A Manual of

ENGINEERING GEOMETRY AND GRAPHICS

for Students and Draftsmen

THE ENGINEERING DRAWING SERIES

ENGINEERING DRAWING

FRENCH AND VIERCK *Engineering Drawing*
Eighth Edition, 715 pages, 6 × 9, 1288 illustrations

McGRAW-HILL TEXT-FILMS FOR ENGINEERING DRAWING
A Series of Directly Correlated
Motion Pictures and Filmstrips (8 films)

VIERCK, COOPER, *Engineering Drawing Problems*
AND MACHOVINA Series 2, 11 × 17
Engineering Drawing—Basic Problems
Series A, 8½ × 11

LEVENS AND EDSTROM *Problems in Engineering Drawing*
Series III, 8½ × 11 (Series IV in preparation)

RUSS *Quiz Questions to Accompany Engineering Drawing*

FRENCH AND TURNBULL *Lessons in Lettering*
Book I—Vertical Single Stroke Lettering
Third Edition, 40 pages, 9 × 6

Book II—Inclined Single Stroke Lettering
Third Edition, 40 pages, 9 × 6

MECHANICAL DRAWING

FRENCH AND SVENSEN *Mechanical Drawing*
Fifth Edition, 437 pages, 6 × 9, 618 illustrations

McGRAW-HILL TEXT-FILMS FOR MECHANICAL DRAWING
A Series of Directly Correlated Motion
Pictures and Filmstrips

LEVENS AND EDSTROM *Problems in Mechanical Drawing*
Problems in Mechanical Drawing, Second Course

GEOMETRY AND GRAPHICS

SHUPE AND MACHOVINA *Engineering Geometry and Graphics*
First Edition, 348 pages, 6⅛ × 9¼, 443 illustrations

SHUPE, MACHOVINA,
AND HANG *Engineering Geometry and Graphics Problems*

A Manual of
ENGINEERING GEOMETRY
AND GRAPHICS
for Students and Draftsmen

HOLLIE W. SHUPE

Professor of Engineering Drawing
The Ohio State University

PAUL E. MACHOVINA

Associate Professor of Engineering Drawing
The Ohio State University

McGRAW-HILL BOOK COMPANY, INC.

New York   Toronto   London

1956

A MANUAL OF ENGINEERING GEOMETRY AND
GRAPHICS FOR STUDENTS AND DRAFTSMEN

Library of Congress Catalog Card Number 55-11569

THE MAPLE PRESS COMPANY, YORK, PA.

PREFACE

The content of drawing courses for engineering students has been largely confined in the past to representational drawing and engineering (descriptive) geometry. With the importance of the problem-solving side of graphics becoming increasingly apparent, drawing courses in many places now are being broadened to include more of "analytic" graphics. This book is designed to aid in the trend by providing, in addition to the text material needed in engineering geometry, material for a more general coverage of graphic solutions.

It is presumed that the student about to use this text has received training in the use of drawing equipment and knows the basic principles of plane and solid geometry, algebra, and logarithms. The book may be used in a course following one that presents the representational phases of the drawing program through the use of a representational-drawing type text such as "Engineering Drawing," by French and Vierck, or it may be used in the initial course of a drawing sequence if supplemented by material on the use of drawing equipment.

The theory of orthographic projection is presented in connection with engineering geometry and employs reference planes placed in convenient positions. Folding lines and plane traces are not used. Wherever applicable, drawings showing problem solutions are separated into stages to illustrate the step-by-step procedure and to avoid complexity.

The subjects included for a more general coverage of graphic solutions conform with those usually found in first-year drawing courses so devoting time. Fundamentals are emphasized and treatments generalized to permit wide latitude in applications. For instance, the subject of vectors is treated simply as vectors, and not as a specific type, in order that the principles may be readily applied to all types of vector quantities. Experience with these subjects should greatly increase the student's appreciation for the value of graphic methods.

The text has been developed and used in mimeographed form over a period of years in courses taught by the authors and their colleagues at The Ohio State University. An expression of appreciation is made to these associates and others for their helpful suggestions.

HOLLIE W. SHUPE
PAUL E. MACHOVINA

CONTENTS

CHAPTER 1

INTRODUCTORY

1.1. The drawings employed in modern engineering, science, and technology may be classified into two general categories: *representational* and *graphic solutions*. Representational drawings serve primarily as the medium for transmitting information for the use and benefit of others, while graphic solutions are drawings made to obtain solutions to problems and often are of direct benefit only to the maker. The field of graphic solutions is vast, ranging from problems of a purely numerical nature to those typified by machine-design layouts, developments, etc. The more common, basic aspects of this field are described in this text.

The reader is familiar with representational drawings of the "engineering-drawing" type. Such drawings are characterized by their finished appearances, their completeness in portrayal of the information covered, and the contrasting weights of their lines, some of which are relatively heavy. In contrast, graphic solutions are distinguished by their uniformly fine lines, the accuracy with which they are prepared, and sometimes the incompleteness of explanation for others of the factors involved. Certain types are often prepared for general use, and so, in a sense, are also representational.

All the problems dealt with in graphic solutions are fundamentally mathematical in nature. Their solution by graphic means is made possible through using a *graphic symbolism* in place of the more familiar numerical and algebraic symbols. Solutions via the graphic and the usual algebraic routes might thus be regarded as companions in a mathematical sense.

The basis for graphic solutions is essentially geometry, making use of the theorems and postulates from branches of that subject. In a sense, graphics may be thought of as being applied geometry—an application in which the geometric entities (e.g., points and lines) themselves are the symbols. As such, graphics constitutes a direct approach for problems of a geometric nature and, with other problems, applies these entities as symbols to effect an analogous representation.

Accepting graphic symbolism may at first be troublesome because of the extensive training received in other symbolism. For example, the individual is schooled from childhood in the use of Arabic numerals for representing magnitudes. He may not recognize that Arabic numerals in

1

themselves are but symbols and that, at other places and in different times, various symbols have been used for this purpose.

In graphics, quantities are ordinarily expressed by the lengths of lines or by distances that are symbolic of numerical values or magnitudes when the scale of the drawing is known. Thus, on a drawing where unity is symbolized by a distance of, say, $\frac{1}{10}$ in., a line 4 in. in length represents a magnitude of 40. Furthermore, in analogous representations, the unit *distance* might stand for a second, an hour, or a day of *time*, a pound or a ton of *force*, a foot-second or a mile per hour of *velocity*, etc., just as readily as an actual distance which it commonly symbolizes on representational drawings. The importance of scales in graphics should be evident. With certain phases a special knowledge of scales is necessary in order to construct particular scales needed for solutions.

Graphic methods for solving problems offer certain advantages. The representation and processes are direct and natural, frequently corresponding more closely with the natural aspects of the problem. The inherent pictorial quality may provide a better understanding of the problem and its solution and reduce the possibilities for errors. From a practical standpoint, solutions for certain types of problems are often quicker and occasionally are available graphicly when impractical or even impossible algebraicly; scientific research makes fairly wide use of graphics, often for these reasons alone. Sometimes a combination of graphic and algebraic methods is found to be advantageous. Experience with the subject not only will broaden one's background but should lead to a better understanding of formal mathematics.

The student is undoubtedly aware of the value of graphics and is able to apply it in some lines of work, for example, in representational drawing, possibly in mapping, in charts and graphs which are used to present numerical data effectively, etc. In addition, the student should be able, without further formal instruction, to solve problems involving plane geometry on the drawing board by applying his knowledge of drawing and geometry. Similarly, he probably can accomplish other solutions, such as with simple equations—finding roots of an equation or of simultaneous equations—by plotting on coordinate systems. Solutions to these and many other problems are potential when an awareness is developed of the possibilities in applying graphics.

Although the use of drawings for solving problems dates back to antiquity, graphics has yet to be developed as a modern continuous science. Deterrents may have included the restriction placed by the Euclidean school on measurements in geometry and the general association of graphic solutions with coordinate systems, hence with their limitations. Within more recent years, the advantages offered by the subject have received attention, and development has taken place especially along lines where applications are of particular practical value.

The phases of graphic solutions covered in this text are ones that, in general, have been fairly highly developed. The one receiving greatest attention here is engineering geometry and is the graphic counterpart of solid analytic geometry in mathematics. It has been treated more thoroughly because it has long been considered an essential subject in engineering studies. This viewpoint is due not only to the problem-solving aspects of the subject but especially to the excellent training it affords in thinking in three-dimensional space—an essential asset to most engineers. Engineering geometry is used in solving space problems through direct representations and other problems through analogous representations.

The remaining phases of graphics treated herein deal mainly with solutions reached through analogous representations. The data are frequently equational in nature. In most instances, the treatments are somewhat abbreviated because of space limitation. Sufficient material is presented, however, to provide the student with a general background of information and in the hope that an awareness of the value of graphic methods will be developed. The bibliography provides an avenue through which further knowledge may be gained.

ACCURACY, PRECISION IN LAYOUT, AND EQUIPMENT

1.2. Factors Affecting Accuracy in a Graphic Solution. The degree of accuracy in numerical answers found by graphic methods is limited by practical considerations. However, it is usually possible to obtain such answers to a degree of accuracy greater than that called for with most practical problems.

Other than for accuracy of the original data, the various factors that may affect the accuracy of a graphic solution are either directly or indirectly under the control of the draftsman. All such factors should be given consideration before starting a solution, and tolerances covering the working conditions and for performing the drafting established so that the end result will have the desired accuracy. Consequently, if an answer of maximum possible accuracy is required, steps must be taken so that the over-all conditions are as accurate as the available starting data.

The factors which should be given consideration are accuracy of the data, accuracy desired in the result, scale of the drawing, accuracy of equipment, type of construction employed, care exercised by the draftsman, and effect of atmospheric conditions on the working surface. These items are considered in the following paragraphs.

1.3. Accuracy of Data and of Results, and Scale of the Drawing. For most engineering problems, data are obtained or results are utilized, or both, by making measurements. The measurements are made with various devices ordinarily employing scales, and scales, incidentally, are graphic contrivances. The number of significant digits contained in the values obtained through such measurements is dependent upon the scale used. It should be borne in mind that absolute accuracy in measurement is not attainable and, in solving a problem by any method, the answer can be accurate to no more significant digits than the number of digits in the factor containing the least. Hence, the limiting element to the accuracy of an answer lies directly in the accuracy of the data and indirectly in the scales used if measurements were involved in obtaining the data. Graphic methods, therefore, can furnish answers of maximum accuracy provided the scale employed in the solution is readable to a number of significant digits commensurate with that of the data and provided due consideration is given to the other factors affecting accuracy as enumerated in the previous paragraph.

The foregoing discussion should be borne in mind when choosing the scale for a solution. Often there will be a tendency to use an unnecessarily large scale on the assumption that a more accurate answer will result. Such a scale will lead to a larger drawing which not only will make precision more difficult to maintain but will also require more time.

1.4. Drafting Equipment. For the most part, the equipment used in graphic solutions is the same as that employed for general drafting purposes. Special equipment may be desirable when much work of specialized type or very large layouts are to be handled. It should be evident that all equipment must be in good condition. T squares and other straightedges should be tested for straightness, and triangles for perpendicularity. Since such equipment is subject to change, the tests should be repeated occasionally.

Inasmuch as precise work demands fine lines and accurate constructions, hard pencils that will not require frequent resharpening are preferred. For most work, 4H to 6H pencils are recommended, and a hard-surface paper should be used with such pencils. A needle-point scriber and metal drawing surfaces may be used for work requiring great precision. Inking may be called for occasionally, especially when the drawing is to be applied as a calculating device for repeated use, as with nomograms.

Special attention should be paid to the draftsman's scales. The more accurate "engine-divided" scales are preferred to the less expensive "printed" kind. Since a variation in unit length may exist between two draftsman's scales of similar type, the *same* draftsman's scale should be used throughout a given solution.

1.5. Care in Constructions. Much of the layout work in a typical problem consists of geometric constructions. When precision is paramount, it becomes increasingly important to select constructions and perform them in a manner least likely to introduce inaccuracies. Common sense should be a guide in such matters. For example, the magnified presentations in Fig. 1.1 compare the exactness of position for points determined by two cases of intersecting lines. Avoid locating a point by the intersection of lines making a relatively small angle, as in (1).   Greater accuracy can be expected from the intersection of more nearly perpendicular lines, as in (2). Also, where the location of a point on a line at an angle through the use of a long projector might prove inaccurate, location through transfer of a measurement might be preferred.   The use of two such methods together will frequently provide a check.   To avoid unnecessarily long projections and permit compactness, it may be desirable to overlap constructions.   The simplest construction should ordinarily prove to be the most accurate and, in general, will be the most advantageous.   Attention should be given to

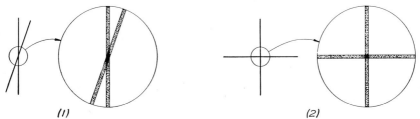

FIG. 1.1. Comparative location of point.

the effect of cumulative errors and constructions employed which minimize them.

1.6. Drafting—Lines and Measurements.   Ordinarily, lines should be made as fine as possible so as to approach the theoretical lines of pure geometry.   With the use of hard pencils kept well sharpened, line widths of but a few one-thousandths of an inch can be maintained.

Linear measurements can be made easily to the closest one-hundredth of an inch, for which purpose a scale with the inch subdivided into fiftieths is most convenient.   By using a magnifying glass in connection with a scale subdivided in one-hundredths of an inch, one can make measurements within a few one-thousandths of an inch.   When distances are to be laid out very precisely with a scale, points are best marked with a needle point by making a very slight prick in the paper.

Common protractors usually will not provide the accuracy necessary for angular measurements.   In this event, precision vernier protractors may be used or the angle laid out through the use of the trigonometric tangent of the angle by making right-angle measurements.

1.7. Effect of Atmospheric Conditions on the Working Surface.   Materials upon which drawings are made may be affected by changes in humidity and temperature.   Paper, especially, will exhibit considerable change in shape and size with variation in humidity.   To minimize the effect of such variation, solutions should be completed in as short a time and under as uniform conditions as possible.   When precision is important and controlled atmospheric conditions are not at hand, metal drawing surfaces are often used.   A scriber is employed with soft metals or with special coated sheets that are available.   Pencil drawings may be made on metal surfaces prepared with a special paint for such work. Another material recommended as being dimensionally stable is glass cloth, a tracing cloth made of glass fiber and available in a form accepting pencil lines.

GRAPHIC ARITHMETIC

1.8. Elementary addition, subtraction, multiplication, etc., performed graphicly provide a convenient introduction to the field of graphic solutions. The solutions in themselves are of but academic interest, since the processes are ordinarily more consuming of time than the usual methods. The principles are important, however, when a step in arithmetic is included as part of a larger, more embracing solution. It should also be observed that certain branches of graphics are based to a certain extent on these principles. For example, sliding scales or slide rules follow the principles of graphic addition and subtraction.

1.9. Representing Numbers. The magnitudes of the quantities involved in the problem must first be considered, and a scale selected that will keep the solution within practical confines. To represent a number n, a distance equivalent to n times the *unit distance* (distance selected to represent 1) is laid off *directly* through the use of the scale graduations and calibrations.

1.10. Graphic Addition and Subtraction. To add the numbers a and b, distances representing a and b, respectively, are laid off end to end on a

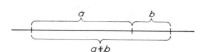

Fig. 1.2. Graphic addition.

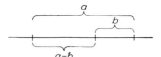

Fig. 1.3. Graphic subtraction.

straight line (Fig. 1.2). The sum of $a + b$ may be read with the scale from the total distance. To subtract b from a, the distances are laid off as before but with one measured in a direction opposite to the other (Fig. 1.3). The difference in distances when read with the scale yields the answer to $a - b$.

1.11. Graphic Multiplication and Division. These may be performed through the use of similar triangles. Several procedures are possible. Figure 1.4 illustrates one by which the product of a times b is obtained. In the figure, distances representing a and b are laid off, one along each leg of any angle, measuring from the vertex. The distance representing *one unit* is laid off on one leg of the angle, again measuring from the vertex. Line CD is drawn, and EF constructed parallel. By similar triangles, $x/b = a/1$. Hence, $x = a \times b$.

Figure 1.5 illustrates the division of c by d. The distances representing c, d, and *unity* are laid off along the legs of any angle, measuring from the vertex as shown. *GH* is drawn, and *JK* constructed parallel. **Again** by similar triangles, $y/c = 1/d$. Hence, $y = c/d$.

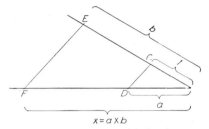

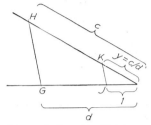

FIG. 1.4. Graphic multiplication.   FIG. 1.5. Graphic division.

1.12. Mean Proportional, Square Root, and Reciprocals. The mean proportional between two quantities and a special case yielding square roots are available graphicly through the geometric principle that lines joining the ends of a diameter with a point on the circle form a right angle.

To find the mean proportional *b* between two quantities *a* and *c*, first lay off distances representing the two quantities end to end on a straight line (Fig. 1.6). Using mid-point *G* of line *DF* as the center and with *GD* as the radius, draw the semicircle as shown. Draw the perpendicular *HE*,

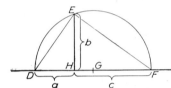

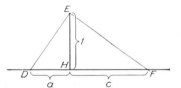

FIG. 1.6. Mean proportional graphicly.   FIG. 1.7. Reciprocals graphicly.

thus establishing a distance representing the mean proportional *b*. By similar triangles, $a/b = b/c$.

Square roots may be found through the construction of Fig. 1.6 by laying off *a* to represent unity. Doing so, $1/b = b/c$. Hence, $b = \sqrt{c}$.

A similar construction (Fig. 1.7) may be used to obtain reciprocal values. In the figure, the right triangle *DEF* is constructed with the perpendicular *EH* equal to unity and with either *a* or *c* representing a quantity for which the reciprocal is sought. Since $a/1 = 1/c$, then $a \times c = 1$. Hence, *a* and *c* are reciprocals.

ENGINEERING GEOMETRY

1.13. Engineering geometry is a branch of graphics investigating the relationships, properties, and measurements of solids, surfaces, lines, and angles, as required in many engineering problems which deal with three-dimensional or space relationships. The subject uses geometric constructions in orthographic projection views as the means of graphicly solving these problems.

Since a knowledge of geometric forms is important in comprehending text discussions, some of the forms are presented in Figs. 1.8 to 1.10 as review.

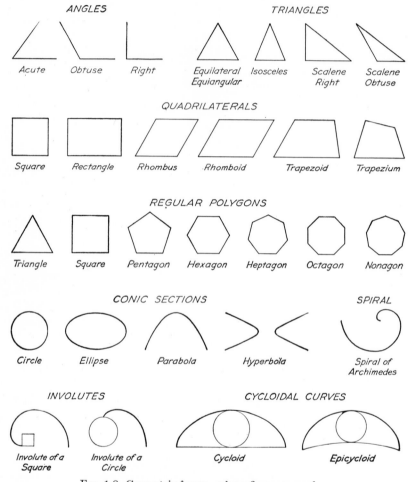

FIG. 1.8. Geometric forms—plane figure examples.

1.14. Edges, Corners, and Surfaces vs. Lines, Points, and Planes. The student is accustomed to handling and visualizing solid objects and is familiar with their basic geometric elements such as edges, corners, and surfaces. Ordinarily, an engineering-geometry problem is more concerned with the object elements than with the object itself, and usually, only a relatively few of the total geometric elements actually enter into the solution of the problem. In many instances, the solution merely employs these entities as symbols in analogous representations, hence as unrelated to an actual solid object. In either case, the representation of irrelevant elements in a graphic solution is unproductive and wasteful; therefore such elements are usually omitted. This leads to drawings where an object edge becomes a line, a corner a point, and a surface a plane, all perhaps

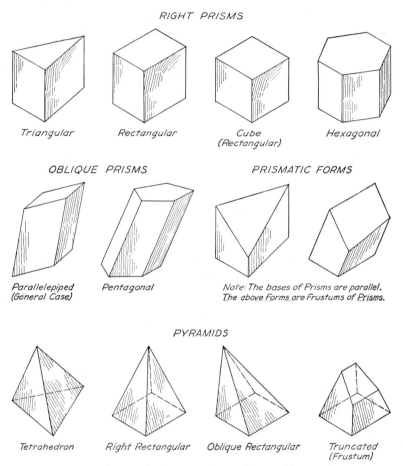

RIGHT PRISMS

Triangular   Rectangular   Cube   Hexagonal
                                   (Rectangular)

OBLIQUE PRISMS   PRISMATIC FORMS

Parallelepiped   Pentagonal   Note: The bases of Prisms are parallel.
(General Case)   The above Forms are Frustums of Prisms.

PYRAMIDS

Tetrahedron   Right Rectangular   Oblique Rectangular   Truncated
                                                           (Frustum)

FIG. 1.9. Geometric forms—prism and pyramid examples.

appearing unconnected by other elements. Paradoxically, such simplification often hampers visualization, hence is frequently an initial difficulty for the student.

A rectangular prism is shown in Fig. 1.11(1). It will be apparent that the lettered points shown in (2) are positioned similarly with respect to the corners of the prism. The line BC in (2) is similar to the edge BC of the prism, and the plane $DEFG$ of (2) can be likened to the prism surface $DEFG$. The three sets of parallel edges of the prism could be represented by lines drawn through the corresponding points of (2), and the perpendicular relationships of the edges and surfaces of the prism could be shown by using corresponding lines and planes in the presentation of (2). The noteworthy difference between these two presentations is that edges and surfaces (of objects) are limited in extent while lines and planes are not.

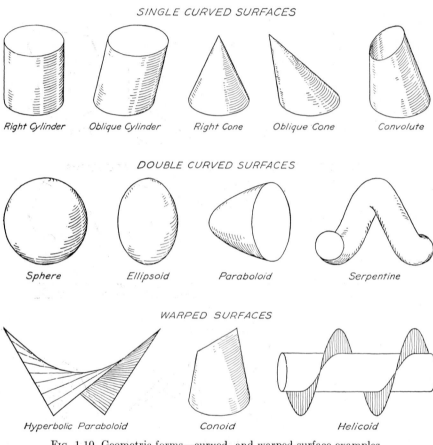

SINGLE CURVED SURFACES

Right Cylinder   Oblique Cylinder   Right Cone   Oblique Cone   Convolute

DOUBLE CURVED SURFACES

Sphere   Ellipsoid   Paraboloid   Serpentine

WARPED SURFACES

Hyperbolic Paraboloid   Conoid   Helicoid

FIG. 1.10. Geometric forms—curved- and warped-surface examples.

Perpendicular and parallel relations of lines to lines, lines to planes, and planes to planes must be established or determined in a great many problems. All these relationships can be compared with those seen in a rectangular prism.

1.15. Problem Presentations. The problems of this text are presented in several ways. Pictorial sketches and orthographic views are used in many instances, while word descriptions alone suffice in others. A system of coordinates, coupled with word descriptions, is also used.

The coordinate system permits the plotting of the front and top views of a point by listing relative width, height, and depth, in that sequence.

Hence, point $A(2,3,5)$ is located in Fig. 1.12 by the following procedure: The capital letter names the point. The first numeral positions both the top and front views of point A on a line 2 in. to the right of the left border

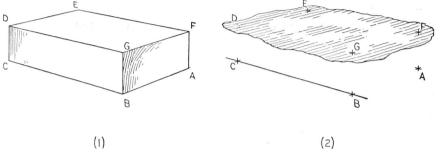

(1)   (2)

Fig. 1.11. Edges, corners, and surfaces vs. lines, points, and planes.

line. The second numeral fixes the front view of point A on a line 3 in. above the bottom border line of the sheet. (The subscript $_F$ is used to denote the front view of the point.) The third numeral locates the top view of point A on a line that is 5 in. above the bottom border line.

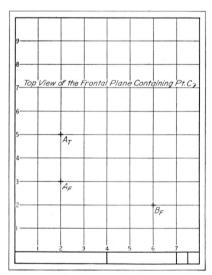

Fig. 1.12. Coordinate plotting of points.

There will be instances where two of the three principal dimensions required to locate a point are known, but not the third. Unknown coordinates will be indicated by the letter X. The front view of point $B(6,2,X)$ is shown in Fig. 1.12, but the top view of point B cannot be fixed until other portions of the particular problem are solved.

In a few problems, there may be only one coordinate of a point known when the problem is stated; such a point might be $C(X,X,7)$. This original information restricts point C to the frontal plane that is represented in the top view by a line that is 7 in. above the bottom border line of the sheet.

Views other than the front and top views will generally be required. They may be drawn by using the usual projection routines, as described in Chap. 2.

CHAPTER 2

ORTHOGRAPHIC PROJECTION

2.1. Representational drawings are often supplemented with size descriptions, material specifications, and, at times, manufacturing processes; as such they become the working drawings of industry. Individual pieces are produced with constant reference to these working drawings. The assembly of pieces into consumer goods follows the assembly drawings of the working-drawing sets. Representational drawings, therefore, are a vital part of the economic structure and must be accomplished with both accuracy and speed.

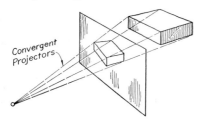 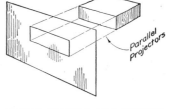

PERSPECTIVE PROJECTION   ORTHOGRAPHIC PROJECTION

FIG. 2.1. A pictorial comparison of perspective and orthographic projections.

Photography is a medium commonly used for shape description. The graphical counterpart of photography is the subject of *perspective projection*. In both photography and perspective, the representation of three-dimensional relationships can be pictorially shown, but the designer cannot photograph an object that has not yet been made. Perspective projections of a designer's imagined objects are sometimes used to convey his ideas to engineering draftsmen, but the possibility of using perspective in working drawings is limited.

All projection drawings are recorded on surfaces by the intersection of a system of straight-line projectors with those surfaces. The projectors are from the various features that are to be recorded. These projectors may be either parallel or convergent. Converging projectors are used in perspective projections, which pictorially show the length, breadth, and thickness of an object. The true shape of surfaces is not usually shown in such a view. A projection made with parallel projectors onto a plane that is parallel to the surface represented will show the actual shape of

13

that surface. It should not be presumed, however, that all projections of this type are specifically drawn to determine the true shapes of surfaces. A comparison of convergent and parallel projectors is given in Fig. 2.1.

In *orthographic projection*, the projectors for any single recording are parallel to each other. These recordings, or *views*, are made onto planes of projection that are perpendicular to their respective projectors. Since a two-dimensional drawing cannot adequately represent spatial relationships by itself, two or more orthographic views must be drawn if three-dimensional conditions are to be shown. This requirement is met by using two planes of projection that are at right angles to each other.

2.2. Principal Planes of Projection and Principal Views (Fig. 2.2). The principal planes of projection are the mutually perpendicular *horizontal*, *frontal*, and *profile* planes. Views recorded upon these planes are the principal views. Principal views are projected as follows: (1) front and rear views onto frontal planes, (2) top and bottom views onto horizontal planes, and (3) right- and left-side views onto profile planes.

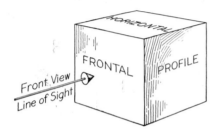

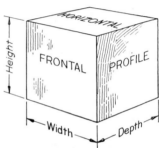

FIG. 2.2. Principal planes of projection.   FIG. 2.3. Principal dimensions.

2.3. Principal Dimensions. *Height, width,* and *depth* dimensions are respectively perpendicular to the horizontal, profile, and frontal planes (see Fig. 2.3). They are the most commonly used dimensions of all in the study of orthographic projection. Length, breadth, and thickness, being object dimensions, have no compulsory relationship to the principal dimensions of height, width, and depth. Whenever possible, however, objects will usually be positioned with their plane surfaces parallel to the principal planes of projection; length, breadth, and thickness then become coincidental with the height, width, and depth dimensions of the orthographic projections.

2.4. The Meaning of Lines in Orthographic Projections. Lines are used in orthographic views to represent three different conditions: an intersection between two surfaces, an edge view of a surface, and a limiting element of a surface. Examples of each are shown in Fig. 2.4. In (1), the

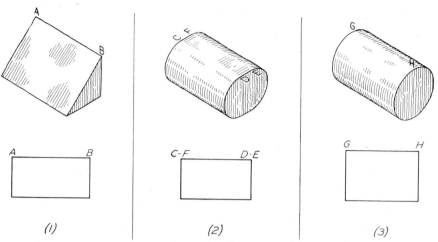

Fig. 2.4. The meaning of lines in orthographic projection.

edge AB is represented in the orthographic view by line AB. The horizontal surface $CDEF$ is shown orthographically by a single line in (2). The upper limiting element of the cylinder is represented by line GH in the orthographic view of (3).

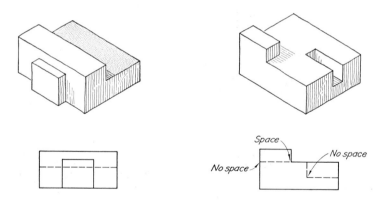

Fig. 2.5. Dotted-line representation of hidden detail.

Fig. 2.6. Dotted-line delineation.

The complete graphical shape description of an object requires the representation of all its many features, visible and hidden. Visible details are shown with solid lines, but hidden details are conventionally represented by lines made up of short dashes, sometimes called *dotted lines*. The shaded surface of the object shown pictorially in Fig. 2.5 is represented by the dotted line drawn in the orthographic view.

Careful delineation results in greater legibility of any drawing. Dotted

lines should be somewhat lighter in weight than solid lines in order to create
a subdued effect for the hidden details they represent.   Dotted lines should
always start with a dash except when they appear as extensions of solid
lines (see Fig. 2.6).

2.5. Adjacent Views (Fig. 2.7).   Adjacent orthographic views (views in
direct projection with each other) must be recorded on planes of projection

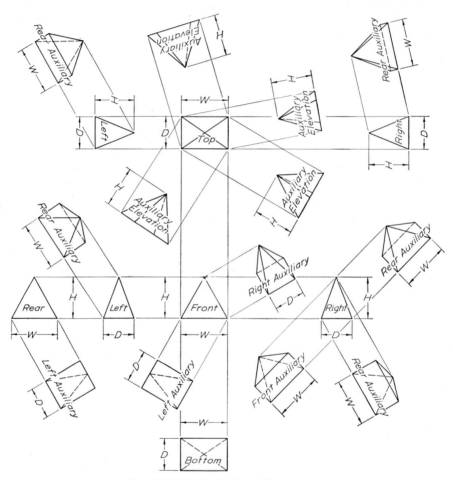

Fig. 2.7. Principal and auxiliary views.

that are perpendicular.   For example, the front, right-side, rear, and left-
side views may all be drawn adjacent to the top view, since the planes on
which they are recorded are all perpendicular to the horizontal plane on
which the top view is drawn.   Similarly, the right-side, bottom, left-side,
and top views may all be drawn adjacent to the front view.   The top,

front, bottom, and rear views may all be drawn adjacent to either side view.

Views recorded on planes other than the principal planes of projection will often be required. If drawn adjacent to the top view, they are *auxiliary elevations*. *Right* and *left auxiliary views* are drawn adjacent to the front view. *Front* and *rear auxiliaries* are drawn adjacent to the side views. *Oblique views*, recorded on planes of projection that are not perpendicular to any of the principal planes of projection, are drawn adjacent to auxiliary views. An oblique view must be projected from an auxiliary view that is recorded on a plane perpendicular to the projection plane on which the oblique view is recorded.

2.6. Two Perpendicular Dimensions of an Orthographic View. It should be noted in Fig. 2.7 that all views adjacent to the top view show the dimension of height in true length. Views adjacent to the front view all show depth. Width is seen in all views adjacent to either side view.

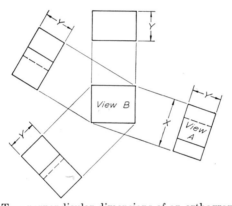

FIG. 2.8. Two perpendicular dimensions of an orthographic view.

A fixed pattern exists with regard to the two perpendicular dimensions of any one view. In view A of Fig. 2.8, the dimension X is projected from view B. Dimension Y is seen in all views adjacent to view B. If view B is the front view, dimension Y is depth, but if view B is the top view, dimension Y is height. Such dimensions as Y are measured from a reference plane that is perpendicular to the dimension.

2.7. Procedure for Drawing a Third Orthographic View, Two Views Being Given. The principle of the two perpendicular dimensions of an orthographic view is used whenever two adjacent orthographic views are given and a third view is required.

In Fig. 2.9(1), the top and front views of a tetrahedron are drawn. A view of the tetrahedron seen looking in the horizontal direction PO is required. Since the required view will be recorded on a vertical plane of projection, the view is positioned adjacent to the top view. In (2), the dimension X is projected from the top view to the new view.   The recognition that dimensions X and Y are perpendicular permits the establishment of a horizontal reference plane (HRP) parallel to dimension X and perpendicular to dimension Y, as shown in the auxiliary elevation of (3).   This same reference plane is established in the front view of (4), where the true

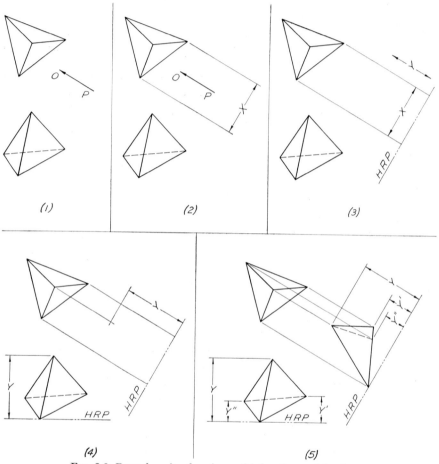

Fig. 2.9. Procedure for drawing a third orthographic view.

lengths of dimensions Y can be measured.   In (5), the auxiliary view is completed, using a combination of projection from the top view and measurement of heights from the front view.

The views of Fig. 2.10 further illustrate the principle being considered. The top and front views are given.   A view seen looking in the frontal direction OP is required.   The required view shows depth, so a frontal reference plane (FRP), perpendicular to depth, is established.   Depth measurements are taken from the top view and recorded in the auxiliary view (i.e., dimension Y). The dimension X is projected from the front view.

2.8. An Oblique View, Seen Looking in a Specified Direction. It should be noted in the examples of Figs. 2.9 and 2.10 that *a view seen looking in any specified direction is recorded adjacent to a view whose line of sight is perpendicular to the specified direction.* Hence, in Fig. 2.9, the required

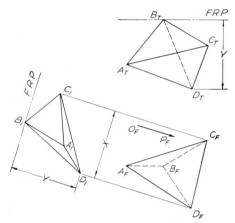

FIG. 2.10. A view seen looking in a specified frontal direction.

view is adjacent to the top view, since the vertical line of sight for the top view is perpendicular to the specified horizontal line of sight PO. Simi-

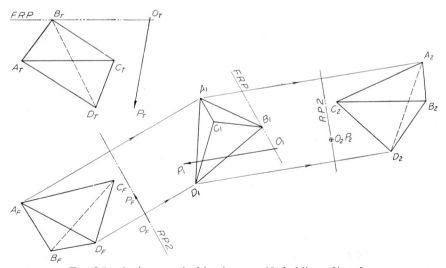

FIG. 2.11. A view seen looking in a specified oblique direction.

larly, in Fig. 2.10, the required view is adjacent to the front view, since the line of sight for the front view is perpendicular to the required line of sight.

If the specified line of sight is oblique, the required view cannot be placed adjacent to any principal view since none of them is a view projected at right angles to the specified oblique line of sight.   An auxiliary view whose line of sight is perpendicular to the specified one must first be drawn.   The required view can then be drawn adjacent to this auxiliary view.   In Fig. 2.11, the top and front views of a tetrahedron, together with the oblique line of sight *OP*, are given.   A right auxiliary view projected from the front view at right angles to *OP* is drawn first.   The required oblique view is then projected from this auxiliary view.   It should be noted that *RP2* is perpendicular to the projectors from the right auxiliary in all views adjacent to that auxiliary.

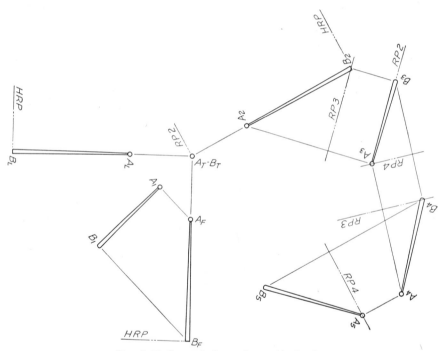

FIG. 2.12. Several views of a vertical pole.

2.9. Orientation.   When one reads any orthographic view, the ability to orient oneself to gravity will be of considerable assistance in visualizing three-dimensional conditions.   Several orthographic views of a vertical flagpole *AB* are shown in Fig. 2.12.   All views have been lettered with the top of the letters toward the top of the pole to assist the reader in orienting himself with regards to each view.

Although the usual concern in orientation is with the vertical direction, the front-to-rear and left-to-right directions are of equal importance. In Fig. 2.13, the edge AB serves to illustrate the left-to-right direction, while the edge BC allows for a study of the front-to-rear direction. The views are lettered with regard to gravity.

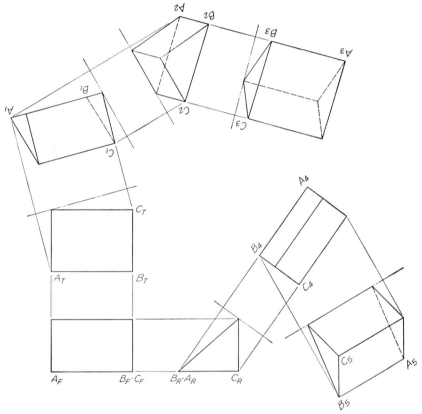

FIG. 2.13. Several views of a triangular prism.

2.10. Selection of Views in Representational Drawing. Three-dimensional relationships may be shown with any pair of adjacent orthographic views. This fact alone, however, does not permit an arbitrarily selected pair of views to represent adequately the shape of three-dimensional features. The views must be selected so that the shape of an object is apparent to the reader of those views. In Fig. 2.14, a quadrilateral prism is represented. The given views indicate the three-dimensional relationships between the edges and surfaces of the prism, but these views do not show (nor do they permit the reader to assume) specific angular values that exist between those edges and surfaces.

Six different objects are represented in Fig. 2.15. The shape of any one of them cannot be described by only the top and front views, since

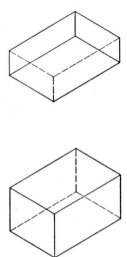

FIG. 2.14. An arbitrarily selected pair of views of a quadrilateral prism.

all these objects appear identical in those views. The triangular prism, cylinder, and rectangular sheet, however, can each be described with the given front and side views; the top views are not required in these representations.

Three views of a rectangular prism are drawn in Fig. 2.16(1). The

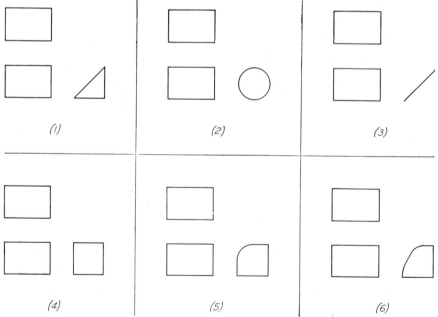

FIG. 2.15. Objects having identical top and front views.

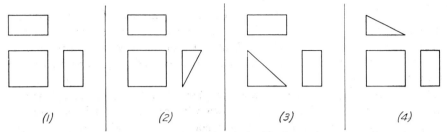

FIG. 2.16. Objects having two views identical with those of a rectangular prism.

rectangular shapes of two of these views are repeated in (2), (3), and (4). A comparison of these representations will show that a rectangular prism can never be completely described by two adjacent orthographic views when those views have their lines of sight perpendicular to surfaces of the object.

Rectangular prisms and objects similar to those shown in Fig. 2.15(5) and (6) require three orthographic views for their proper shape description. No two of these three views can be taken at 180° with respect to each other.

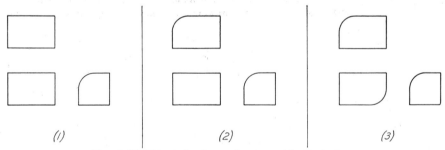

FIG. 2.17. Objects having at least one identical view.

Figure 2.15(5) is repeated in Fig. 2.17(1). The objects shown in Fig. 2.17(1) and (2) have identical front and side views, but since the rear portion of the first object is basically rectangular, the top view cannot be omitted in describing the shape of this object. The top and side views shown in (3) are the same as those in (2); however, the front views show a difference between these objects.

It should be apparent that an accurate shape description of a surface will be had if the observer looks at the surface along a line of sight perpendicular to that surface. All other views will show the surface in a distorted manner. This difference in appearance may be readily illustrated if the student will take a rectangular sheet of paper and view it according to the following four-position sequence: (1) Look perpendicular to the sheet; it will appear as a rectangle and in its true proportion. (2) Look perpendicular to two of the edges of the sheet, but not perpendicular or parallel to the other two edges; the sheet will appear as a rectangle, but not in its true proportion. (3) Look parallel to the plane of the paper; the sheet will appear as a straight line. (4) Look at the sheet in any other direction; it will appear as a parallelogram, with the corner angles appearing as other than right angles.

2.11. Selection of Views in Other Graphical Solutions. Although three-dimensional relationships may be shown with any pair of adjacent orthographic views, many of the graphical solutions to engineering geometry problems are accomplished by using specific pairs of such views. (For example, problems that involve rotating parts are usually solved with a normal view and an end view of the rotation axis.) The analysis of any problem of this type, therefore, should include a study of the orthographic views needed for the solution and of the means by which such views can be most effectively produced.

PROBLEMS

Group I. Principal Views

2.1. Four blocks are shown in Fig. 2.18. Freehand orthographic views of each block are to be drawn as follows: Divide the drawing sheet into four quadrants. In the

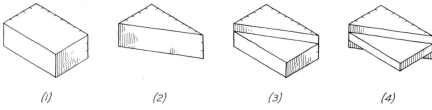

(1)   *(2)*   *(3)*   *(4)*

Fig. 2.18. Blocks.

upper left corner, draw the top, front, and right-side views of the rectangular prism. In the upper right corner, draw the top, front, and right-side views of the triangular prism. In the lower left corner of the drawing sheet, draw the three orthographic views that best describe the object shown in (3). Three orthographic views of the tenoned block are to be drawn in the lower right corner of the sheet. Proportions for each block may be determined by reference to the uniformly spaced markings along the outline edges of each pictorial sketch.

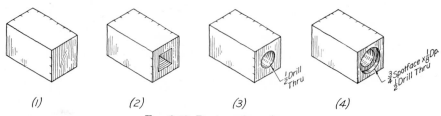

(1)   *(2)*   *(3)*   *(4)*

Fig. 2.19. Rectangular prisms.

2.2. Four rectangular prisms are shown in Fig. 2.19. Freehand orthographic views of each prism are to be drawn as follows: Divide the drawing sheet into four quadrants.

Draw the top, front, and side views of each prism; one quadrant of the drawing sheet is to be used for each object in the manner indicated for Prob. 2.1. The uniformly spaced markings are at intervals of ¼ in.

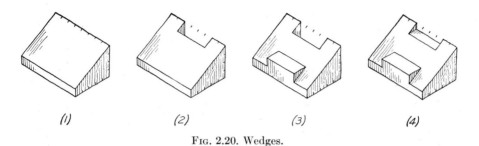

(1)   *(2)*   *(3)*   *(4)*

Fig. 2.20. Wedges.

2.3. Four wedges are shown in Fig. 2.20. Freehand orthographic views are to be drawn of each wedge. The drawing sheet is to be divided and used in a manner similar to that described above.

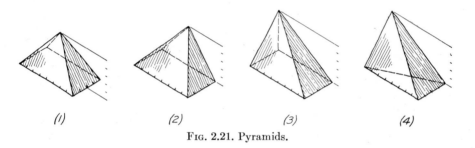

(1)   *(2)*   *(3)*   *(4)*

Fig. 2.21. Pyramids.

2.4. Four pyramids are shown in Fig. 2.21. In each quadrant of the drawing sheet, draw the top, front, and side views of one of these pyramids.

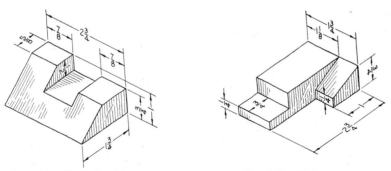

Fig. 2.22. Slotted guide.   Fig. 2.23. Wedge stop.

2.5. Draw the top, front, and side views of the slotted guide shown in Fig. 2.22.

2.6. Draw the top, front, and side views of the wedge stop shown in Fig. 2.23.

2.7. Draw the top, front, and side views of the duplex wedge shown in Fig. 2.24.

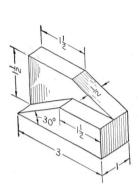

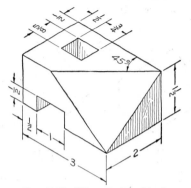

FIG. 2.24. Duplex wedge.   FIG. 2.25. Clipped slide block.

2.8. Draw the top, front, and side views of the clipped slide block shown in Fig. 2.25.
2.9. Draw the top, front, and side views of the bracket shown in Fig. 2.26.

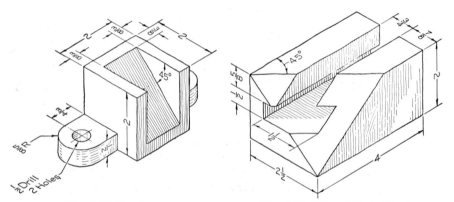

FIG. 2.26. Bracket.   FIG. 2.27. Clipped T-slot block.

2.10. Draw the top, front, and side views of the clipped T-slot block shown in Fig. 2.27.
2.11. In Fig. 2.28 the front and right-side views of a dual-purpose wedge are given. Draw the top, front, and right-side views of the wedge.

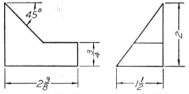

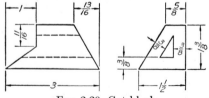

FIG. 2.28. Dual-purpose wedge.   FIG. 2.29. Cut block.

2.12. In Fig. 2.29 the front and partial right-side views of a cut block are given. Draw the top, front, and left-side views of the block.

2.13. In Fig. 2.30 the top and front views of a triangular pyramid are given. Draw the top, front, and left-side views of the pyramid.

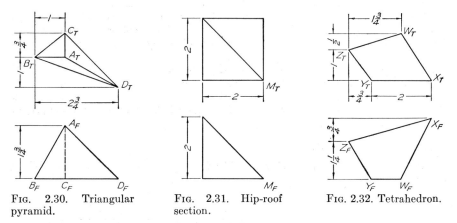

Fig. 2.30. Triangular pyramid.

Fig. 2.31. Hip-roof section.

Fig. 2.32. Tetrahedron.

2.14. In Fig. 2.31 the top and front views of a hip-roof section are given. Draw the top, front, and right-side views of the section.

2.15. In Fig 2.32 the outline of a tetrahedron is shown in the top and front views. Draw the top, front, and either side views of the tetrahedron.

2.16. Line $A(2\frac{1}{2},5,7\frac{1}{2})$ $B(2\frac{1}{2},1,7\frac{1}{2})$ is the axis of a 2-in.-diameter right-circular cylinder. This cylinder is cut by plane $C(1,5,8)$ $U(3,2\frac{1}{2},9)$ $T(4,1\frac{1}{4},6)$. Draw the top, front, and right-side views of the curve cut on the cylinder by the limitless plane CUT.

Group II. Auxiliary Views

2.17. Draw the orthographic views required for the shape description of the clip angle shown in Fig. 2.33.

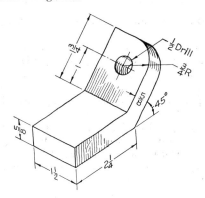

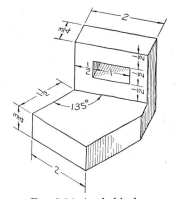

Fig. 2.33. Clip angle.

Fig. 2.34. Angle block.

2.18. Draw the orthographic views required for the shape description of the angle block shown in Fig. 2.34.

2.19. Triangle $R(1,2,8\frac{1}{2})$ $S(2\frac{1}{2},0\frac{1}{2},8\frac{1}{2})$ $T(3\frac{1}{2},3,8\frac{1}{2})$ is the base and $D(1,2,5)$ $E(2\frac{1}{2},0\frac{1}{2},6\frac{1}{2})$ $F(3\frac{1}{2},3,7\frac{1}{2})$ is the truncating surface of a prism. Draw the view of DEF that is seen by looking in the direction $O(7,1,3)$ $P(5,1,5)$.

2.20. Points $A(1,1,7)$, $B(2,0\frac{1}{2},8\frac{1}{2})$, $C(4,3,8)$, and $D(4,1,5)$ are the four corners of a tetrahedron. Draw the top and front views of the tetrahedron and another view of this pyramid as seen when the line of sight is DA.

2.21. Square $S(1,1,6)$ $Q(3,1,6)$ $R(3,1,8)$ $E(1,1,8)$ is the base of a right pyramid whose altitude is $2\frac{1}{2}$ in. long. *Scale:* full size. Draw the top, front, and right auxiliary (whose frontal line of sight is downward and at an angle of $30°$ with the horizontal) views of this pyramid.

2.22. Point $C(2,2,7)$ is the center of a 2-in.-diameter sphere. *Scale:* full size. Point N is the uppermost point on the spherical surface. Point Q is the point of the sphere that is farthest to the rear. The point of the surface that is farthest to the right is point E. Draw the view of the sphere for which the line of sight is NQ. Identify points C, N, E, and Q in all views drawn.

Group III. Oblique Views

2.23. Draw the orthographic views required for the shape description of the oblique clip angle shown in Fig. 2.35.

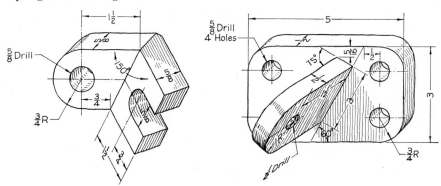

FIG. 2.35. Oblique clip angle.   FIG. 2.36. Transverse connector.

2.24. Draw the orthographic views required for the shape description of the transverse connector shown in Fig. 2.36.

2.25. The lower base of a cube is $J(1,1,5)$ $K(3,1,5)$ $L(3,1,7)$ $M(1,1,7)$. Draw the top, front, auxiliary, and oblique views of the cube, the last view being the one seen when looking in the direction $Z(3,3,7)J$.

2.26. Points $R(0\frac{1}{2},0\frac{1}{2},7)$, $S(0\frac{1}{2},2\frac{1}{2},8\frac{1}{2})$, $T(2\frac{1}{2},2\frac{1}{2},6)$, and $V(3\frac{1}{2},0\frac{1}{2},7)$ are the four corners of a tetrahedron. Draw the top, front, auxiliary, and oblique (whose line of sight is TV) views of the tetrahedron.

2.27. Point $P(6,1,7\frac{1}{2})$ is the center of a $2\frac{1}{2}$- by 2- by 1-in. rectangular prism. The $2\frac{1}{2}$-in. edges are horizontal-frontal, and the 1-in. edges are vertical. The line of sight for an oblique view of this prism is the body diagonal from the lower left rear corner. *Scale:* full size. Draw the top, front, auxiliary, and indicated oblique views of the prism.

CHAPTER 3

DEFINITIONS AND BASIC VIEWS OF POINTS AND LINES

3.1. A *point* is that which has neither parts nor extent but position only. A *line* is a continuous extent of only one dimension (i.e., a line has length, but not breadth or thickness).

3.2. Location of a Point. The location of any point can be given in terms of three mutually perpendicular measurements from a known point.

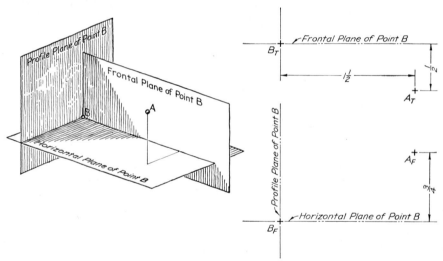

Fig. 3.1. Location of a point from a known point.

In orthographic projection the dimensions of height, depth, and width are best employed. A relative height is given when it is said that a point is *above* or *below* another point; *in front of* or *behind* indicates a depth relationship; to the *right* or *left* is a width notation. In Fig. 3.1, point *A* is given. Point *B* is located with reference to point *A* according to the following: *B* is ¾ in. below *A*, ½ in. behind *A*, and 1½ in. to the left of *A*.

3.3. The Seven Straight-line Positions. A line parallel to a plane of projection receives its name from that plane. Thus, a horizontal line is a line parallel to the horizontal plane of projection, a frontal line is a line parallel to the frontal plane of projection, and a profile line is a line parallel to the profile plane of projection. When a line is parallel to two of the

29

projection planes, it takes the name of both (i.e., horizontal-frontal, horizontal-profile, and frontal-profile). The frontal-profile line is more commonly termed a *vertical* line. A line not parallel to any of the three principal planes of projection is an *oblique* line. Figure 3.2 shows the various positions of straight lines; each of them should be visualized by the student, using a pencil held in the position the line occupies in space.

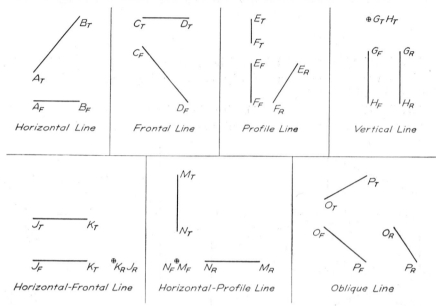

FIG. 3.2. Examples of the seven straight-line positions.

For purposes of brevity, the term *line*, as used throughout this text, shall mean a *straight* line. Other lines will be identified by name, e.g., circle, ellipse, etc.

3.4. Location of a Line. If any two points of a line are located, the line itself will be positioned in space. Such points, while they limit the line segment between the points, do not limit the extent of the line.

3.5. Location of a Point on a Line. In Fig. 3.3, the line AB is given together with the requirement of determining the location of a point P on the line. Point P is to be $\frac{1}{2}$ in. in front of point A. An edge view of the frontal plane containing P is established in the top view. The point in common between that plane and the line AB is point P. The front view is secured by projecting from the top view.

Had the given line been profile, the front view of point P could not have been determined by projection from the top view. The height of point P could be found by drawing a side view (see Fig. 3.4).

3.6. Normal Views of a Line. Any view for which the line of sight is perpendicular to a line is a *normal* view of that line. Such a view will show the actual distance between points of the line and is, therefore, often called a true-length view of the line. If the student will hold his pencil as a model of a line in space, he will see that an infinite number of normal views of any line can be secured, for the given line may be likened to the axle of a wheel having many spokes (all perpendicular to the axle) and these spokes simply represent the many lines of sight along which normal views of the given line can be secured.

In Fig. 3.2, it will be noted that horizontal lines are shown true length in the top view, that the front view is a normal view of all frontal lines, and

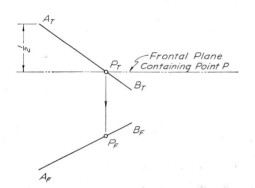

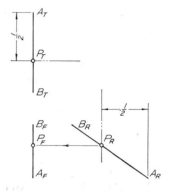

FIG. 3.3. Location of a point on an oblique line.

FIG. 3.4. Location of a point on a profile line.

that the side view is a normal view of all profile lines. The lines of sight for principal views are not perpendicular to oblique lines, so none of the principal views would be a normal view of an oblique line.

3.7. Normal View of an Oblique Line. In Fig. 3.5, the top and front views of an oblique line AB are shown. A normal view of the line is seen when it is viewed in the horizontal direction OP, a line of sight perpendicular to AB. A second normal view of AB could be secured by looking in the frontal direction RS, another line of sight perpendicular to AB. OP and RS are but two of the many lines of sight that are perpendicular to AB, but for most practical purposes the normal view of an oblique line will be determined by looking in either a horizontal or frontal direction. If a side view is given, then a profile line of sight perpendicular to the oblique line is equally advantageous.

3.8. End View of a Line. Normal and end views of lines are views with which the student has had experience. To secure any orthographic view, it is necessary to have an end view of the line of sight for that view. The required view is projected from a normal view of the line of sight. In Fig. 3.5, it is apparent that the top view is a normal view of the line of sight OP and that the auxiliary view (a normal view of AB) would show an end view of *OP*. Hence, if the problem requires that an end view of a line be secured, it will be necessary first to draw a normal view of the line. In Fig. 3.6, the solution is shown.

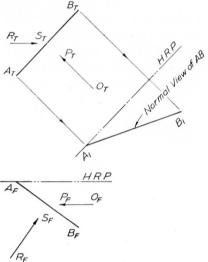

FIG. 3.5. Normal views of an oblique line.

If a view adjacent to an end view of a line is required, that view will be a normal view of the line regardless of the direction of projection from the

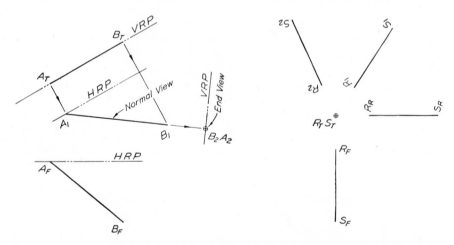

FIG. 3.6. End view of an oblique line.

FIG. 3.7. Views adjacent to an end view of a line.

end view. Therefore, it can be stated with the positiveness of a rule that in orthographic projection *all views adjacent to an end view of a line are normal views of that line* (see Fig. 3.7).

3.9. True Length of Line Segments by the Cone Method. In Fig. 3.8(1), the given line segment is AB. In (2), a right-circular cone is established having a vertical axis, its vertex at A, and point B on the circle of its base.

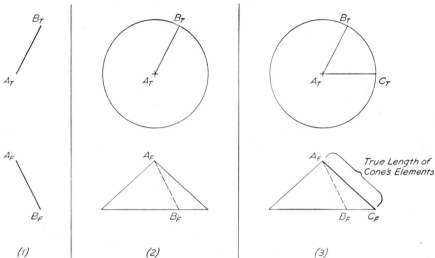

FIG. 3.8. True length of a line segment by the cone method.

AC is a frontal element of the cone; therefore, the front view is a normal view of AC. Since all elements of the cone are equal in length, the true length of AB is determined in (3) by simply measuring the normal view of AC.

The true length of a line segment may be found by this method through the use of any right-circular cone having the given segment as an element. The solution is expedited if the given views show, respectively, the normal and end views of the axis of the cone.

PROBLEMS

Group I. Location of a Point on a Line. Intersecting Lines

3.1. In Fig. 3.9 determine the setback of the building line from the Side Street curb line so that visibility can be maintained from a point on the centerline of Main Street 60 ft east of the east curb line of Side Street to a point on the east curb line of Side Street that is 40 ft from the south curb line of Main Street. The plat is horizontal.

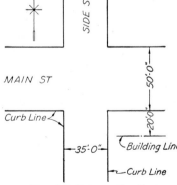

FIG. 3.9. Intersecting lines.

3.2. In Fig. 3.10 determine the elevation at which the line of sight from transit telescope T intersects the stadia rod SR.

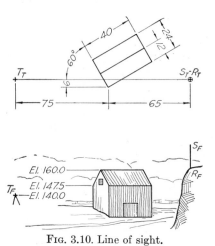

FIG. 3.10. Line of sight.

3.3. *a.* Line $A(3,1,7)$ $B(1,X,7)$ intersects line $P(1,1,8)$ $Q(3,4,5)$. Draw the front view of AB.

b. The horizontal-frontal line $M(5,X,8)$ N intersects the line $Y(7,1\frac{1}{2},5)$ $Z(7,3,7\frac{1}{2})$ at point N. Draw the top and front views of line MN.

Group II. Normal Views of Lines

3.4. Determine the true length of each of the 12 guy wires that aid in the support of the billboard shown in Fig. 3.11.

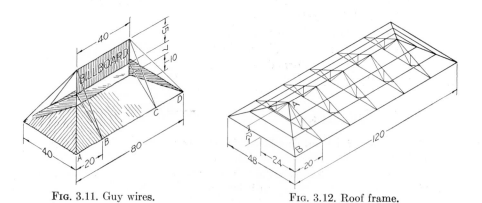

FIG. 3.11. Guy wires.   FIG. 3.12. Roof frame.

3.5. Determine the true length of the hip rafter AB shown in Fig. 3.12.

3.6. Determine the true length of each member of the tripod shown in Fig. 3.13.

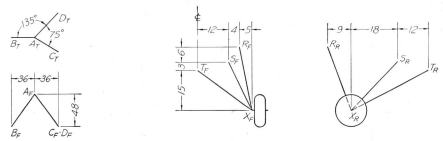

FIG. 3.13. Tripod.   FIG. 3.14. Landing gear.

3.7. Determine the true length of the landing-gear members TX, SX, and RX shown in Fig. 3.14.

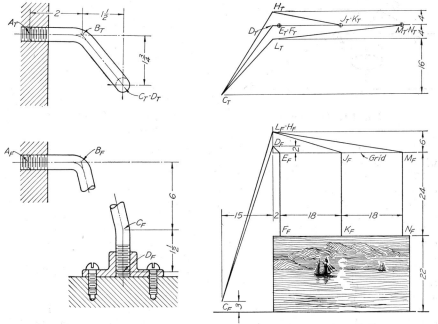

FIG. 3.15. Support rod.   FIG. 3.16. Back-cloth lines.

3.8. In Fig. 3.15 a rod has been threaded at both ends and then bent to the $ABCD$ shape shown. Determine the true length of rod that was required for this finished product. (Disregard bend allowances, and determine the required length as the summation of AB, BC, and CD.)

3.9. The back cloth for a theatrical production is shown in Fig. 3.16. Determine the minimum length for the short line ($CDEF$), the centerline ($CHJK$), and the long line ($CLMN$) for the back cloth positioned as shown. (Disregard the additional lengths required for fastening purposes.)

3.10. In Fig. 3.17 three guy wires are attached to a horizontal collar on the cylindrical stack at points E, A, and C, respectively. These wires are secured to the ridge at points F and B and to the eave at point D, as shown. Allow 18 in. per guy wire for fastening purposes. Determine the total length of wire required for these three guys.

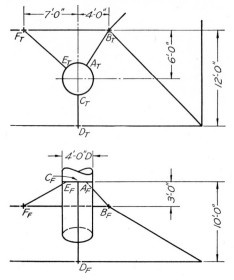

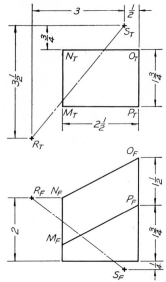

FIG. 3.17. Guy wires.   FIG. 3.18. Drilled, truncated prism.

3.11. Lines $A(1,1\frac{1}{2},7)$ $B(3,3,8\frac{1}{2})$, $BC(4\frac{3}{4},X,7\frac{1}{2})$, and $BD(4\frac{3}{4},X,7\frac{1}{2})$ are three wires of equal length. Complete the front view to show wires BC and BD.

3.12. Square $A(1,1,6)$ $B(1,1,9)$ $C(4,1,9)$ $D(4,1,6)$ is the base of a pyramid. All edges of the pyramid are equal in length. Draw the top and front views of the pyramid.

3.13. A trapeze bar is suspended 48 in. below its horizontal support. The suspension cables are 36 in. apart. How much will the bar be raised by twisting it through 90°?

3.14. Two pulleys lie in the same plane. They are both 2 in. in diameter, and their centers are at points $C(1\frac{1}{2},3,6)$ and $R(5,1,7)$, respectively. *Scale:* full size. Determine the length of the shortest belt that can be used to run on these pulleys.

3.15. The end A of rod $A(4,1,9)$ $B(1,4,7)$ is fixed. End B is to be moved 2 in. to the right, 1 in. below, and forward of its present position. *Scale:* full size. Draw the top and front views of the rod in its new position.

3.16. End R of straight rod $R(4,0\frac{1}{2},8\frac{1}{2})$ $S(2,3,5\frac{1}{2})$ is fixed. End S is to be moved 4 in. to the right and $\frac{3}{4}$ in. below its present position. End S is to remain forward of end R. *Scale:* full size. Draw the top and front views of the rod in its new position.

3.17. A cable runs directly from pulley $A(1,3,6)$ to pulley $B(4,1\frac{1}{4},7\frac{1}{2})$. An addition to the control system requires a change in the path of the cable. The new path runs the cable over pulley A, then vertically downward over a pulley C, then horizontally to pulley B. *Scale:* $\frac{1}{2}'' = 1'\text{-}0''$. Determine the additional cable length required by this change. (Disregard pulley diameters.)

3.18. Chute $A(1,3\frac{1}{2},8)$ $B(4\frac{1}{4},1,6)$ is too steep. The loading point A must remain in its present position. The discharge end of the chute is to be moved by elevating the support at B 6 ft and moving that support 4 ft to the rear and 2 ft to the left of its present position. *Scale:* $\frac{1}{4}'' = 1'\text{-}0''$. Determine the length of the chute that overhangs the support at the discharge end of the chute.

3.19. Points $A(1\frac{1}{2},1,5\frac{1}{2})$, $B(3,1,8\frac{1}{2})$, and $C(4\frac{1}{2},1,5\frac{1}{2})$ are the centers of cubes whose volumes are 1 cu in. each. Surfaces of these cubes are horizontal, frontal, or profile. A $3\frac{1}{2}$-in.-diameter sphere is placed in the cup formed by these cubes. *Scale:* full size. Draw the top and front views of the sphere and cubes.

Group III.   End View of a Line

3.20. In Fig. 3.18 a rectangular prism has been truncated by plane *MNOP*. Line *RS* is the axis of a $\frac{3}{4}$-in.-diameter hole that is to be drilled through this solid. Draw a view of the truncated prism that shows the circular right section of the hole in its true shape.

3.21. Control cable $A(3,1,9)$ $B(6,3\frac{1}{2},7)$ passes through the parallelogram hole $R(4,2\frac{1}{2},8)$ $S(5,2\frac{1}{2},9)$ $T(6,1\frac{1}{2},8)$ U of a bulkhead. Determine the minimum clearance between the cable and the sides of the hole. *Scale:* $\frac{1}{4}'' = 1'\text{-}0''$. If point A is fixed, locate a new position for point B so that the cable will pass through the exact center of the hole. (The length of AB is to remain unchanged. Disregard sag.)

3.22. *Note:* The following problem, while actually a problem requiring the normal view of lines, is solved by drawing an end view of one of the lines.

Draw a view in which line $A(1,2\frac{1}{4},7\frac{1}{2})$ $B(2\frac{1}{2},0\frac{1}{2},7)$ and line $C(3,2,6)$ $D(2\frac{1}{2},2\frac{1}{2},8\frac{1}{2})$ are both shown in true length.

DEFINITIONS AND BASIC VIEWS OF PLANES—
DEVELOPMENT OF POLYHEDRONS

4.1. A *plane* is a continuous magnitude that has two dimensions (such as length and breadth, but not thickness). If a line is drawn between any two points of the plane, it will be wholly within that magnitude.

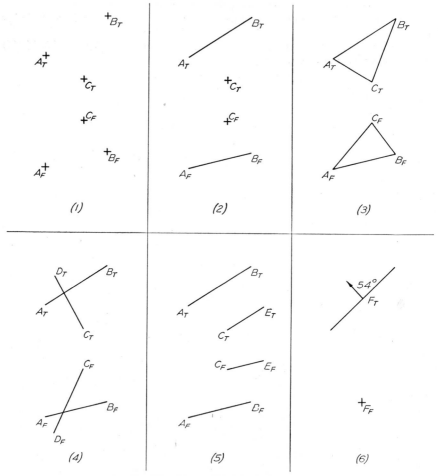

FIG. 4.1. Representations of an oblique plane.

4.2. Representation of a Plane. Figure 4.1 shows six ways of representing a plane in orthographic projection. In (1), three noncollinear points are used; in (2), a line and a point not on the line represent the plane; in (3), a plane figure is employed; in (4), two intersecting lines are used; in (5), two parallel lines represent the plane; and in (6), the method of strike and dip is shown.

4.3. Plane Nomenclature. The student is familiar with the terms *horizontal, frontal,* and *profile.* However, in brief review the following should be recalled: (1) In a horizontal plane no point of the plane is above or below

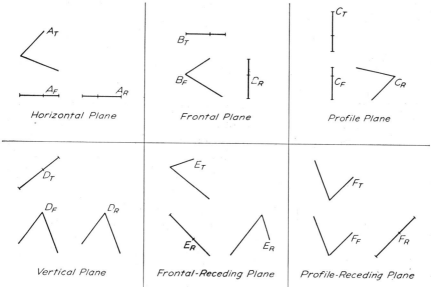

Fig. 4.2. Examples of planes parallel and/or perpendicular to the principal planes of projection.

any other point of the plane; (2) in a frontal plane no point of the plane is in front of or behind any other point of the plane; (3) in a profile plane no point of the plane is to the right or left of any other point of the plane.

In Fig. 4.2, it may be seen that horizontal planes are perpendicular to both the frontal and profile planes of projection, since the front and side views both show the horizontal plane ABC appearing as a straight line. Similarly, note may be taken of the fact that frontal planes are perpendicular to both the horizontal and profile planes of projection while profile planes are perpendicular to the horizontal and frontal planes of projection.

All vertical planes are perpendicular to horizontal planes. The names *frontal receding* and *profile receding* are assigned, respectively, to planes perpendicular to either the frontal or profile planes of projection.

Planes not perpendicular to any of the three principal planes of projection are oblique planes.

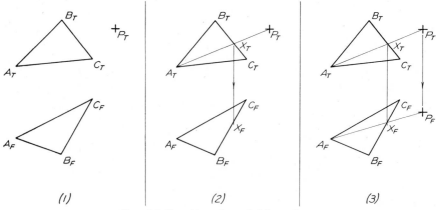

Fig. 4.3. Location of a point in a plane.

4.4. Location of a Point in a Given Plane (Fig. 4.3).   In (1), plane ABC and the top view of point P, a point in the plane, are given.   To locate the front view of point P the line AP is drawn in the top view, as shown in (2). Point X, the intersection of AP with BC, is projected from the top view to the front view.   The front view of line AX is drawn, and point P projected to it from the top view, as shown in (3).

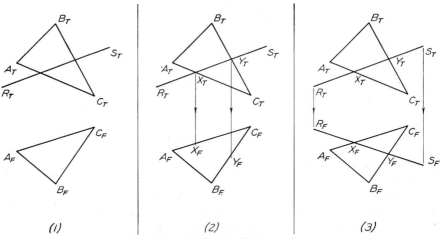

Fig. 4.4. Location of a line in a plane.

4.5. Location of a Line in a Given Plane.   To locate a line in a given plane, it is necessary only to establish two points of the line by the procedure outlined in the preceding paragraph.   The points selected should be as widespread as conditions of the problem will permit in order to ensure accuracy of the position of the line.

In Fig. 4.4(1), plane ABC and the top view of line RS, a line in plane ABC, are given. In (2), the intersections X and Y of line RS with lines AC and BC, respectively, are projected to the front view. Line XY is drawn in the front view, and points R and S are projected from the top view to the front view, as shown in (3).

Projection procedures between the top and front views are less flexible if the given plane is presented with a profile line. An additional line of the plane can be of material assistance in such a case. In the problem of

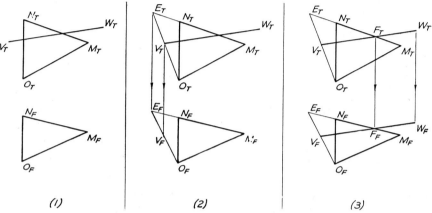

(1) (2) (3)

Fig. 4.5. Use of an additional line in the location of a line in a plane.

Fig. 4.5, the line OV is used to bypass the profile-line presentation. The given data are shown in (1). In (2), the top view of OV is drawn, and point E, its intersection with line MN (extended), is projected to the front view. Point V is located in the front view by projecting from the top view to the front view of OE. Point F, the intersection of lines VW and MN, is projected to the front view. Line VF is drawn as shown in (3). Point W is then projected from the top view.

4.6. Horizontal, Frontal, and Profile Lines of an Oblique Plane. In engineering geometry one of the simplest yet most useful constructions is the establishment of a line that will be shown true length in one of the given views.

In Fig. 4.6(1), the top and front views of plane ABC are presented. The top view is a normal view of all horizontal lines, so the line AH, established as horizontal in the front view, will be shown in true length in the top view. It will be remembered from solid geometry that when a third plane intersects two parallel planes, the resultant lines of intersection are parallel. If the original problem had been to establish the horizontal line of plane ABC that contains point C, then two horizontal planes, one at the height of point C and the other at the height of point A, could be used. The intersection CJ of the upper horizontal plane and plane ABC is parallel to AH and so drawn in all views.

The front view is a normal view of all frontal lines. In Fig. 4.6(2), the frontal line *BF* is first established in the top view, a view showing an edge view of all frontal planes. Point *F*, on *AC*, is projected to the front view, where the line *BF* is then drawn. Had it been required to determine the frontal line of plane *ABC* that contains point *C*, the line parallel to *BF* through *C* would be that line (*CK*).

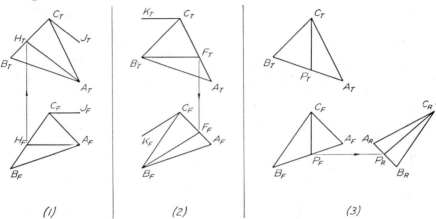

FIG. 4.6. Horizontal, frontal, and profile lines of an oblique plane.

The side view is a normal view of all profile lines. If the requirement had been to locate a line of plane *ABC* that would be true length in the side view, then the profile line *CP* could have been established. This line is first drawn in the front view and then in the side view by the projection of point *P* from the front view [Fig. 4.6(3)].

4.7. Edge Views of Planes. In Fig. 4.2, it may be observed that (1) a horizontal plane is perpendicular to the frontal and profile planes and appears as a line in both the front and side views, (2) a frontal plane is perpendicular to both the horizontal and profile planes and appears as a line in the top and side views, (3) a profile plane is perpendicular to both the horizontal and frontal planes and appears as a line in the top and front views, (4) all vertical planes are perpendicular to the horizontal plane and appear as lines in the top view. From these descriptions, it can be deduced that *any plane perpendicular to a second plane will appear as a line in a normal view of the second plane.*

It should then be realized that every edge view of a plane shows one system of parallel lines of that plane appearing as points; e.g., the profile lines of a horizontal plane appear as points in the front view, an edge view of the plane. Frontal lines of a horizontal plane appear as points in the side view, another edge view of the horizontal plane. Conversely, *an edge view of a plane will be had if an end view of any line in the plane is secured.*

In Sec. 3.8, it was determined that an end view of a line can be only adjacent to the normal view of the line. Hence, to secure an edge view of plane ABC [Fig. 4.7(1)], a line of the plane is established that is normal in one of the given views, e.g., the horizontal line AH. This determines the direction for a line of sight that will give an end view of AH and, therefore, an edge view of plane ABC. In (2), the end view of the frontal line FB is used to obtain another edge view of plane ABC.

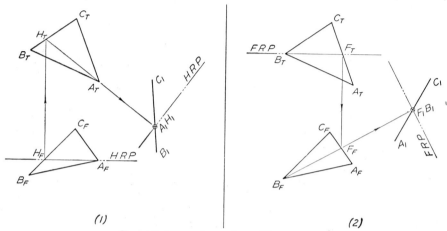

FIG. 4.7. Edge views of an oblique plane.

4.8. Strike and Dip. In Sec. 4.2, the method of representing a plane by strike and dip was mentioned. This representation is especially useful to mining engineers and geologists; however, the method permits the ready visualization of planes by anyone familiar with its basic principles.

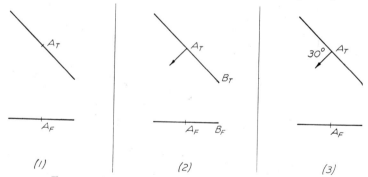

FIG. 4.8. Representation of a plane by strike and dip.

The *strike* of a plane is the direction of horizontal lines of the plane. The *dip* of a plane is the angle of depression between the plane and horizontal planes. In addition to strike and quantity of dip, it is necessary to describe the general *direction of dip*, since two planes can be passed through a horizontal line and make the same angle (other than 0 or 90°) with the horizontal.

In Fig. 4.8(1), a horizontal line containing point A is drawn. A plane containing this line, that dips 30° in a southwesterly direction, is required.

(North is toward the rear in the given problem.)   The general direction of dip is indicated in the top view of (2), with a short arrow drawn at right angles to AB.   In (3), the amount of dip is added to the symbol to complete the description of the plane.

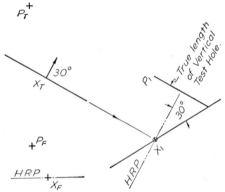

Fig. 4.9. Problem employing strike-and-dip representation.

A basic problem employing the strike-and-dip presentation of a plane is shown in Fig. 4.9.   The plane that strikes and dips through point X represents a vein of ore.   Point P, on the hillside, locates where a vertical test drill hole is to be bored to the vein.   The length of this hole is to be determined.   An end view of the strike line is secured, and the edge view of the plane is drawn there.   The true length of the vertical test hole is seen in this view, a normal view of all vertical lines.

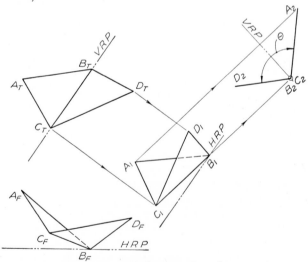

Fig. 4.10. Angle between two planes.

4.9. Angle between Two Given Planes.   The true size of the angle between two planes is seen in a view that shows an end view of the line of intersection the planes.   In Fig. 4.10, the normal view of the angle between planes ABC and BCD is identified in the oblique view where BC appears as a point. Either the angle θ or the angle $360° - \theta$ might be given as the angle between the surfaces ABC and BCD. There is a difference, however, between these angles and the ones that may be given between the *limitless planes* of ABC and BCD, because in the latter instance either θ or $180° - \theta$ might be given. $360° - \theta$ would not be given for the angle between the limitless planes.

4.10. Normal Views of Planes. Reference to Fig. 4.2 will illustrate that the top view is a normal view of all horizontal planes, that the front view

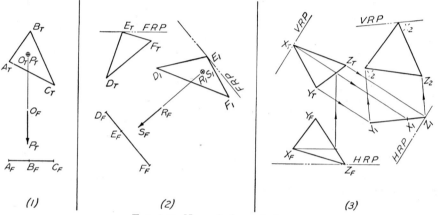

FIG. 4.11. Normal views of planes.

is a normal view of all frontal planes, and that the side view is a normal view of all profile planes. Regardless of the position that a plane occupies in space, it is only necessary to look perpendicularly at it in order to secure its normal view. In Fig. 4.11(1), the vertical line of sight OP is perpendicular to the horizontal plane ABC; hence, the top view, showing an end view of OP, is a normal view of plane ABC.

Further study of Fig. 4.11(1) will allow for the realization that a *normal view of a plane is projected perpendicularly from an edge view of that plane.* An end view of the line of sight for the normal view of a plane will be seen in the normal view of the plane, and normal views of that line of sight will be seen in all edge views of the plane.

In Fig. 4.11(2), the front view is an edge view of plane DEF. Line RS, a frontal line of sight perpendicular to plane DEF, is shown in the front view. The auxiliary view shows an end view of RS and a normal view of DEF. In (3), the normal view of the oblique plane XYZ is secured after an edge view of that plane was first obtained. (The line of sight for the normal view of XYZ was not physically drawn on the paper but was visualized in the original analysis of the problem.)

4.11. Angle between Intersecting Lines. The student should again follow the procedure outlined in Sec. 2.10 to observe that angles and plane figures appear different from separate points of view. Obviously, then, the only views in which angles between intersecting lines can be measured or in which specified plane figures can be laid out will be normal views of the planes of those angles and figures. There are two such views for every plane, the lines of sight being at an angle of 180° to each other; e.g., the right- and left-side views are both normal views of all profile planes.

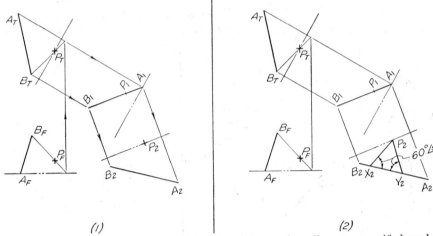

(1)   *(2)*

FIG. 4.12. Lines through a given point, intersecting a given line at a specified angle.

A typical problem that requires a normal view of a plane follows. In Fig. 4.12, point P and line AB are given. It is required to locate all lines containing point P that will intersect line AB and make angles of 60° with AB. The problem is analyzed as requiring a normal view of plane ABP, for in no other view can the 60° angles be established. In (1), the edge and normal views of plane ABP are drawn. Lines PX and PY are located in the normal view of plane ABP, both intersecting line AB and making angles of 60° with that line, as shown in (2). Points X and Y can then be projected to the original views if required.

4.12. Angle between a Line and an Oblique Plane. The true size of the angle between a line and a plane is seen in a view that is both a normal view of the line and an edge view of the plane.

In Fig. 4.13(1), the given line is AB and the given plane is XYZ. An edge view of XYZ is projected from the top view, and a normal view of the plane is projected from its edge view, as shown in (2). A normal view of line AB (and another edge view of plane XYZ) is projected from the normal view of plane XYZ, in (3). The true size of the required angle is seen in that view.

4.13. Development of Polyhedrons (Fig. 4.14). In many engineering constructions full-size patterns of some or all surfaces of an object are required. If these surfaces are plane or single curved, their patterns may

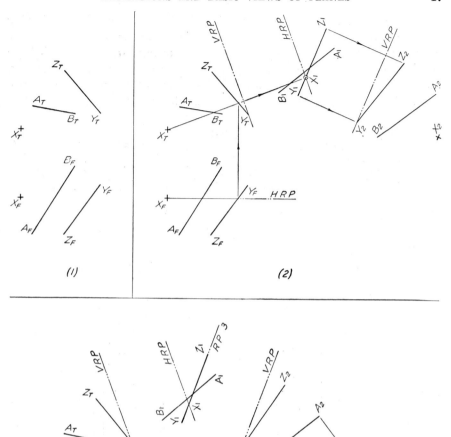

(1)

(2)

(3)

Fig. 4.13. Angle between an oblique line and an oblique plane.

be accurately determined. Such surfaces are said to be developable, and the complete surface laid out in a plane is called the *development* of that surface.

If it is required to develop the lateral surfaces of a polyhedron, the normal views of those surfaces are obtained and then joined at their common edges.

The experienced draftsman will probably shorten this procedure by finding the true lengths of the several edges of the polyhedron, using the cone method described in Sec. 3.9. If a surface is triangular, its size and shape are determined by this procedure. If the surface is other than triangular, then its *shape* must be fixed by placing diagonals on the surface or otherwise finding the true size of the angles between adjacent edges.

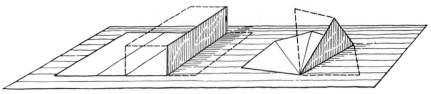

FIG. 4.14. Development of polyhedrons.

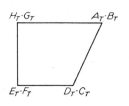

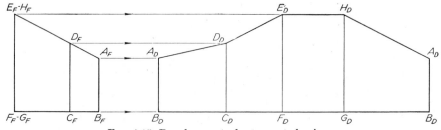

FIG. 4.15. Development of a truncated prism.

4.14. Development of a Truncated Prism. Two orthographic views of a truncated prism are shown in Fig. 4.15. The development of the lateral surfaces is started on the arbitrarily chosen shortest edge AB. In the unrolling of these surfaces, edges BC, CF, FG, and GB develop as a straight line, since each is perpendicular to the lateral edges of the prism. This straight line $BCFGB$ is the *stretch-out* for the pattern. The true size and shape of surface $ABCD$ are drawn by obtaining the true lengths of AB and CD from the front view and the true length of BC (the shortest distance between AB and CD) from the top view. Similarly, the surfaces $CDEF$, $EFGH$, and $GHAB$ are added in sequence to the pattern.

It should be noted that the orthographic views drawn in Fig. 4.15 show, in one instance, the true length of the lateral edges and, in the other, the true length of the distances between them. Such a pair of views is necessary for an accurate and rapid solution to the development problem. It should also be noted that this pattern is *inside up*. Differing circumstances will cause some objects to be developed with their exteriors rather than interiors face up on the pattern.

4.15. Development of a Pyramid (Fig. 4.16). The development of the surfaces of a triangular pyramid is started by determining the true lengths of its six edges. Recognition that edge VA is frontal and that AC is horizontal permits their true lengths being secured from the given views. The

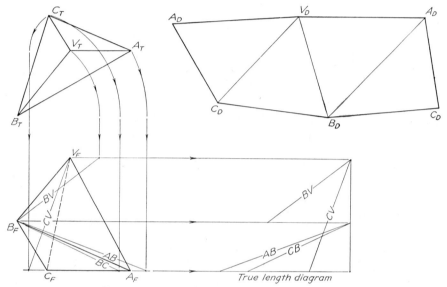

FIG. 4.16. Development of a triangular pyramid.

cone method may be used to find the true lengths of edges BV, CV, AB, and BC as shown by the construction overlaying the top and front views. It is obvious that some confusion results by following this practice. The front view appears quite involved, and with a more complicated object the complexity of the view and the overlaying construction may result in an erroneous development.

True lengths of the edges may be determined by means of a true-length diagram, a variation of the cone method. The horizontal projection length of an edge (seen in the top view) is used as one leg of a right triangle whose other leg is equal to the height between the extremities of that edge. The hypotenuse of the triangle is the true length of the edge. The student is urged to check the construction for any true length shown to verify this fact.

All four of the surfaces of the pyramid are developed, exterior up, in the pattern. The true lengths of the several edges are used to determine the normal views of each triangular surface, and the surfaces are joined along common edges.

4.16. Practical Considerations. The developments described in the foregoing sections have been made without considering the practical requirement of fastening the sheets after they have been cut and bent into the desired geometric forms. Additional material is usually left adjacent to the edges to be joined, except when a separate angle is fastened to both sides of the joint or when the joint is buttwelded.

One-half of the piece is all that need be developed if the piece is symmetrical, provided the drawing clearly shows the pattern centerline. Angles of each bend must be indicated, and if the piece is nonsymmetrical the developments must be marked for bending up or down.

Added interest in developments may be realized if each student will solve one of the problems in Group VI of this chapter, and then cut and form the resulting pattern into a model of the subject piece.

PROBLEMS

Group I.   Location of Points and Lines in Planes

4.1. Points $D(2,1,X)$, $E(4,4,X)$, and $F(4,X,8)$ are points in plane $A(3,3,7)$ $B(6,1,8)$ $C(7,4,6)$. Locate points D and E in the top view and point F in the front view.

4.2. Plane $M(3,0\frac{1}{2},7\frac{1}{2})$ $N(5,4\frac{1}{2},8\frac{1}{2})$ $O(7,2\frac{1}{2},5)$ contains point $P(6,1\frac{1}{2},X)$. Draw the top, front, and left-side views of (a) the profile line PQ that intersects line NO at Q, (b) the frontal line QR that intersects the line OM at R, and (c) the horizontal line RS that intersects line MN at S.

4.3. The plane surfaces $A(0\frac{1}{2},0\frac{1}{2},6)$ $B(2,2,8\frac{1}{2})$ $C(4\frac{1}{2},1\frac{1}{2},6)$ and $ABD(2\frac{1}{2},4,6)$ are to be supported by a brace across their dihedral angle. One end of the brace is to be at point $P(1\frac{3}{4},X,6\frac{1}{2})$ in plane ABD. The brace is to make equal angles with both surfaces. Draw the top and front views of the brace, and determine its length.

Group II.   Strike and Dip

4.4. Determine the strike and dip of plane $A(6\frac{1}{2},2,4)$ $B(4\frac{1}{2},0\frac{1}{2},6\frac{1}{2})$ $C(2,3,5\frac{1}{2})$.

4.5. a. Line $D(6,5\frac{1}{2},8\frac{1}{2})$ $G(3\frac{1}{2},5\frac{1}{2},7\frac{1}{4})$ is in a plane that dips 45° to the left rear. Points $E(5,X,7)$ and $F(3\frac{1}{2},X,8)$ lie in this plane. Locate points E and F in the front view.

b. Line $M(1,0\frac{1}{4},3\frac{1}{2})$ $N(3,0\frac{1}{4},2\frac{1}{2})$ is a strike line of a plane that dips 60° forward and to the left. Points $O(2\frac{1}{2},2,X)$ and $P(3\frac{1}{2},1\frac{1}{4},X)$ lie in this plane. Locate points O and P in the top view.

4.6. Line $S(1,2,8)$ $K(5,2,6)$ is a tunnel in the Simpson seam. Point $C(3,4,5)$ is the top of a vertical shaft that serves the seam at a depth of 300 ft. *Scale:* $1'' = 100'$. Determine the strike and dip of the Simpson seam.

4.7. Points $A(4\frac{1}{2},2,5)$, $B(5,3\frac{1}{2},7\frac{1}{2})$, and $C(7,1\frac{1}{2},6)$ are survey stations in the Steam-coal seam. Determine the strike and dip of this seam.

4.8. Line $J(4,2,6)$ $K(6,2,8)$ is a strike line of a vein of ore. The vein dips 30° in a southeasterly direction. Points $P(6,X,6)$ and $N(6,X,5)$ are survey stations in the mine operating this vein. If the elevation of K is 300 ft above sea level, what are the elevations of points P and N? *Scale:* $1'' = 200'$.

4.9. Points $A(1,4,5)$, $B(3,4,8)$, and $C(6,3,6)$ are the tops of vertical test drill holes that have been sunk to the Mac seam. The holes at A and C reached the seam after 300 ft of drilling. Hole B was only 100 ft deep when it reached the seam. *Scale:* $1'' = 100'$. Determine the strike and dip of the seam. How deep would a drill hole started at $D(4,3,7)$ be when it reached the seam?

4.10. Line segment $C(1,2\frac{1}{2},6)$ $F(4,2\frac{1}{2},7)$ is one diagonal of a regular hexagon. The plane of the hexagon dips 60° in a southeasterly direction (north being to the rear). Draw the top and front views of the hexagon.

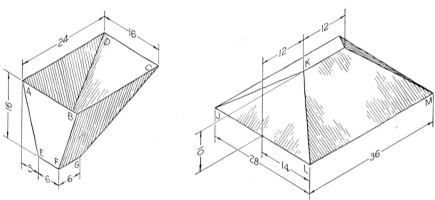

Fig. 4.17. Hopper.   Fig. 4.18. Hip roof.

Group III. Angle between Planes. Edge Views of Planes

4.11. Determine the true size of the dihedral angles between the lateral surfaces of the hopper shown in Fig. 4.17.

4.12. Determine the true size of the angle between the roof surfaces JKL and KLM shown in Fig. 4.18.

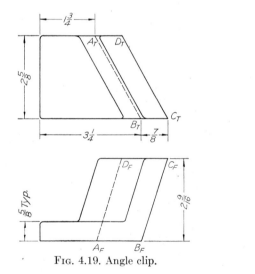

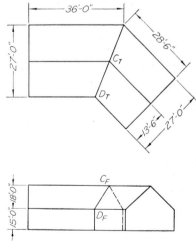

Fig. 4.19. Angle clip.   Fig. 4.20. Valley flashing.

4.13. In Fig. 4.19 through what angle from its present position must the clip angle be rotated about AB to permit the milling of surface $ABCD$ in a horizontal working position?

4.14. In Fig. 4.20 determine the angle that a piece of sheet metal must be bent from the flat to form the flashing for valley CD.

4.15. The front and half-top views of a square-based pyramidal roof framing of a cupola are shown in Fig. 4.21. The hip rafters are beveled so that the top surfaces of the jack rafters are in the planes of the beveled surfaces. Determine the angle between the beveled surfaces of one of these hip rafters.

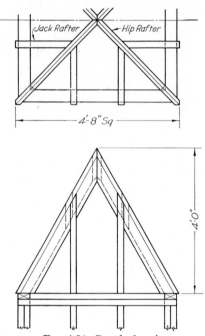

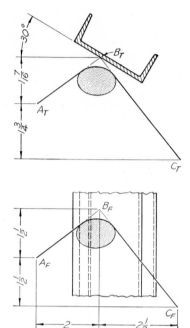

FIG. 4.21. Cupola framing.   FIG. 4.22. Pulley bracket.

4.16. A control cable whose centerlines are AB and CD runs over the pulley shown in Fig. 4.22. Preliminary to the design of the pulley bracket, the angle between the mounting surface (vertical face of the channel) and the plane of the pulley (ABC) must be determined. Find the true size of this angle.

4.17. Determine the true size of the angle between the windshield planes $ABCD$ and $CDEF$ shown in Fig. 4.23.

4.18. In a transport airplane, a cubical junction box is centered on bus bar BR, with two of its surfaces perpendicular to BR as in Fig. 4.24. Determine the angle between these surfaces and the plane of the nose rib.

4.19. Determine the angles that the plane of plate $A(4,1,6)$ $B(5\frac{1}{4},1,5)$ $C(6\frac{1}{4},2\frac{1}{2},6)$ $D(5,2\frac{1}{2},X)$ makes with the horizontal, frontal, and profile planes of projection. Identify the true size of each angle with an appropriate letter (that is, H, F, or P).

4.20. Draw an auxiliary elevation and a right auxiliary view that shows the plane $M(1,1,6\frac{1}{2})$ $N(4,1,6)$ $O(2,3,8)$ appearing as a line.

4.21. Determine the true size of the dihedral angle between plane $A(1\frac{1}{2},3\frac{1}{2},7\frac{1}{2})$ $B(2\frac{1}{2},0\frac{1}{2},3\frac{3}{4})$ $C(5\frac{1}{2},2,8)$ and plane $BCD(5,4,6)$.

4.22. Two flat plates have been welded together along line $D(7,3\frac{1}{2},7\frac{1}{2})$ $C(4,1,4)$. Point $A(7,2,6)$ is in the plane of one of these plates; point $B(6,1,8)$ is in the plane of the other plate. Determine the true size of the angle between these plates.

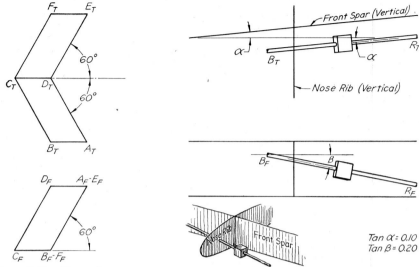

FIG. 4.23. Two-piece windshield.

FIG. 4.24. Oblique junction box.

$Tan\ \alpha = 0.10$
$Tan\ \beta = 0.20$

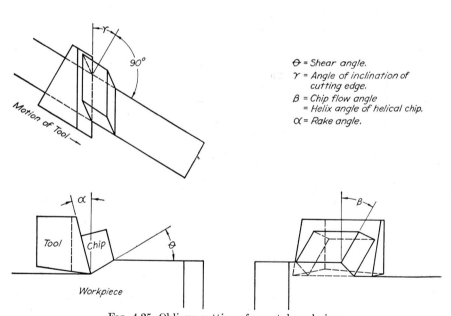

θ = Shear angle.
γ = Angle of inclination of cutting edge.
β = Chip flow angle
  = Helix angle of helical chip.
α = Rake angle.

FIG. 4.25. Oblique cutting of a metal workpiece.

4.23. Fig. 4.25.   In the oblique cutting of a metal workpiece by a single straight cutting edge, the true rake angle is the measure of the angle between the tool face and a plane perpendicular to the direction of tool travel.   Determine the true rake angle when $\alpha = 15°$ and $\gamma = 30°$.

Group IV.　Normal Views of Planes

4.24. The top and front views of a concrete footer are given in Fig. 4.26. Determine the normal views of each lateral surface as a preliminary step in the design of the form-work for this footer.

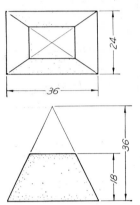

Fig. 4.26. Pier footer.

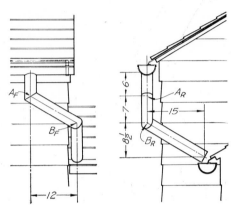

Fig. 4.27. Roof leader.

4.25. Rain water is drained from the upper eaves trough shown in Fig. 4.27 to the lower one by the three-piece roof leader. Preliminary to cutting the straight length of leader required to make this three-piece assembly, the true size of the angles at *A* and *B* between adjacent piece centerlines is required. Determine the size of these angles to the nearest whole degree.

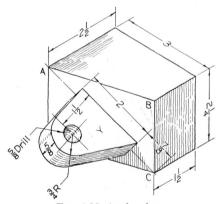

Fig. 4.28. Anchor lug.

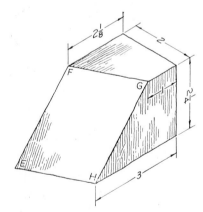

Fig. 4.29. Truncated prism.

4.26. Draw the views and/or partial views necessary for the complete shape description of the anchor lug shown in Fig. 4.28.

4.27. Draw a normal view of surface *EFGH* shown in Fig. 4.29.

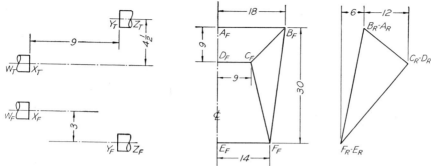

Fig. 4.30. Ogee connection.   Fig. 4.31. Landing-gear truss.

4.28. In Fig. 4.30 two horizontal-frontal pipe lengths are represented by their axes *WX* and *YZ*, respectively. These pipes are to be connected by means of a symmetrical ogee curved pipe. Determine the radius of bend and the bend angle for one-half of the ogee pipe.

4.29. In Fig. 4.31 the front and right-side views of the tube centerlines of a landing-gear truss are given. Determine the true size of the angles between adjacent tubes.

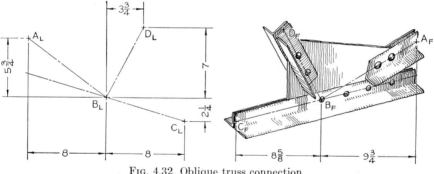

Fig. 4.32. Oblique truss connection.

4.30. In Fig. 4.32 three members of an obliquely positioned truss have *AB*, *BC*, and *BD* as their respective gauge lines. Determine the true size of the angles *ABC*, *ABD*, and *DBC* preparatory to designing the gusset plate. (All gauge lines shown are coplanar.)

4.31. The compound centerline of a control cable is $A(0,1,5)$ $B(2,1,6)$ $C(5,2\frac{1}{2},6)$ $D(6\frac{1}{4},1\frac{1}{4},4)$. Pulleys of 2-in. diameter are used at the B and C turns. Locate the top and front views of the pulley centers. *Scale:* full size. (Neglect cable diameter.)

4.32. Line segment $A(7,3,5)$ $D(4,2,7)$ is one diagonal of a regular hexagon. Point $K(7,1,8)$ is in the plane of the hexagon. Draw the top and front views of the hexagon.

4.33. Points $A(1,1\frac{1}{4},7)$, $B(3,3\frac{1}{2},8\frac{1}{2})$, and $C(3\frac{1}{2},1\frac{3}{4},6)$ are on the circumference of the inscribed circle of a regular hexagon. Two sides of the hexagon are horizontal. Draw the top and front views of the hexagon.

4.34. Lines $R(1,1,7)$ $S(3,3,8\frac{1}{2})$ and $ST(5,2,5)$ are the centerlines of a cable. A 4-in.-diameter pulley carries the cable around the turn at S. *Scale:* full size. Locate the center of the pulley.

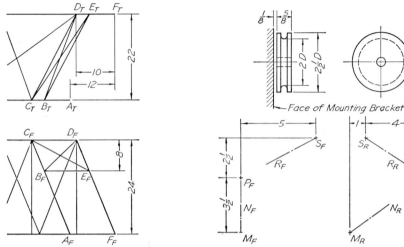

FIG. 4.33. Skew bridge end panel.   FIG. 4.34. Pulley, cable, and guard pins.

4.35. Draw a normal view of the end panel $ABCDEF$ shown in Fig. 4.33.

4.36. Lines MN and RS are the centerlines of a $\frac{1}{2}$-in.-diameter cable that runs on the pulley shown in the detail drawing of Fig. 4.34. These centerlines, if extended, intersect at point P. To prevent the cable from jumping the pulley should it slacken suddenly,

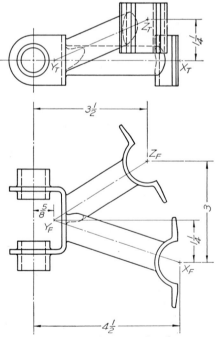

FIG. 4.35. Welded support bracket.

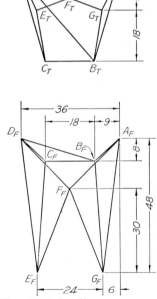

FIG. 4.36. Landing-gear upper truss.

¼-in.-diameter guard pins are to be positioned opposite the points of tangency between cable and pulley. Clearance between the guard pins and the pulley is to be $\frac{1}{16}$ in. The guard pins are to project $\frac{7}{8}$ in. from the face of the mounting bracket. The mounting bracket is to the rear of the cable. Draw a normal view of the mounting-bracket face, showing the pulley and guard-pin locations.

4.37. In Fig. 4.35 determine the true size of the angle XYZ between the support-bracket tubes.

4.38. Tubing centerlines for the upper truss of a commercial aircraft landing gear are shown in Fig. 4.36. Determine the true lengths of the several tubes (measured to center-line intersections) and the true size of the angles between adjacent tubes.

4.39. The equilateral triangle MNO lies in plane $M(2\frac{1}{2},0\frac{1}{2},8\frac{1}{2})$ $N(0\frac{1}{2},3\frac{1}{2},7\frac{1}{2})$ $P(4\frac{1}{2},1\frac{1}{2},5\frac{1}{2})$. Point O is the nearer to point P of the two possible positions. Draw the top and front views of triangle MNO.

4.40. Points $A(1\frac{1}{2},1,8)$, $B(3\frac{1}{8},4\frac{1}{4},5\frac{1}{2})$, and $C(4\frac{1}{4},2\frac{3}{8},6\frac{5}{8})$ are on the circumference of a circle that circumscribes the regular pentagon $PQRST$. Point P is 1 in. above point A and to the left of A. Draw the top and front views of the pentagon.

4.41. Draw the top and front views of the bisector of angle $A(2\frac{1}{2},1,8\frac{1}{2})$ $B(2\frac{1}{2},4,6)$ $C(6,2,4)$.

4.42. Points $C(1\frac{1}{2},3,5)$ and $F(3\frac{1}{2},2,8\frac{1}{2})$ are diagonally opposite corners of a regular hexagon. The hexagon lies in plane $CFJ(0\frac{1}{2},1,6\frac{1}{4})$. Draw the top, front, edge, and normal views of the hexagon.

Group V. Angle between a Line and a Plane

4.43. Determine the true size of the angle between line $M(1,3,5)$ $N(4,1,7)$ and plane $A(2,1,8)$ $B(4,3,6)$ $C(5,1,5)$.

4.44. Determine the true size of the angle that line $J(4,2,6)$ $K(6,3,7)$ makes with plane $Q(1,1\frac{3}{4},8)$ $R(2\frac{1}{2},3,7\frac{1}{2})$ $S(4,0\frac{1}{4},5\frac{1}{2})$.

4.45. Determine the true size of the angle between line $A(1,1,6)$ $P(2\frac{1}{2},3\frac{1}{4},5)$ and plane $B(3,3\frac{1}{2},7)$ $C(4,2,5)$ A.

Group VI. Development of Polyhedrons

4.46. Lay out the pattern for the sheet-metal air scoop shown in Fig. 4.37.

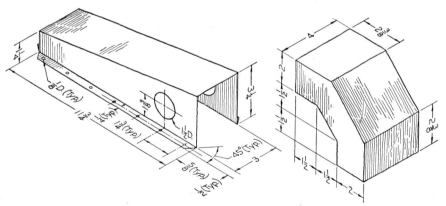

FIG. 4.37. Air scoop.   FIG. 4.38. Rectangular duct elbow.

4.47. A two-by-four duct is turned through 90° by the elbow shown in Fig. 4.38. Develop the surfaces of this elbow. (Disregard flanges, tabs, and all other securement means.)

4.48. Develop the lateral surfaces of the hopper shown in Fig. 4.39.

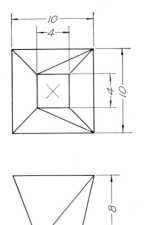

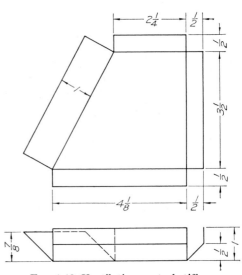

FIG. 4.39. Hopper.   FIG. 4.40. Ventilating-control stiffener.

4.49. Develop the surfaces of the ventilating-control stiffener shown in Fig. 4.40.

4.50. Points $A(0\frac{1}{2},1,8)$, $B(2,1,5)$, $C(4,2,7)$, and $D(1,3\frac{1}{2},6)$ are the four corners of a tetrahedron. Develop the surfaces of this pyramid into a one-piece pattern inside up.

CHAPTER 5

INTERSECTIONS OF LINES, PLANES, AND POLYHEDRONS

5.1. The many problems involving planes can be solved only through the use of intersecting lines. Two lines intersect if there is a point common to both lines. In Fig. 5.1, point X is common to lines AB and CD; hence these lines intersect.

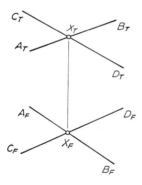

Fig. 5.1. Intersecting lines.

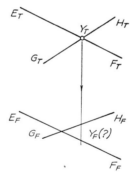

Fig. 5.2. Nonintersecting lines.

An appearance of intersection as seen in only one view does not assure an intersection between two lines. In the top view of Fig. 5.2, point Y appears to be on both EF and GH; however, the front view shows that Y cannot be on both. Lines EF and GH, therefore, do not intersect.

5.2. Visibility of Skew Edges. Skew edges exist in most structures, and the necessity of determining their visibility in the several views drawn is ever present. The top and front views of the four corners of a tetrahedron are shown in Fig. 5.3(1). The *outline* is always visible and is so drawn in (2). To determine the visibility of edges AC and BD in the top view, it is merely necessary to find which edge passes over the other. The intersecting-line principle is employed for this purpose.

In Fig. 5.3(3), the lines of edges AC and BD are drawn in lightly. A vertical line XY that intersects both AC and BD is established. Point X on AC is over point Y on BD; therefore, AC is above BD and is visible in the top view. The top view is completed in (4). A horizontal-profile line

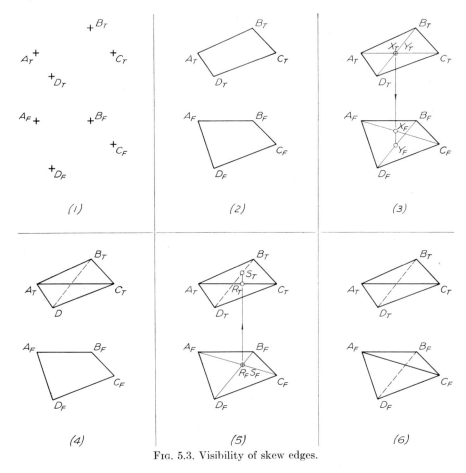

Fig. 5.3. Visibility of skew edges.

RS is drawn between edges AC and BD. Whichever edge this line intersects in front of the other is visible in the front view. The construction is shown in (5), and the front view completed, as shown in (6).

Although edge AC is visible in both the top and front views the student should realize that edge AC is hidden in as many views as it is visible. For example, the front view shows AC visible, but AC is hidden in the rear view.

5.3. Intersection of a Given Line and a Given Plane (Edge-view Solution). A line will intersect a plane at a single point if it is neither in the plane nor parallel to it. This point of intersection is immediately determined in all edge views of the plane, as shown in Fig. 5.4. The intersection

X of the oblique line MN and the frontal receding plane ABC is identified in the front view, an edge view of ABC. The top view of X is located by

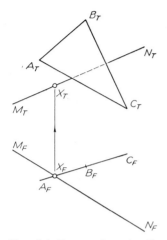

FIG. 5.4. Intersection of a line and a frontal-receding plane.

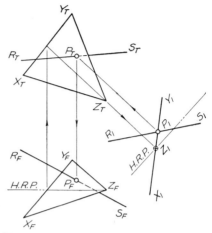

FIG. 5.5. Intersection of a line and an oblique plane.

projection from the front view. Note that point X lies outside the limits of triangle ABC; however, this is of no consequence, since the plane is limitless.

When the given plane is oblique and, therefore, does not appear as a line in any principal view, an auxiliary view that shows the edge view of the plane must be drawn for a solution by this method (see Fig. 5.5).

5.4. Intersection of Two Given Planes (Edge-view Solution). The line of intersection between two planes can be determined by finding the intersections of two lines of one plane with the other plane. In Fig. 5.6, the lines AB and BC intersect plane XYZ at points M and N, respectively. Hence, line MN is the line of intersection between planes ABC and XYZ.

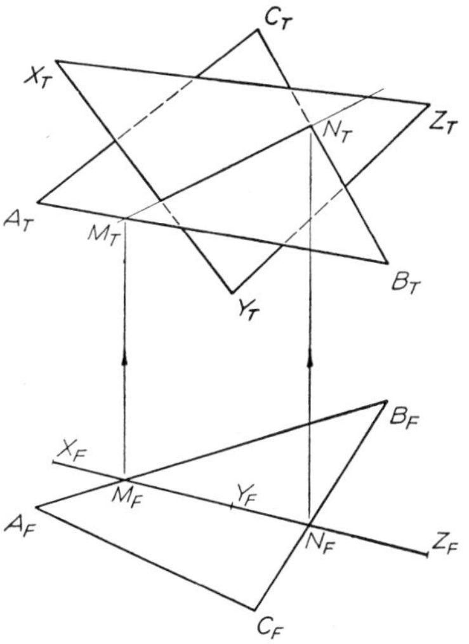

The points of intersection between the lines of one plane with the other plane are not immediately seen in any of the principal views when both of the planes are oblique; however, an edge view of one of the planes will effect the same presentation as that shown in Fig. 5.6.

FIG. 5.6. Intersection of two planes.

5.5. Cutting-plane Solutions to Intersection Problems. A comparison of the number of steps taken with the expected accuracy of the solution presents an inverse ratio in the solution of engineering-geometry problems. Auxiliary views must be drawn in the edge-view solutions previously described. Such solutions are not overly long, but shorter constructions will be usually preferred. Cutting planes permit shorter procedures.

5.6. Intersection of a Given Line and a Given Oblique Plane (Cutting-plane Solution). The intersection of a line and an oblique plane can be determined through the use of a cutting plane that contains the given line. A cutting plane that appears as a line in one of the given views is usually selected. This permits a readily determined line of intersection between the given plane and the cutting plane, in a manner similar to the solution shown in Fig. 5.6. If the given line is not parallel to this line of intersection, they will intersect, and their intersection is the required point, common to both the given line and the given plane. The given line and plane are parallel if the line of intersection between the cutting plane and the given plane is parallel to the given line.

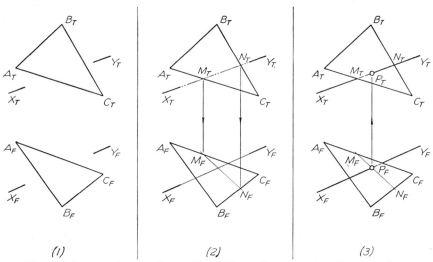

(1)   *(2)*   *(3)*

Fig. 5.7. Intersection of a line and an oblique plane—cutting-plane solution.

In Fig. 5.7(1), plane ABC and line XY are given. A vertical cutting plane containing line XY is established in (2). It intersects plane ABC along line MN. Lines MN and XY intersect at point P, the required intersection between line XY and plane ABC, as shown in (3).

5.7. Intersection of Two Given Planes (Cutting-plane Solution). The intersection of two planes may be found by using the foregoing procedure to determine two points on the required line of intersection. In Fig. 5.8(1), the given planes are ABC and XYZ. In (2), the solution is tentatively started by attempting to determine the intersection of line AB with plane

XYZ. Line AB is parallel to plane XYZ, since line MN is parallel to AB. Such a start, therefore, gives no point on the required line of intersection. In (3), the intersection of line XZ with plane ABC is determined to be point P, through the use of a vertical cutting plane containing line XZ. The line

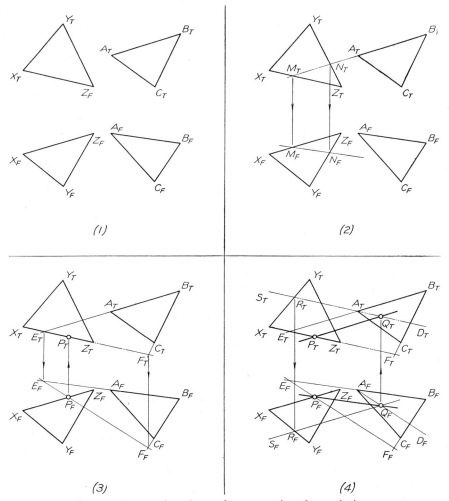

FIG. 5.8. Intersection of two planes—cutting-plane solution.

of intersection between the cutting plane and plane ABC meets line XZ at an angle which permits the accurate determination of point P. A cutting plane parallel to the previous one is used to determine a second point on the intersection of the given planes. In (4), this second cutting plane cuts line AD on plane ABC and line RS on plane XYZ. AD and RS intersect at point Q. The line intersection between planes ABC and XYZ is the line PQ.

The solution to the foregoing problem does not require the determination of a second point on the line of intersection. The line of intersection is parallel to line AB, since AB is parallel to plane XYZ.

5.8. Line through a Given Point and Intersecting Each of Two Given Skew Lines. This problem is solved by finding the intersection of one skew line with the plane of the other skew line and given point. In Fig.

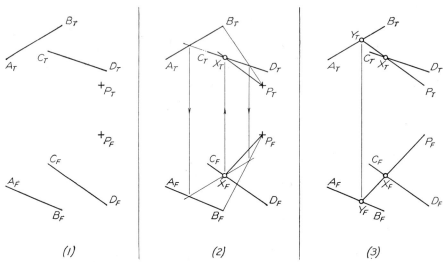

FIG. 5.9. Line through a given point and intersecting both of two given skew lines.

5.9(1), AB and CD are the skew lines and P is the point through which the required line must pass. In (2), the intersection X of line CD with plane ABP is determined. The required line is PX. To verify the result, the intersection Y of line PX with line AB is found and checked for projection accuracy between the views, as shown in (3).

5.9. Intersection of a Polyhedron and a Plane. The intersection of a line and an oblique plane is efficiently found through the use of a cutting plane. The intersection of several lines with an oblique plane can best be accomplished by securing an edge view of the oblique plane.

An illustration of the latter solution is shown in Fig. 5.10. The top and front views of that portion of pyramid $VABC$ that is below plane XYZ are required. The edge view of plane XYZ is determined in (2). The intersections of plane XYZ with edges VA, VB, and VC are seen immediately in this view and projected back to the other views. The completed top and front views of the truncated pyramid are shown in (3).

5.10. Intersection of Two Polyhedrons. The intersection of two polyhedrons is basically a series of plane intersections. It must be remembered, however, that the edges and surfaces of a polyhedron are limited whereas theoretical intersections deal with lines and planes unrestricted as to length and extent. Since the intersection of two planes is a line, the intersection of two polyhedrons will be a series of edges, representative of such lines, connected so as to form a continuous intersection that returns upon itself. In some instances there will be more than one line of intersection, e.g., when one geometric mass is extended on both sides of a second geometric mass.

The intersection of the two prismatic masses indicated in Fig. 5.11(1) is determined by finding a series of surface intersections. The surfaces $ABJK$ and RST intersect on JK, and since the edge view of both surfaces is seen in the top view, that line appears as a point in the top view. If JK were

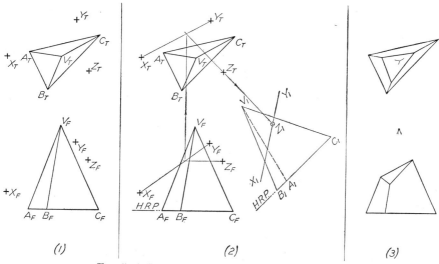

FIG. 5.10. Intersection of a plane and a pyramid.

extended, it would be seen that it would continue on surface RST but not on surface $ABJK$; hence, the next part of the line of intersection between the solids will be between surfaces RST and AKC. This is found by determining the intersection of line AC with plane RST, then connecting this point U and point K. The actual intersection terminates at point L, for the intersection lies entirely on the surfaces of both solids, and surface RST is bounded by edge RL. In (3), the intersection of surfaces AKC and RVW is next determined. The lateral edge CM of surface AKC intersects surface RVW at point M; hence, LM is the line of intersection between AKC and RVW.

The sequence continues with finding the intersection of surfaces BCM and RVW; edge BC intersects plane RVW at point X, so MN (of line MX) is that intersection. The intersection of surfaces WNT and $BCNJ$ follows, as shown in (4). Edge BJ intersects plane WNT at point Y. Limited by their edges, the intersection of surfaces WNT and $BCNJ$ is NO. The completion of the intersection between the prismatic masses is effected by connecting points O and J, thus establishing the intersection of surfaces BCN and RST.

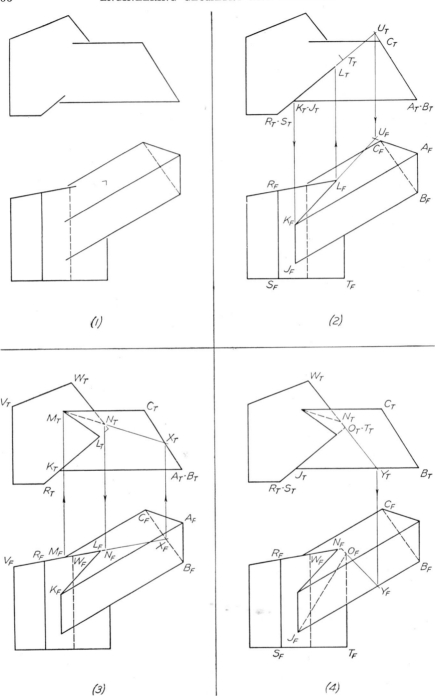

Fig. 5.11. Intersection of two polyhedrons.

PROBLEMS

Group I.   Visibility of Skew Edges

5.1. *a.* Points $A(0\frac{1}{2},1,6)$, $B(2,1,8)$, $C(3\frac{1}{2},4,5)$, and $D(1,4,8)$ are the four corners of a tetrahedron.   Complete the top and front views.

b. Points $J(4\frac{1}{2},2,5)$, $K(6\frac{1}{2},1,5)$, $L(7\frac{1}{2},4,7)$, and $M(5\frac{1}{2},4,8)$ are the four corners of a tetrahedron.   Complete the top and front views.

Group II.   Intersection of Lines and Planes

5.2. In Fig. 5.12 point A is the top of a television sending antenna.   For the purpose of this problem the ridge XY is considered as a straight line.   The following distances are

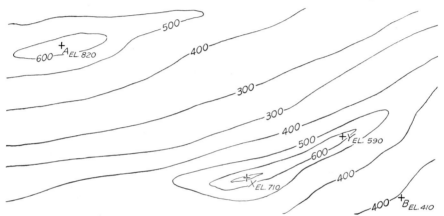

Fig. 5.12. Antenna heights.

known: $AX = 7\frac{1}{4}$ miles, $XY = 3\frac{1}{3}$ miles, $AY = 9\frac{1}{2}$ miles, $XB = 5$ miles, and $YB = 2\frac{2}{3}$ miles.   Determine the minimum height above the ground for a receiving antenna based at point B to be able to receive the signal from point A on a straight line.

5.3. In Fig. 5.13 line AB is the centerline of a railroad track.   The valley XY is spanned with a trestle, and the adjacent mountains are tunneled in prolongation of AB. The mountain sides are to be considered as planes WXY and XYZ for the purposes of this problem.   Locate the tunnel entrances on each mountain side.

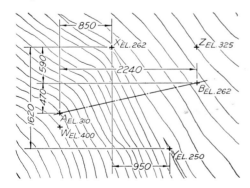

Fig. 5.13. Tunnel entrances.

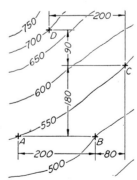

Fig. 5.14. Vertical air shaft.

5.4. In Fig. 5.14 points A, B, and C are on the outcrop of a vein of ore. A vertical shaft is to be drilled to the vein from point D. Determine the elevation at which the shaft will intersect the vein.

5.5. Locate the point of intersection between line $L(1,1,7)$ $N(6,5,7)$ and plane $A(2,3,6)$ $B(3,4,8)$ $C(5,1\frac{1}{2},6\frac{1}{2})$.

5.6. Determine how far the inclined tunnel $S(4,3,8)$ $T(3\frac{1}{2},2\frac{3}{4},7\frac{1}{4})$ must be extended beyond point T to intersect the $A(1\frac{1}{2},2,7\frac{1}{2})$ $B(4\frac{1}{2},1,6\frac{1}{2})$ $C(3,3,5\frac{1}{2})$ vein of ore. *Scale:* $1'' = 100'$.

5.7. The basic problem of shades and shadows involves the intersection of a line and a plane. The line is the interrupted light ray; the plane is the surface upon which the shadow is cast. Point $L(2,4,6)$ is a light source. Determine the shadow of point $P(4,2,7)$ that is cast upon the horizontal plane containing point $H(7,1,6)$.

5.8. A $1\frac{1}{2}$-in. cube is resting on a horizontal table surface, with its surfaces parallel to the principal planes of projection. A light source at infinity lights the cube from the direction $A(1,3,6)$ $B(2,2,7)$. Draw the outline of the shadow of the cube cast on the table surface.

5.9. Points $J(2,4\frac{1}{2},7)$, $K(3\frac{1}{4},1\frac{1}{2},8\frac{1}{2})$, $L(6,3,8)$, and $M(5\frac{1}{2},5,6)$ are the corners of a piece of sheet metal that has been bent along KL. Locate the top and front views of the centers of the holes that must be drilled through this material to permit passage of the straight wire $R(1\frac{1}{4},3\frac{1}{2},8)$ $S(7,4,6\frac{1}{2})$.

5.10. Points $A(4\frac{1}{2},2,5)$, $B(5,3\frac{1}{2},7\frac{1}{2})$, and $C(7,1\frac{1}{2},6)$ are in a vein of ore. Point $K(6\frac{1}{2},4\frac{1}{2},7\frac{1}{2})$, on the covering hillside at an elevation of 890 ft above sea level, is the location where an air shaft is to be vertically drilled to the vein. *Scale:* $1'' = 100'$. At what elevation will this shaft reach the vein? A horizontal tunnel from point $L(6,3\frac{1}{4},5\frac{1}{4})$ bearing due north is also proposed. Determine the true length of such a tunnel from point L to the vein.

5.11. Points $A(2\frac{1}{4},2\frac{1}{4},7\frac{1}{2})$, $B(4,4\frac{1}{2},7\frac{1}{2})$, $C(6,2\frac{1}{2},5\frac{1}{2})$, and $D(5,0\frac{1}{2},8\frac{1}{2})$ are the four corners of a tetrahedron. In the top and front views, mark the points of intersection between line $R(3\frac{1}{2},4\frac{1}{4},8\frac{1}{2})$ $S(5\frac{1}{2},1\frac{1}{4},5\frac{1}{4})$ and the surfaces of the tetrahedron.

5.12. Draw the top and front views of a line that passes through point $P(2,3,7\frac{1}{2})$ and intersects both line $A(2\frac{1}{2},2\frac{3}{4},7\frac{3}{4})$ $B(4\frac{1}{2},4,6\frac{1}{2})$ and line $C(3\frac{3}{4},3,8)$ $D(6\frac{1}{4},2,7)$.

5.13. Draw the top and front views of a line through point $G(5\frac{1}{2},2\frac{1}{2},6\frac{1}{2})$ that intersects both lines $H(2,2\frac{1}{2},7\frac{1}{2})$ $J(4,1,8\frac{1}{2})$ and $M(4\frac{1}{2},1\frac{1}{4},6)$ $N(4\frac{1}{2},3\frac{1}{4},8)$.

Group III.   Intersection of Planes

5.14. Draw the top and front views of the line of intersection between planes $A(1,4\frac{1}{2},6\frac{1}{2})$ $B(4,1\frac{1}{2},8\frac{1}{2})$ $C(7,2\frac{1}{2},4\frac{1}{2})$ and $R(3,1\frac{1}{2},7\frac{1}{2})$ $S(7,4\frac{1}{2},8\frac{1}{2})$ $T(6,0\frac{1}{2},4\frac{1}{2})$.

5.15. Draw the top and front views of the line of intersection between planes $K(0\frac{1}{2},2\frac{1}{2},8\frac{1}{2})$ $L(2,5\frac{1}{2},5\frac{3}{4})$ $M(3\frac{1}{2},0\frac{1}{2},5\frac{3}{4})$ and $R(3,5\frac{1}{2},8\frac{1}{2})$ $S(6\frac{1}{2},0\frac{1}{4},5\frac{3}{4})$ $T(7\frac{3}{4},4\frac{3}{4},8\frac{1}{2})$.

5.16. Line $K(2,3,6)$ $L(2,3,8)$ lies in a plane that has a 30° dip to the right. Line $S(5,2,7)$ $T(7,2,7)$ lies in a plane that has a 45° dip to the front. Draw the top and front views of the line of intersection between these planes.

5.17. Line $A(3,3,6)$ $B(5,3,7)$ is a strike line of a vein that dips 30° in a southeasterly direction. Line $C(3,2,8)$ $D(5,2,6)$ is a strike line of a vein that dips 60° in a northeasterly direction. Draw the top and front views of the line of intersection between these veins. (A horizontal-profile line points northward to the rear.)

5.18. A vein of ore intersects the surface of the ground along a line termed the outcrop of the vein. The ground surface, for the purpose of this problem, is defined by the limitless plane $A(2,3,7\frac{1}{2})$ $B(3\frac{1}{2},1,8)$ $C(4\frac{1}{2},2,6)$. Line $R(5,2\frac{1}{2},8)$ $S(7,2\frac{1}{2},7\frac{3}{4})$ is in the plane of an ore vein; the vein dips 30° forward and to the right. Draw the top and front views of the outcrop.

5.19. Points $A(2,2,7)$, $B(3\frac{1}{2},1,8\frac{1}{2})$, and $C(4\frac{1}{2},1\frac{1}{2},7)$ are in the hanging wall of a coal seam. This seam is 3 ft thick. Show the outcropping of this seam on the horizontal ground surface that contains point $G(7,3,8)$. *Scale:* $1'' = 10'\text{-}0''$.

5.20. Line $R(5,2\frac{1}{2},6\frac{1}{2})$ $S(7,2\frac{1}{2},7\frac{1}{2})$ is a line in an ore vein. The vein dips 30° in a southeasterly direction. Draw the top and front views of the outcrop of this vein on the ground surface $A(2,3,7\frac{1}{2})$ $B(3\frac{1}{4},1\frac{1}{4},8\frac{1}{4})$ $C(4\frac{1}{4},2\frac{1}{4},6\frac{1}{4})$.

5.21. Point P is common to plane $A(2\frac{1}{2},2,6)$ $B(5\frac{1}{2},2,8)$ $C(4,2\frac{3}{4},5\frac{1}{4})$, plane $K(0\frac{1}{2},2\frac{1}{2},8\frac{1}{2})$ $L(2,5\frac{1}{2},5\frac{3}{4})$ $M(3\frac{1}{2},0\frac{1}{2},5\frac{3}{4})$, and plane $R(3,5\frac{1}{2},8\frac{1}{2})$ $S(6,1,6)$ $T(7,4\frac{1}{2},8)$. Locate point P in both the top and front views.

5.22. Determine the center and diameter of the largest sphere that can be contained within the tetrahedron $A(2,1\frac{1}{2},6)$ $B(3\frac{1}{2},0\frac{1}{2},7\frac{1}{2})$ $C(4,1\frac{1}{2},5)$ $D(2\frac{1}{2},3,7\frac{1}{2})$.

Group IV.   Intersection of Polyhedrons

5.23. Draw the top and front views of the building shown in Fig. 5.15(1). A chimney whose top is level with the uppermost ridge of the roof is shown in the detail at (2).

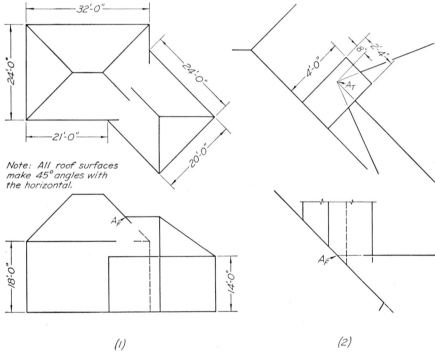

(1)   *(2)*

Fig. 5.15. Roof intersections.

Show the various intersections between the chimney surfaces and the roof surfaces in all views drawn.

5.24. Planes $A(1,3\frac{1}{2},7\frac{1}{2})$ $B(3\frac{3}{4},3\frac{1}{2},6)$ $C(3,1,8)$ and $ABD(2\frac{1}{2},1,6)$ are limited only by edge AB for the purposes of this problem. A duct whose right section is a foot square is centered on $Q(2\frac{1}{4},X,6\frac{1}{2})$ in plane ABD. The lateral edges and surfaces of the duct are perpendicular to ABD. Two of the duct-surface intersections with ABD are horizontal. *Scale:* $\frac{3}{4}'' = 1'\text{-}0''$. Determine the diameter of the smallest circular opening in plane ABC that will permit the duct to pass through plane ABC.

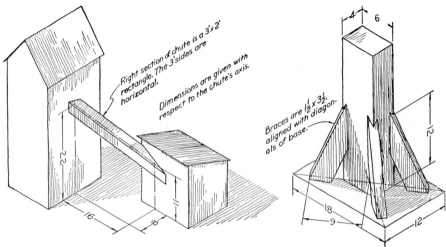

FIG. 5.16. Oblique chute.   FIG. 5.17. Braced post.

5.25. Draw the top, front, and right-side views of the rectangular chute shown in Fig. 5.16.

5.26. Detail one of the braces shown in Fig. 5.17.

5.27. A 2-in. cube is positioned with its surfaces parallel to the principal planes of projection.   The intersection of this cube with a plane that dips forward and to the right is a regular hexagon.   Draw the edge and normal views of the hexagon.

CHAPTER 6

PARALLEL RELATIONSHIPS OF LINES AND PLANES

6.1. Parallel lines appear either parallel or coincident *in all orthographic views*. This principle of parallel-line relationship allows for accurate and rapid solutions to many plane and space problems.

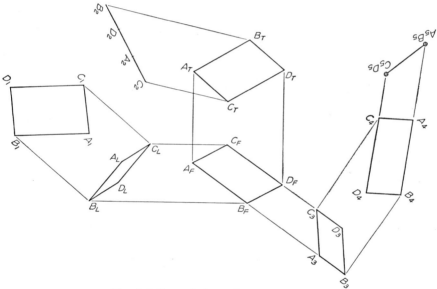

Fig. 6.1. Several views of a parallelogram.

6.2. Parallel Lines. Several different views of a parallelogram are drawn in Fig. 6.1. Note that the parallel-line principle of the preceding paragraph is borne out in all of these orthographic views. However, one view by itself is not adequate for the representation of parallel lines. For example, it will be seen in Fig. 6.2(1) that the lines WX and YZ appear parallel in the top view, but the front view shows that the lines are not parallel.

Two lines are usually parallel if they appear parallel in each of two adjacent views. When those views both show an edge view of planes parallel to both lines, those lines are not necessarily parallel. In Fig.

71

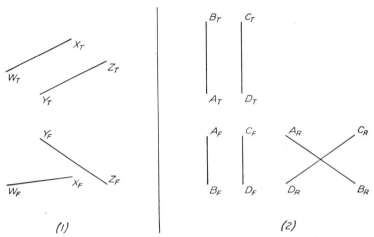

FIG. 6.2. Views in which nonparallel lines appear parallel.

6.2(2), the lines AB and CD appear parallel in both the top and front views. Both lines are profile lines, and the top and front views are edge views of

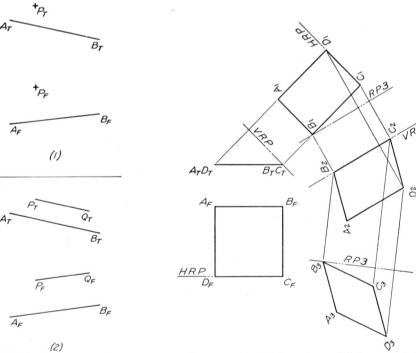

FIG. 6.3. Line through a given point and parallel to a given plane.

FIG. 6.4. Application of parallel-line principles.

profile planes.   Visualization of the lines, as identified by the four lettered points, will enable the student to realize that the lines are not parallel.   The side view also shows that the lines have different directions.

6.3. Line through a Given Point and Parallel to a Given Line. In Fig. 6.3(1), the line AB and the point P are given.   It is required to establish a line through P that will be parallel to AB.   In each view the required line PQ is drawn through P parallel to AB, as in (2).   The selection of point Q is arbitrary and used only for identification purposes.

Several views of a square are shown in Fig. 6.4.   The opposite sides of a square, being actually parallel, will appear parallel in all views.   If two of the four sides are located in any one view, the other two sides can be determined by the use of parallel relationships.   Corners B, C, and D were located by projection and measurement in each of the auxiliary and oblique views.   Corner A was positioned by drawing the sides opposite BC and CD parallel to their respective opposites.   For purposes of accuracy and to check the previously located corners, the location of corner A should be checked by measurement and back projection in each new view.

6.4. Fundamental Principle of Parallel Line and Plane Relationships. Any plane that contains one of two parallel lines is parallel to the second line.

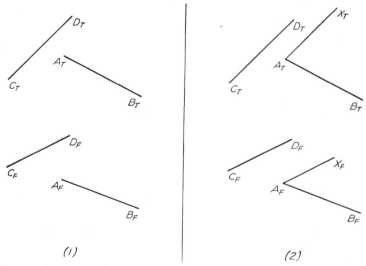

(1)   *(2)*

Fig. 6.5. Plane containing a given line and parallel to a second given line.

6.5. Plane Containing One Given Line and Parallel to a Second Given Line. In Fig. 6.5, the problem of establishing a plane through a given line AB and parallel to the given line CD is presented.   The solution is effected by establishing a line parallel to CD that also intersects line AB. In the immediate problem, the line AX is drawn parallel to CD; plane ABX is the required plane.   The given data are presented in (1); the solution in (2).

6.6. Plane through a Given Point and Parallel to Both of Two Given Skew Lines. The solution of this problem is realized by establishing two lines intersecting at the given point, each of which is parallel to one of the

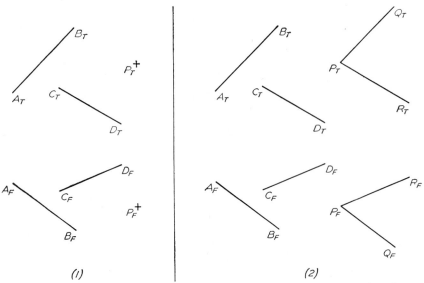

FIG. 6.6. Plane through a given point and parallel to both of two given skew lines.

given skew lines. In Fig. 6.6(1), point P and the skew lines AB and CD are given. In (2), the line PQ is drawn parallel to line AB, and the line PR is drawn parallel to line CD. PQR is the required plane.

6.7. Parallel Planes. In establishing a plane parallel to a given plane, a second requirement must be given to limit the problem to one solution.

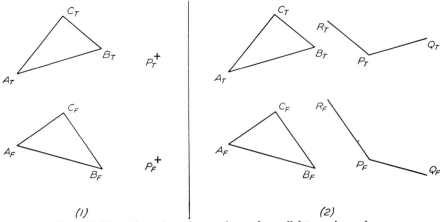

FIG. 6.7. Plane through a given point and parallel to a given plane.

The additional specification may require the plane to be passed through a given point, or it may specify position and distance relationship between the two planes.

In Fig. 6.7(1), a plane parallel to plane ABC and containing point P is required. It is necessary only to establish two lines through point P that are respectively parallel to any two nonparallel lines of plane ABC. In (2), the line PQ is drawn parallel to AB, and the line PR is drawn parallel to BC. Plane PQR is the required plane.

When it is specified that a plane is to be established parallel to a given plane and a distance X from the given plane, two solutions to the problem are possible. A further specification is needed to limit the number of solutions to one.

In Fig. 6.8(1), the given plane is ABC. A plane parallel to ABC, a distance X from the given plane and generally above it, is required. Lines EF and FG are drawn in the top view and designated as lines of the required

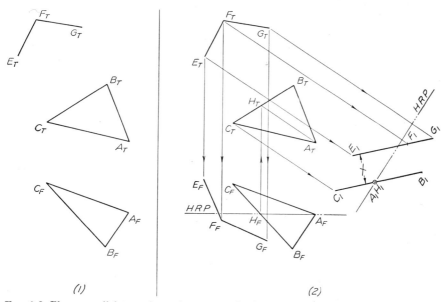

(1)   *(2)*

FIG. 6.8. Plane parallel to a given plane, a specified position and distance from the given plane.

plane. A horizontal line of plane ABC is drawn in (2) to determine a line of sight for an edge view of the planes. The required plane is established in the auxiliary elevation. Points E, F, and G are located in the auxiliary view by projection from the top view. The heights of these three points with respect to the horizontal reference plane are then transferred from the auxiliary to the front view, where the points are located on the proper projectors from the top view.

PROBLEMS

Group I. Parallel Lines

6.1. Draw the top, front, and right-side views of the truncated duct shown in Fig. 6.9.

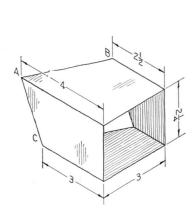

FIG. 6.9. Truncated rectangular duct.   FIG. 6.10. Clipped step block.

6.2. Draw the top, front, and right-side views of the clipped step block shown in Fig. 6.10.

6.3. Parallelogram $A(2,1\frac{1}{2},9)$ $B(1,2,8)$ $C(3,1,6)$ D is the lower base of a prism. $CE(5,3,5\frac{1}{2})$ is one of the equal-length lateral edges of the prism. Draw the top and front views of the prism.

6.4. The edges of an equilateral parallelepiped are 2 in. long. Three of these edges lie on line $A(2,2,6)$ $B(4,2,8)$, line $AC(5,1,7)$, and line $AJ(4,4,6)$, respectively. Draw the top and front views of the parallelepiped.

Group II. Lines Parallel to Planes

6.5. In Fig. 6.11 the curves RT and SU are the linear directrixes of a cylindroid. All elements of this surface are parallel to its plane director ABC. Draw the top and front views of element RS.

6.6. The oblique line $A(3,4,6)$ $B(7,X,5)$ and the horizontal line $BC(6,X,X)$ are both parallel to plane $R(1,3,7)$ $S(3,0\frac{1}{2},8)$ $T(4,2,5)$. Complete the top and front views to show both AB and BC.

Group III. Planes Parallel to Lines

6.7. In Fig. 6.12 lines WX and YZ are elements of a conoid. All elements of a conoid are parallel to its plane director. Draw the top and front views of a plane containing point A that could be the plane director of this surface.

6.8. Plane $R(7,2,6)$ $S(5,3,X)$ $T(5,1,X)$ is parallel to both line $A(1,1,8\frac{1}{2})$ $B(4,2,6)$ and line $J(1,3,6)$ $K(4,0\frac{1}{2},7)$. Draw the top and front views of triangle RST.

6.9. The parallel centerlines $A(5,1,8\frac{1}{2})$ $B(7\frac{1}{2},2\frac{1}{2},6\frac{1}{4})$ and $C(6,3,8\frac{1}{2})$ D of two $3\frac{1}{4}$ OD pipes pass through a frontal wall surface whose plane contains point A and a profile wall surface whose plane contains point B. An insulation box made of $\frac{3}{4}$-in.-thick material covers these pipes from wall to wall. The sides of the box have a 2-in. clearance

from the pipe surfaces.   The right section of the box is rectangular.   *Scale:* $1\frac{1}{2}'' = 1'\text{-}0''$.
Draw the top and front views of the insulation box.

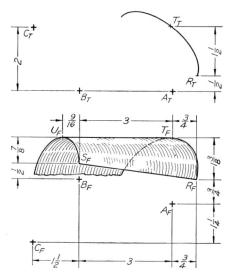

FIG. 6.11. Elements of a cylindroid.

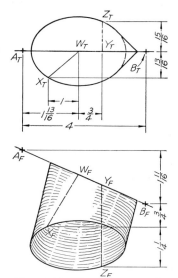

FIG. 6.12. Plane director of a conoid.

Group IV.   Parallel Planes

6.10. Plane $D(4,X,7\frac{1}{2})$ $E(6\frac{1}{2},X,8\frac{1}{2})$ $K(5\frac{1}{2},2\frac{3}{4},6\frac{1}{2})$ is parallel to plane $A(1,2\frac{1}{4},5\frac{3}{4})$ $B(2,3\frac{1}{4},8)$ $C(3\frac{1}{4},0\frac{1}{2},7)$.   Draw the front view of triangle DEK.

6.11. Point $P(4,2\frac{1}{2},X)$ is one corner of a $2\frac{1}{2}$-in. square.   This square is to the right of point P and in a plane that is parallel to plane $A(2,4,8\frac{1}{4})$ $B(6\frac{3}{4},1,7\frac{1}{2})$ $C(5\frac{1}{4},0\frac{1}{2},6\frac{1}{4})$, 2 in. from plane ABC and in front of ABC.   Two sides of the square are frontal.   *Scale:* full size.   Draw the top and front views of the square.

6.12. Planes $R(4\frac{1}{4},X,8\frac{1}{2})$ $S(6,X,7\frac{1}{2})$ $T(5\frac{1}{4},X,6\frac{1}{4})$ and $A(1,1\frac{1}{4},7\frac{1}{4})$ $B(2\frac{1}{4},3\frac{1}{2},8\frac{1}{2})$ $C(3\frac{1}{4},2\frac{1}{2},6)$ are parallel and have a 2-in. clearance.   Plane RST lies behind plane ABC.   *Scale:* half size.   Draw the front view of triangle RST.

6.13. Plane $P(1\frac{1}{2},X,6\frac{1}{2})$ $Q(4,X,5\frac{1}{2})$ $R(3\frac{1}{4},X,7\frac{1}{2})$ is parallel to plane $J(0,3,7\frac{1}{2})$ $K(4,1,6\frac{1}{2})$ $L(2\frac{1}{2},4,5)$.   The planes have a $\frac{3}{4}$-in. clearance between them, and plane PQR is above plane JKL.   *Scale:* full size.   Draw the front view of triangle PQR.

6.14. Line $A(1,4,7)$ $B(4,2,8)$ is the intersection of a vertical cliff with the hanging wall of a vein of copper ore.   The vertical distance between the hanging and foot walls of the vein is 6 ft.   A test drill hole strikes the hanging wall at point $T(5,3\frac{1}{2},6)$.   Determine the thickness and the strike and dip of the vein.   (Hanging and foot walls are the top and bottom surfaces of the vein, respectively.)

CHAPTER 7

PERPENDICULAR RELATIONSHIPS OF LINES AND PLANES

7.1. The theoretical problems of perpendicular lines and planes have innumerable applications in industry; e.g., wheels, gears, cams, and the like are applied problems of planes perpendicular to lines. The determination of clearances involves measurements along lines perpendicular to other lines and planes. The basic principles of perpendicular relationships are few but of such importance that many courses in engineering geometry are designed to stress these relationships.

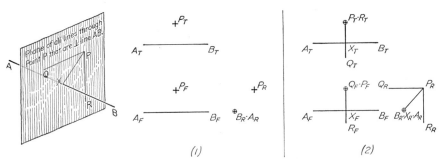

(1)   *(2)*

FIG. 7.1. Lines through a given point and perpendicular to a horizontal-frontal line.

7.2. Perpendicular Lines. Reference to the illustration described at the end of Sec. 2.10 will permit a better understanding of the fundamental principle of perpendicular lines: *Two perpendicular lines appear perpendicular in any view that shows a normal view of either or both of the lines.* The word *perpendicular*, as used herein, expresses a 90° relationship in direction only. In order to be perpendicular, two lines need not intersect.

In Fig. 7.1(1), where the problem is to establish a line through point P perpendicular to the horizontal-frontal line AB, an infinite number of solutions are available. In (2), the lines PQ and PR determine the profile plane containing all lines through point P that are perpendicular to line AB; lines PQ and PR are but two of these many lines. The line PX, which is perpendicular to and intersects line AB, is also shown in (2).

In Fig. 7.2, three different positions of a rectangle are shown. In (1), the front view is a normal view of both AB and BC, and the angle between

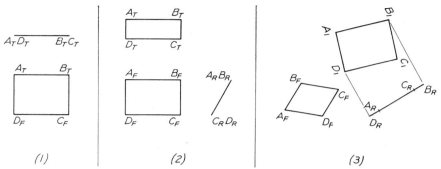

FIG. 7.2. An illustration of the perpendicular-line principles.

these sides appears as a right angle.   In (2), the front view is a normal view of side AB, but not of side BC; however, in this view the angle between these sides still appears to be 90°.   In (3), the front view shows neither AB nor BC in true length, and the angle between them does not appear as a right angle but as obtuse in that view.   Further examination of the front view in (3) shows that the angle BCD appears as an acute angle, whereas in actuality it, too, is a right angle.

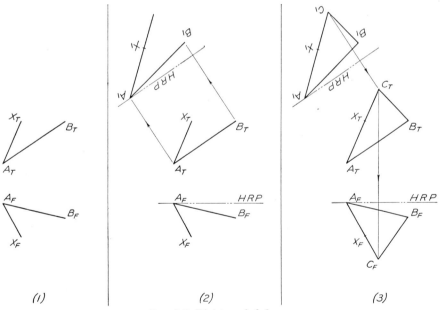

FIG. 7.3. Right-angled figure.

An example of a problem requiring the use of perpendicular-line principles is shown in Fig. 7.3. AB is one of the legs of a right triangle that has its third corner C on line AX.   The top and front views of the triangle are required. The given data are drawn in (1). An analysis of the problem indicates that a normal view of the leg AB is required, for in such a view the right angle between the two legs will show in its true size. In (2), the normal view of AB is secured. The line of the second leg is established at right angles to AB, as shown in (3). The intersection of this constructed line with AX locates the third corner of the triangle.

The foregoing problem could have been solved by securing a normal view of plane ABX. Such a solution requires an additional view, however, and unless a normal view of the plane is required for other reasons, the solution shown in Fig. 7.3 is usually preferred.

7.3. Shortest Distance from a Point to a Line. Perpendicular-line principles are employed in determining the shortest distance between a point and a line. Such a distance would be measured on a line through the given point that intersects and is perpendicular to the given line.

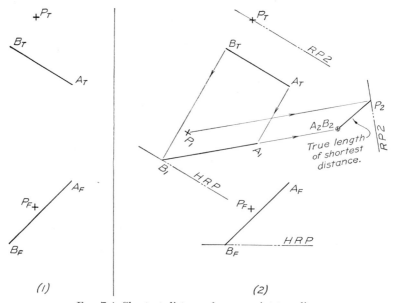

Fig. 7.4. Shortest distance from a point to a line.

In the problem of Fig. 7.4, the shortest distance from point P to line AB is required. Since *an end view of a line shows the true length of all lines that are perpendicular to it*, the solution is determined in a view that shows an end view of line AB.

7.4. Line through a Given Point and Perpendicular to Both of Two Nonparallel Given Lines. While there are many lines that can be passed through a given point and perpendicular to a given line, there is but one answer to the present problem. The given lines and point are presented in

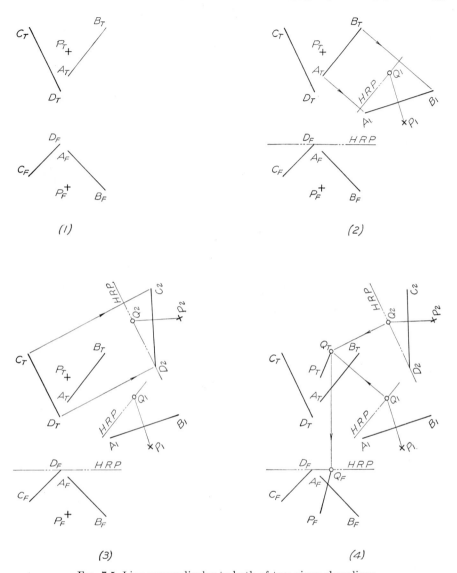

Fig. 7.5. Line perpendicular to both of two given skew lines.

Fig. 7.5(1). In analyzing this problem, it should be borne in mind that normal views of each line will show the perpendicular relationship between that line and the required line.

In (2), the view that shows AB in true length also shows the required line PQ perpendicular to AB. The normal view of CD, drawn in (3), permits PQ to be drawn perpendicular to CD in that view. Note that the normal

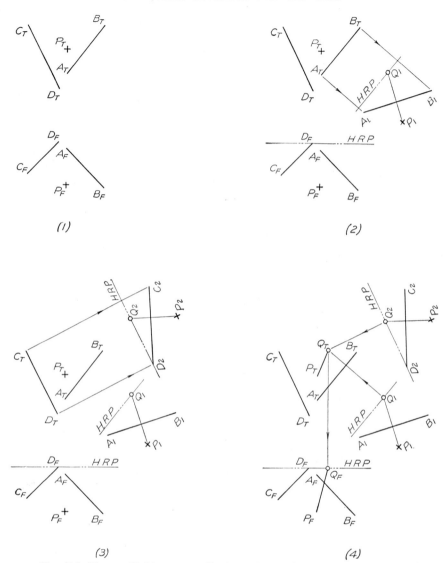

(1)   (2)

(3)   (4)

FIG. 7.5. (*Repeated.*) Line perpendicular to both of two given skew lines.

views of both given lines are projected from the same view.   (This is necessary in order to fix the position of point Q.)   Point Q was arbitrarily selected
in (2) as the intersection of the required line with the horizontal reference
plane HRP.   The location of point Q in (3) can be determined immediately
in this second edge view of HRP.   The top view of point Q is determined by
projecting from both auxiliary views to the top view, as shown in (4).   The
intersection of these projectors fixes the top view of point Q.   The front

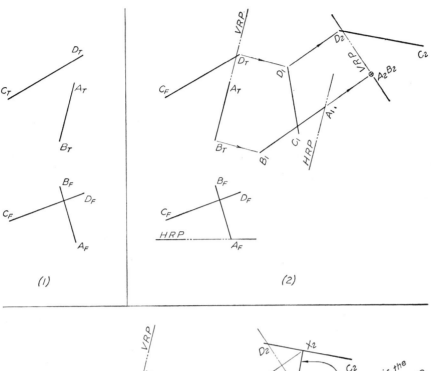

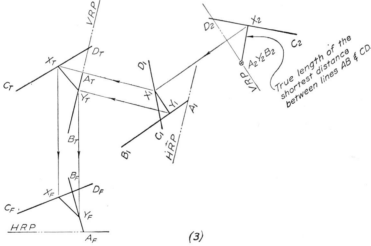

FIG. 7.6. Shortest distance between two skew lines.

view of Q is projected from its top view and positioned on the reference plane.

7.5. Shortest Distance between Two Skew Lines. The shortest distance between two skew lines is measured on a line that is perpendicular to and intersects both skew lines. This problem is found in the connection of two pipes with a third, using right-angled fittings; in locating the shortest

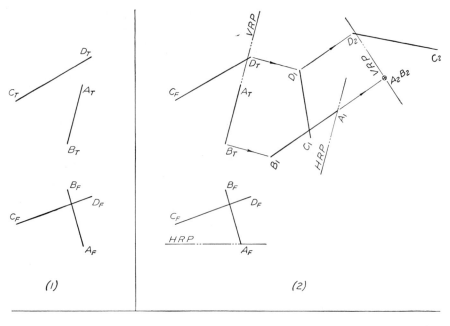

(1)

(2)

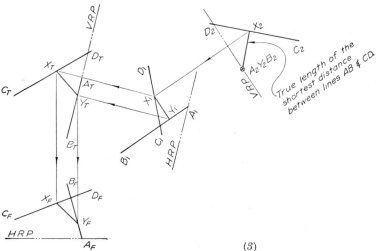

(3)

Fig. 7.6. (*Repeated.*) Shortest distance between two skew lines.

passageway between two tunnels; etc.   The solution is secured through the use of a view that shows an end view of one of the skew lines.   Such a view will be a normal view of the required line and, consequently, will show the perpendicular relationship between the second skew line and the required line.

The problem of Fig. 7.6 illustrates the above-described solution. The given skew lines AB and CD are drawn in (1). In (2), the normal and end views of AB are secured. (It should be noted that although the perpendicular relationship between AB and the required common perpendicular will be seen in the normal view of AB, that view, by itself, is inadequate for positioning the required line.) In the view that shows AB appearing as a point, the common perpendicular is drawn at right angles to CD, as shown in (3). Point X, the intersection of the perpendicular with CD, is projected to the adjacent view. The required common perpendicular XY is drawn at right angles to AB in the normal view of AB.

Should the problem have required only the clearance between the two skew lines, it would have been unnecessary to locate points X and Y in any views other than the oblique view.

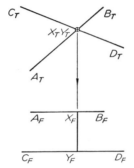

FIG. 7.7. Shortest distance between two horizontal skew lines.

While the foregoing solution works well in the general case, the problem will often occur with one of the given views being a normal view of *both* skew lines. In such a view, the common perpendicular will appear as a point at what appears to be the intersection of those skew lines. The true length of the clearance is seen in all views adjacent to the end view of the required line. In Fig. 7.7, the skew lines are AB and CD. The shortest distance between the skew lines is XY, shown in true length in the front view.

Recognition that the common perpendicular appears in true length in views that show the skew lines appearing parallel to each other may be used to advantage. A plane that contains one of the skew lines and is parallel to the second skew line can be established. An edge view of this plane will show the skew lines appearing parallel to each other; hence, the true length of the shortest distance between them can be measured in such a view.

In Fig. 7.8, the given skew lines are AB and CD. Line AM is drawn parallel to line CD; this construction establishes plane ABM parallel to CD. An edge view of plane ABM is secured in the auxiliary view of (1). The

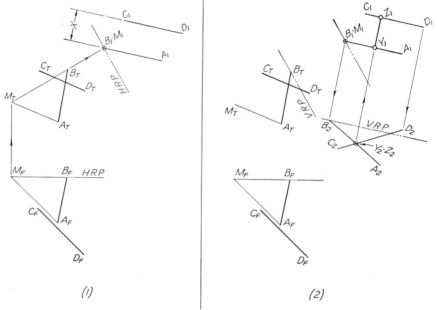

FIG. 7.8. Shortest distance between two given skew lines—parallel-plane method.

clearance between AB and CD is measured as X. If the location of the common perpendicular is required, a view that shows it appearing as a point is necessary. Such a view is drawn in (2). The common perpendicular is determined to be line YZ.

7.6. Principles of Perpendicular Lines and Planes. The fundamental principle of perpendicular-line relationships is the foundation of all solutions to the problems of perpendicular lines and planes. Several additional axioms follow:

1. A line perpendicular to a plane is perpendicular to all lines of that plane.
2. An edge view of a plane is a normal view of all lines perpendicular to that plane.
3. A normal view of a plane is an end view of all lines perpendicular to that plane.

7.7. Line through a Given Point and Perpendicular to a Given Plane (Fig. 7.9). Point P and plane ABC are given in (1). The line PQ, through the given point and perpendicular to the given plane, is required. All lines of plane ABC are perpendicular to the required line. The horizontal line AH and the frontal line FB, both of plane ABC, are used to determine the top- and front-view directions of PQ.

In (2), PQ is shown at right angles to the top view of AH. (This construction is an application of the fundamental principle of perpendicular lines: Two perpendicular lines appear perpendicular in any view that shows a normal view of either or both of the lines. The top view is a normal view of AH; therefore, PQ appears perpendicular to AH in this view.) Similarly,

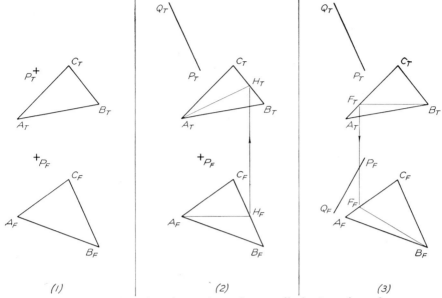

FIG. 7.9. Line through a given point and perpendicular to a given plane.

in (3), the front view of PQ is drawn at right angles to the front view of line FB.

7.8. Line through a Given Point and Perpendicular to Both of Two Non-parallel Given Lines. In Sec. 7.4, a solution for this problem was presented. If the given lines are coplanar then the solution of the preceding

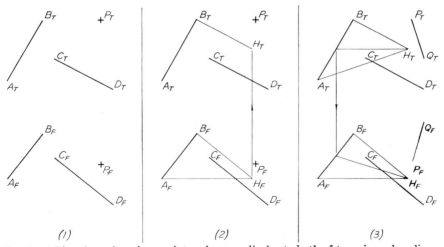

FIG. 7.10. Line through a given point and perpendicular to both of two given skew lines.

paragraph is directly applicable. In the event that the given lines are skew
lines, the procedure of Sec. 7.7 can still be employed advantageously with
modification. A plane that contains one of the skew lines and is also
parallel to the second skew line is first established. The required line is
perpendicular to this plane.

In Fig. 7.10(1), the problem requires a line through point P that will be
perpendicular to both lines AB and CD. In (2), the plane ABH is established parallel to line CD by drawing line BH parallel to CD. The required
line PQ is then drawn perpendicular to plane ABH, as shown in (3).

7.9. Shortest Distance from a Given Point to a Given Plane. The
shortest distance from a point to a plane is measured on a line that contains
the point and is perpendicular to the plane. True length of such a distance
is determined in an edge view of the plane, since it is a normal view of all
lines perpendicular to the plane.

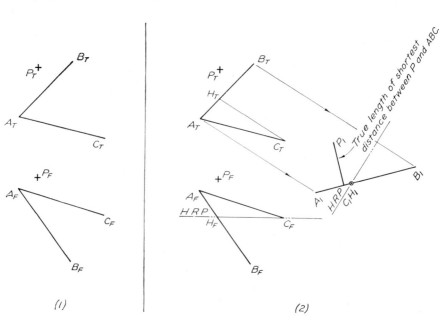

FIG. 7.11. Shortest distance between a point and a plane.

Point P and plane ABC are given in Fig. 7.11(1). An edge view of plane
ABC is drawn in (2). True length of the shortest distance between point
P and plane ABC is identified in this last drawn view.

7.10. Plane through a Given Point and Perpendicular to a Given Line.
In the problem of Fig. 7.12, it is required to establish a plane containing
point P that is perpendicular to line AB. All lines of the required plane will
be perpendicular to AB. Since horizontal and frontal lines are normal in
one each of the given views, the horizontal line PQ and the frontal line PR

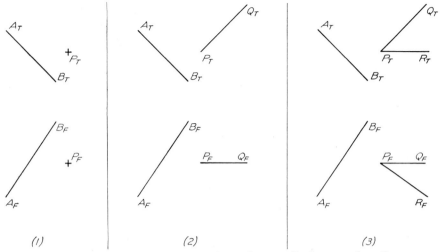

FIG. 7.12. Plane through a given point and perpendicular to a given line.

are used to determine the required plane. Line PQ is drawn at right angles to AB in the top view of (2). The front view of (3) shows PR perpendicular to AB. These two intersecting lines determine the required plane PQR.

7.11. Plane Perpendicular to a Given Plane and Containing a Given Line. If the reader will observe a horizontal surface and hold his pencil at right angles to that surface, he will be able to realize that all planes containing the theoretical line of the pencil will be vertical planes, perpendicular to the

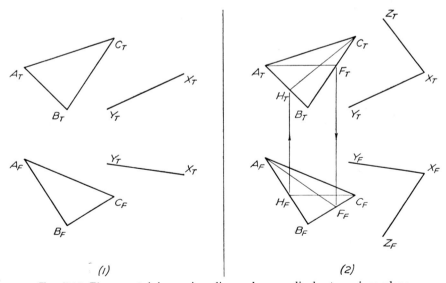

FIG. 7.13. Plane containing a given line and perpendicular to a given plane.

horizontal plane. Hence, if it is required to establish a plane perpendicular to a given plane and containing a given line that is *not* perpendicular to the given plane, the required plane is determined by two intersecting lines: the given line and another that is perpendicular to the given plane.

In Fig. 7.13(1), the given line is XY and the given plane is ABC. A plane containing XY and perpendicular to plane ABC is required. The solution requires that a line through some point of line XY be established perpendicular to plane ABC. In (2), the line XZ is so drawn. The selection of point X as the point of line XY through which the line perpendicular to plane ABC is drawn was arbitrary (the point might have been point Y or any other point of line XY). XYZ is the required plane.

7.12. Plane through a Given Point and Perpendicular to Each of Two Given Planes. Since *all planes containing a line perpendicular to another plane are themselves perpendicular to the other plane,* the solution to the present problem requires simply the determination of two lines through the given point: one line perpendicular to one of the given planes and the second line perpendicular to the other given plane.

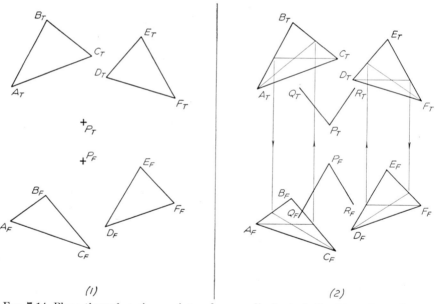

(1)   *(2)*

FIG. 7.14. Plane through a given point and perpendicular to both of two given planes.

In Fig. 7.14(1), point P and planes ABC and DEF are given. In (2), the lines PQ and PR are drawn, PQ perpendicular to plane ABC and PR perpendicular to plane DEF. PQR is the required plane.

7.13. Angle between Two Planes (Perpendicular-line Method). If the angle between two planes is required but the intersection of those planes is not given in the initial data, their intersection may be determined and used as described in Sec. 4.9. The constructions of the preceding section, however, may be used to a decided advantage.

It may be observed in Fig. 7.15 that if two lines (*PQ* and *PR*) are drawn through any arbitrarily selected point *P*, each perpendicular to one of the planes (*ABCD* and *CDEF*), the angle between these lines will be equal to one of the supplementary angles between the planes.

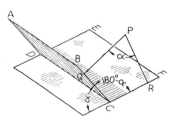

In Fig. 7.16(1), a similar problem is presented. True size of the angle between planes *ABC* and *XYZ* is required. Point *P* is selected at random. Lines *PQ* and *PR*

Fig. 7.15. Angle between two planes—perpendicular-line method.

are drawn, respectively perpendicular to planes *ABC* and *XYZ*, as shown in (2). In (3), the normal view of plane *PQR* is determined. The angle θ, between lines *PQ* and *PR*, is identified as equal in measure to the required angle.

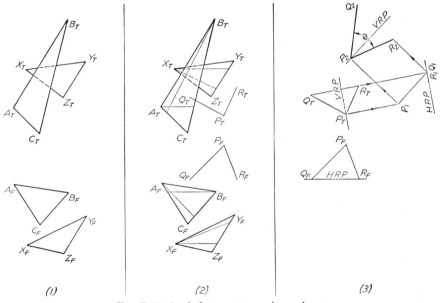

Fig. 7.16. Angle between two given planes.

7.14. Three Mutually Perpendicular Planes.

The presentation of three mutually perpendicular lines and planes occurs repeatedly in the drawing of the many rectangular structures with which an engineer works. When the

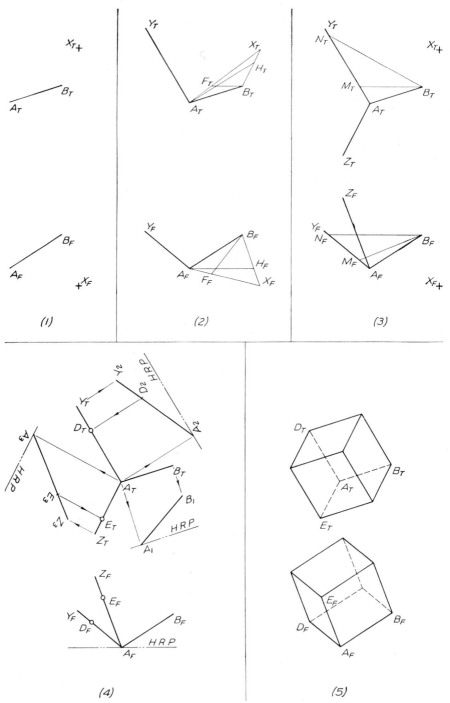

(1)   (2)   (3)

(4)   (5)

Fig. 7.17. Three mutually perpendicular lines and planes.

structure is in a simple position (i.e., when its surfaces are parallel to the principal planes of projection), the presentation is easily accomplished. An obliquely positioned object is more difficult to represent. Such an object may be as presented in Fig. 7.17, where a lower face of a cube lies in plane ABX and AB is the rear edge of that face. These given data are presented in (1). The top and front views of the cube are required.

One of the three edges intersecting at corner A will be perpendicular to plane ABX, and the other two will be in plane ABX. In (2), the line AY is constructed perpendicular to ABX. In (3), the line AZ is drawn perpendicular to plane ABY; AZ is the line of the second edge that lies in plane ABX. The normal views of AB, AY, and AZ are obtained in (4). The edges AD and AE, on lines AY and AZ, respectively, are established equal in length to edge AB, since all edges of a cube are equal in length. Recognition of parallel-line relationships permits a rapid completion of the top and front views of the cube. In (5), the problem is completed.

PROBLEMS

Group I. Perpendicular Lines

7.1. Line segment $A(5,3,4\frac{1}{2})$ $B(4,1\frac{1}{2},7)$ is one leg of a right-angled triangle. The hypotenuse of this triangle lies along the line $AD(2,2\frac{1}{2},5\frac{1}{2})$.

7.2. A right-angled triangle has $B(4,4,8)$ $C(2,1,7)$ as its hypotenuse. The third corner of the triangle is on line $BE(5,2,5)$. Draw the top and front views of the triangle.

7.3. An isosceles triangle has $B(3,3,8\frac{1}{2})$ $C(6,1,8\frac{1}{2})$ as its base. The triangle has a 4-in. altitude, and its vertex is 1 in. higher than point B. *Scale:* full size. Draw the top and front views of the triangle.

7.4. Line segment $M(3,1,9)$ $N(6,3,5)$ is the base of an isosceles triangle whose vertex is a point of line $R(1,4,7)$ $S(6,3\frac{1}{2},6\frac{1}{2})$. Draw the top and front views of the triangle.

7.5. Pipe $A(1,3\frac{1}{2},7\frac{1}{2})$ $B(2,3\frac{1}{2},7)$ is to be connected to pipe $Y(6\frac{1}{2},1,5)$ $Z(7\frac{1}{2},0\frac{1}{4},6)$, using right-angled elbows and straight lengths of pipe that are either vertical or horizontal. Connections are to be made at points B and Y. The shortest total pipe length meeting these conditions is required. *Scale:* $1'' = 1'\text{-}0''$. Draw the top and front views of the connection. If elbows cost 55 cents each and pipe costs 50 cents per foot, what is the total cost of material for this connection? (For the purpose of these calculations determine pipe lengths to the intersection of their centerlines.)

7.6. Point $R(3,2,7)$ is the intersection of the 3-in.-long diagonals of the square base of a right pyramid. Point $Y(3\frac{3}{4},3,8)$ is on the $2\frac{1}{2}$-in. altitude of the pyramid. Point $Z(2,2\frac{3}{4},X)$ is on one of the diagonals of the base. Draw the top and front views of the pyramid. *Scale:* full size.

Group II. Shortest Distance from a Point to a Line

7.7. *a.* Draw the true length of the shortest distance from point $C(1,7,8)$ to line $A(0\frac{1}{2},5,9)$ $B(2,6,9)$.

b. Draw the true length of the shortest distance from point $P(6,6\frac{1}{2},8\frac{1}{2})$ to line $J(5\frac{1}{2},5,9)$ $K(7\frac{1}{2},6,7)$.

c. Draw the true length of the shortest distance from point $Z(1,0\frac{1}{2},4\frac{1}{4})$ to line $X(1\frac{1}{2},2,3)$ $Y(3,0,4)$.

7.8. In Fig. 7.18 lines AB and BC are the centerlines of a sewage system. Permission has been obtained to connect a house sewer from point S to the system. Determine the shortest centerline for the connecting pipe.

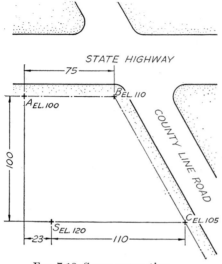

Fig. 7.18. Sewer connection.

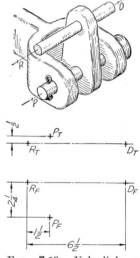

Fig. 7.19. Yoke-link assembly.

7.9. In Fig. 7.19 determine the shortest distance between the axes of the holes that are drilled through the link.

7.10. Line segment $B(1,2,6)$ $S(4,0\frac{1}{2},8)$ is the base of a triangle. Point $V(5,4,5)$ is the vertex of the triangle. Determine the true length of the altitude of the triangle. *Scale:* half size.

7.11. Line $A(3,2,4)$ $B(5,2,8\frac{1}{2})$ is the axis of a 2-in.-diameter right-circular cylinder. What is the diameter of the largest sphere that can be centered at $C(6,3,6\frac{1}{2})$ without intersecting the cylinder? *Scale:* full size.

7.12. Determine the amount of clearance or interference between the 24 OD pipe whose centerline is $A(1,3,6)$ $B(7,1\frac{1}{2},8\frac{1}{2})$ and the 10-ft-diameter spherical tank whose center is $C(3,1,8\frac{1}{2})$. *Scale:* $\frac{1}{4}'' = 1'\text{-}0''$.

7.13. Line $S(1,2,8)$ $K(5,2,6)$ is a strike line of a vein of ore. Point $C(3,4,5)$ is the top of a vertical shaft that serves the vein at a depth of 300 ft below point C. *Scale:* $1'' = 100'$. Draw the top and front views of the shortest tunnel from the bottom of the shaft to a tunnel $KD(6,X,4\frac{1}{2})$ in the ore vein. Determine the true length of this connecting tunnel.

Group III. Line Perpendicular to Both of Two Nonparallel Lines

7.14. Line BE is perpendicular to both line $A(2\frac{1}{2},0\frac{1}{2},8\frac{1}{2})$ $B(4\frac{1}{2},3\frac{1}{2},7\frac{1}{2})$ and line $C(3,2\frac{1}{2},7)$ $D(5,1\frac{1}{2},8\frac{1}{2})$. Point E is 1 in. lower than point B. *Scale:* full size. Draw the top and front views of line BE.

7.15. Line $Y(6\frac{1}{2},4,7\frac{1}{2})$ $Z(5\frac{1}{2},X,X)$ is perpendicular to both line $L(1,4,6)$ $N(4,2,7)$ and line $S(1,1,8)$ $K(3,3,5)$. Draw the top and front views of line YZ.

Group IV. Shortest Distance between Two Skew Lines

7.16. In Fig. 7.20 lines MN, OP, QR, and ST represent power-transmission lines; a telephone line is represented by line AB. Determine the clearance between the telephone line and the nearest of the four power lines.

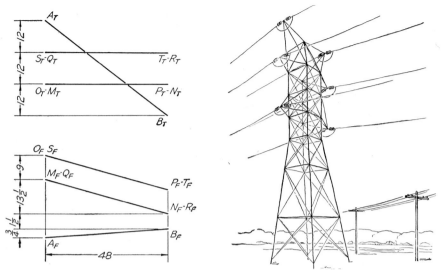

Fig. 7.20. Clearance between power and telephone lines.

7.17. In Fig. 7.21 determine the clearance between the cable centerline *CL* and the triangular brace *RST*.

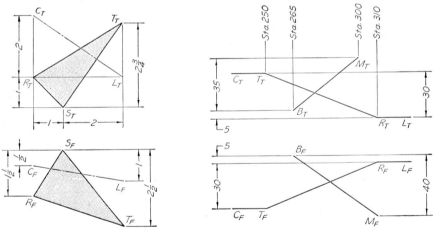

Fig. 7.21. Triangular brace and cable.

Fig. 7.22. Cable clearance.

7.18. In Fig. 7.22 determine the clearance between the bomb-release cable *BM* and the control cable *CTRL*. (The station numbers shown indicate the horizontal distance in inches from the nose of the aircraft. The other dimensions are also in inches.)

7.19. Determine the true length of the shortest distance between line $P(6,1,8)$ $Q(3,1,5)$ and line $Y(6,4,8)$ $Z(6,1\frac{1}{2},5)$. *Scale:* $1'' = 10'-0''$.

7.20. Determine the true length of the shortest distance between the nonintersecting diagonals of any two adjacent faces of a 2-in. cube.

7.21. Draw the top and front views of *JK*, the shortest line segment between line $A(1,3\frac{1}{2},6)$ $B(3,0\frac{1}{2},8)$ and line $C(3,3,5\frac{1}{2})$ $D(2\frac{1}{2},2\frac{1}{2},8\frac{1}{2})$. Determine the true length of *JK*. *Scale:* $3'' = 1'-0''$.

7.22. Tunnel $T(1,2,6)$ $N(4,1,8)$ is to be connected to air shaft $A(3\frac{1}{2},2\frac{1}{2},7)$ $S(3,0\frac{1}{2},6)$ by the shortest possible passageway. Draw the top and front views of this connecting passageway, and determine its length. *Scale:* $1'' = 100'$.

7.23. Preliminary design has established $A(2,1,8)$ $B(5,2\frac{3}{4},6\frac{1}{2})$ as the centerline of a length of 3-in. American Standard welded wrought-iron pipe ($3\frac{1}{2}$ OD), and $C(3,3\frac{1}{2},8)$ $D(5\frac{3}{4},1\frac{1}{2},8\frac{3}{4})$ as the centerline of a length of 2-in. American Standard welded wrought-iron pipe ($2\frac{3}{8}$ OD). *Scale:* half size. Determine the amount of clearance or interference that will result from this design.

7.24. Determine the total distance from point $A(1,3,6\frac{1}{4})$ to point $D(4\frac{1}{2},3,7\frac{1}{2})$ measured along the line $AB(3\frac{1}{2},1,8\frac{3}{4})$ to a point K, then across the line of the shortest distance between lines AB and $C(2,1\frac{1}{2},5)$ D to point L on line CD and then to point D. *Scale:* $1'' = 1'\text{-}0''$.

7.25. Line $S(1,2,8)$ $K(5,2,6)$ is a tunnel in the Bituminous seam. $T(2,3\frac{1}{2},6)$ $N(5,2,7\frac{1}{2})$ is a second tunnel in the same hill mass. *Scale:* $1'' = 200'$. How much longer would a vertical shaft be connecting these two tunnels than the shortest possible connecting shaft?

Group V. Line Perpendicular to a Plane

7.26. Orthographic procedures require that projections onto planes be made through the use of projectors that are perpendicular to the respective planes of projection. Draw the top and front views of the orthographic projection of rectangle $ABCD$ onto plane MNO shown in Fig. 7.23.

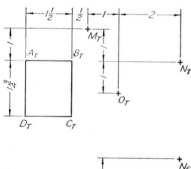

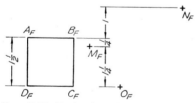

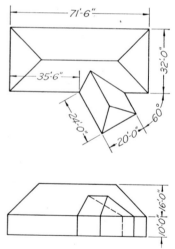

FIG. 7.23. Projection of a plane figure onto an oblique plane.

FIG. 7.24. Wind-pressure directions.

7.27. Wind pressure is exerted on roof surfaces perpendicular to the planes of those surfaces. Draw the top and front views of arrows that will show the direction of force exerted on each roof surface in Fig. 7.24 by wind pressure. Show these arrows intersecting their respective roofs at the center of each area. (All roof surfaces make the same angle with the horizontal.)

7.28. Line $P(5\frac{3}{4},X,7\frac{1}{2})$ $C(4,2\frac{1}{2},6)$ is perpendicular to plane $A(1,X,7)$ $B(2\frac{3}{4},4,8\frac{1}{2})$ $C(4,2\frac{1}{2},6)$. Complete the front view to show line PC and triangle ABC.

7.29. The triangle $A(5,1,8)$ $B(3,3,5\frac{3}{4})$ $C(2,2,7\frac{1}{4})$ is the lower base of a right prism of 1-in. altitude. Draw the top and front views of the prism. *Scale:* full size.

7.30. Line JK intersects both $R(1\frac{1}{2},3\frac{1}{2},6)$ $S(6\frac{1}{2},1\frac{1}{2},7)$ and $A(1\frac{1}{2},0\frac{1}{2},6\frac{1}{2})$ $B(4\frac{1}{4},3\frac{1}{2},8\frac{1}{2})$. Line LM intersects both RS and $BC(6,2,5\frac{1}{2})$. Lines JK and LM are both perpendicular to plane ABC. Draw the top and front views of JK and LM.

Group VI. Shortest Distance from a Point to a Plane

7.31. Determine the true length of the shortest distance from point $P(6,3,6)$ to plane $R(2,1,6\frac{1}{2})$ $S(3\frac{1}{2},4,6)$ $T(4\frac{1}{2},3,8)$. *Scale:* full size.

7.32. How far are the points $K(3\frac{1}{2},3,6)$, $L(4,1,4)$, and $M(7,1,7)$ from plane $A(4,3,8)$ $B(5,0\frac{1}{2},4)$ $C(8,1\frac{1}{2},6)$? *Scale:* half size.

7.33. Determine the true length of the shortest distance from point $D(5,3,6)$ to plane $E(1,1,7)$ $F(2\frac{1}{2},4\frac{1}{2},6\frac{1}{2})$ $G(3\frac{1}{2},3\frac{1}{2},8\frac{1}{2})$. *Scale:* $\frac{1}{4}'' = 1'\text{-}0''$.

7.34. The lower surface of an ore vein is its foot wall. The upper surface of a vein is its hanging wall. Points $O(1,3,5)$, $H(3,1,8)$, and $W(5,2,7)$ are on the hanging-wall outcrop of a vein. Point $F(4,1,6)$ is on the outcrop of the foot wall of the vein. Determine the thickness of this vein. *Scale:* $1'' = 10'\text{-}0''$.

Group VII. Plane Perpendicular to a Line

7.35. In Fig. 7.25 the top and front views of the upper base of a right prism are given in each of the three presentations. The lateral edges of each prism are 1 in. long. Complete the top and front views of each prism.

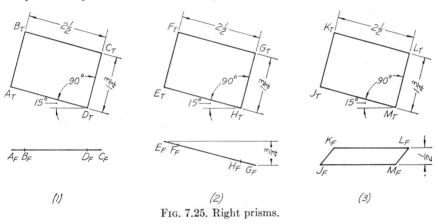

Fig. 7.25. Right prisms.

7.36. Plane $Q(3\frac{1}{2},1\frac{1}{2},7)$ $R(6,X,7)$ $S(2\frac{1}{2},1\frac{1}{2},X)$ is perpendicular to line $P(1\frac{1}{2},3,5)$ Q. Complete the top and front views of triangle QRS.

7.37. Plane $M(3,1,7)$ $N(4,0\frac{1}{2},X)$ $O(6,4\frac{1}{2},X)$ is perpendicular to line $L(1,3,6)$ M. Draw the top view of triangle LMN.

7.38. The plane of the equilateral triangle ABC is perpendicular to line $D(1,4,7)$ $B(3,2,8)$. BC is 2 in. long and frontal. Point A is to the front of B. *Scale:* full size. Draw the top and front views of triangle ABC.

7.39. Point $B(3,1,7)$ is the front corner of the equilateral triangle BCD. The plane of this triangle is perpendicular to line $A(1,3,6)$ B. One side of the triangle is frontal. The sides of the triangle are 2 in. long. *Scale:* full size. Draw the top and front views of triangle BCD.

7.40. Point $K(1,1,5)$ is the vertex and $C(3,1,8)$ is the mid-point of the 2-in. base of a horizontal isosceles triangle. This triangle is the lower lateral face of a right, equilateral-based, triangular pyramid. Point K is the vertex of the pyramid. *Scale:* full size. Draw the top, front, auxiliary, and end views of the pyramid.

7.41. The plane of an isosceles triangle BCD is perpendicular to line $A(1,4,7)$ $B(4\frac{1}{2},2\frac{1}{4},5)$. The vertex angle of this triangle is an acute angle. One of the equal sides of the triangle (CD) is a horizontal line. CD is $2\frac{1}{2}$ in. long and $1\frac{1}{2}$ in. below point B. Both C and D are to the left of B. *Scale:* full size. Draw the top and front views of triangle BCD.

Group VIII. Perpendicular Planes

7.42. Line $R(1,1\frac{1}{2},8)$ $S(3,1\frac{1}{2},6\frac{1}{4})$ is a line of plane RST, which dips 30° to the right rear. The plane of triangle $MNO(3\frac{1}{2},2,8)$ is perpendicular to plane RST. Planes MNO and RST have the same strike. Triangle MNO is an isosceles triangle whose equal sides are 2 in. long and whose base lies in plane RST. *Scale:* full size. Draw the top and front views of triangle MNO.

7.43. The pyramid $V(1\frac{1}{2},4,7)$ $A(0\frac{1}{2},1,7\frac{1}{4})$ $B(2\frac{1}{4},1,5\frac{1}{2})$ $C(3\frac{1}{4},1,9)$ is to be truncated by a plane that is perpendicular to plane VAC. This truncating plane contains points $P(1,2\frac{3}{4},8\frac{1}{4})$ and $Q(3\frac{1}{2},3\frac{1}{2},8)$. Draw the top and front views of the truncated pyramid. Determine the diameter of the circle that will circumscribe the top surface of this truncated pyramid. *Scale:* $3'' = 1'\text{-}0''$.

7.44. Line $A(5\frac{1}{2},X,7)$ $B(7,X,6\frac{1}{2})$ in plane $R(5,1,7\frac{1}{2})$ $S(8,3,6\frac{1}{2})$ $T(6,4,5\frac{1}{2})$ is an edge of square $ABCD$ whose plane is perpendicular to plane RST. Point C is the uppermost corner of the square. Draw the top and front views of square $ABCD$.

Group IX. Angle between Two Planes

The problems of Group III, Chap. 4, may all be assigned for solution by the perpendicular-line method.

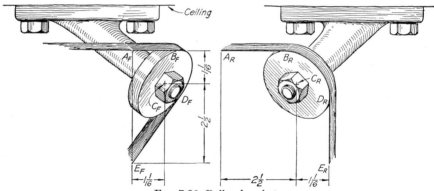

Fig. 7.26. Pulley bracket.

7.45. The belt $ABDE$ runs on the pulley shown in Fig. 7.26. As a preliminary step in the design of the pulley bracket, determine the angle between plane $ABDE$ and the horizontal plane of the ceiling mounting surface.

7.46. Determine the true size of the angle between planes $A(4,4,7\frac{1}{2})$ $B(6,2,6)$ $C(7,3,8)$ and $R(1\frac{1}{2},3\frac{1}{2},7)$ $S(4\frac{1}{2},2\frac{1}{2},5\frac{1}{2})$ $T(2\frac{1}{2},0\frac{1}{2},8\frac{1}{2})$.

7.47. Draw a view that shows the true size of the dihedral angle between planes $D(2,4,6)$ $E(3,0,9)$ $F(5,1,5)$ and $U(3,2,7)$ $V(6,3,9)$ $W(7,0,6)$.

Group X. Three Mutually Perpendicular Planes

7.48. Plane $A(2\frac{1}{2},2,4\frac{1}{4})$ $C(4\frac{3}{4},1\frac{1}{2},5\frac{3}{4})$ $D(5\frac{1}{2},2\frac{1}{4},X)$ is perpendicular to plane $ACB(3\frac{1}{2},1,5\frac{1}{2})$. Locate the top view of point D. Plane $NCM(6\frac{3}{4},X,5\frac{1}{4})$ is perpendicular to both planes ACD and ACB. Locate the front view of point M.

7.49. The diagonals of a specific octahedron are equal in length, and each is the perpendicular bisector of the other two.   One of these diagonals is $A(4\frac{1}{4},1,6\frac{3}{4})$ $B(5\frac{3}{4},3\frac{1}{2},5\frac{1}{4})$. Point $P(3\frac{3}{4},1\frac{3}{4},4)$ is a point on the line of a second diagonal.   Draw the top and front views of the octahedron.

7.50. Plane $A(3,3,7)$ $B(7,2\frac{1}{2},8\frac{3}{4})$ $C(6,0\frac{1}{2},6)$ contains the 2- by 3-in. lower base of a right-rectangular prism whose third dimension is $1\frac{1}{4}$ in.   The 3-in. edges are horizontal. Point $D(3\frac{1}{4},2\frac{1}{2},X)$ of plane ABC is one corner of the base, which lies generally to the right and below point D.   *Scale:* full size.   Draw the top and front views of the prism.

CHAPTER 8

CURVED LINES AND THEIR TANGENTS

8.1. Many engineering problems require a knowledge of curved lines, tangents, and curved surfaces for their solution. The problems may involve objects possessing such features, or it may be that the solution can best be achieved through the introduction of these geometric forms. Problems of the latter type will be found in Chap. 11.

8.2. Curved Lines. A curved line is generated by a point moving in a constantly changing direction. Such lines may be either plane curves or space curves. As in the case of other figures, the appearance of curved lines varies with each change in the observer's location with respect to the lines. Thus, curves appear differently proportioned from what they actually are in most orthographic views. In an extreme instance, a plane curve appears as a straight line (in an edge view of the plane of the curve).

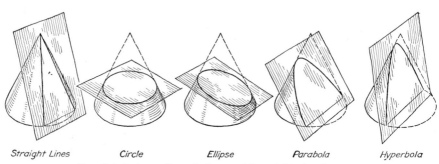

| Straight Lines | Circle | Ellipse | Parabola | Hyperbola |

FIG. 8.1. Intersection of planes with a right-circular cone.

8.3. Conic Sections (Fig. 8.1). The intersections of various planes with right-circular cones (cones of revolution) are *conic sections*. This term applies primarily to the *ellipse, parabola,* and *hyperbola;* however, limiting conditions result in point, line, and circle intersections.

Planes that pass through the vertex of the cone and make an angle with the axis larger than that which the elements make intersect the cone only at the vertex point. Planes through the vertex that make the same angle with the axis as the elements are tangent to the cone. If the plane contains the vertex and makes a lesser angle with the axis than the elements, the intersection is a pair of straight-line elements.

Planes that do not contain the vertex of a right-circular cone have curved-line intersections with that cone. If the plane is perpendicular to the axis of revolution, the curve is a circle. An ellipse is cut on the conic surface by a plane that makes a greater angle with the axis than the elements. The intersection is a parabola when the elements and cutting plane both make the same angle with the axis. If the angle between the plane and the axis is less than the axis-element angle, the resulting intersection is a hyperbola.

8.4. The Circle. A circle is a closed plane curve generated by a point moving so that its distance from a fixed point, the *center*, is constant. The constant distance is the *radius* of the circle. A *diameter* of a circle is a chord that passes through the center of the circle; hence, it is double the radius. The axis of a circle is the line through the center of the circle that is perpendicular to the plane of the circle. In Fig. 8.2, C is the center, BD a diameter, and AX the axis of the circle shown.

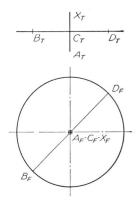

FIG. 8.2. Circle nomenclature.

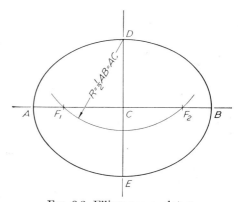

FIG. 8.3. Ellipse nomenclature.

8.5. The Ellipse. An ellipse is a closed plane curve generated by a point moving so that the sum of its distances from two fixed *focal points* is constant. The constant sum is equal to the length of the *major diameter* (the longest of all diameters of the ellipse). The *minor diameter* is the shortest of all the diameters and is perpendicular to the major diameter. In Fig. 8.3, F_1 and F_2 are the foci, AB is the major diameter, and DE the minor diameter of the ellipse.

If the lengths of the major and minor diameters are known, the ellipse may be drawn through points plotted by the procedures indicated in Fig. 8.4. The following is applicable to both (1) and (2) of that figure. On a straight edge of a piece of paper mark the distance ac equal to one-half the major diameter and cd equal to one-half the minor diameter. Move the strip, keeping a on the minor-diameter line and d on the major-diameter line; c

will trace the ellipse during that movement. This method of determining points of the curve requires considerable care if accurate results are to be achieved. Whenever the major and minor diameters are nearly equal, the method shown in (2) should be used.

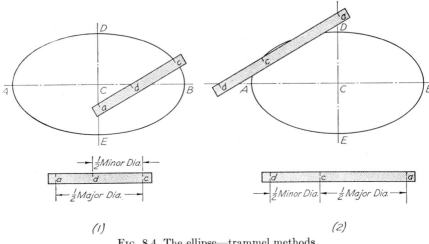

FIG. 8.4. The ellipse—trammel methods.

Any diameter of an ellipse may serve as one of a pair of *conjugate diameters*. A property of conjugate diameters is that each is parallel to the tangents to the curve at the extremities of the other. For any pair of conjugates these tangents form a parallelogram, as shown in the two examples of Fig. 8.5. Points of the ellipse may be determined by the following construction: Divide either of the conjugate diameters into a number of equal parts. Divide the parallelogram sides that are parallel to the other conjugate diameter into the same number of equal parts. Number both sets of these divisions from the extremities of the first conjugate. Draw radiating lines to these numbered divisions from both ends of the second conjugate.

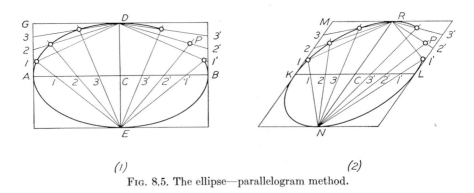

FIG. 8.5. The ellipse—parallelogram method.

Points of the ellipse are determined at the intersection of like-numbered radiating lines.

In Fig. 8.5(1), AB and DE, the major and minor diameters of the ellipse, were given. Point P, a point of the ellipse, is located at the intersection of lines $D2'$ and $E2'$. The conjugate diameters KL and NR were given in (2). Point P, of this second ellipse, is located at the intersection of lines $R2'$ and $N2'$.

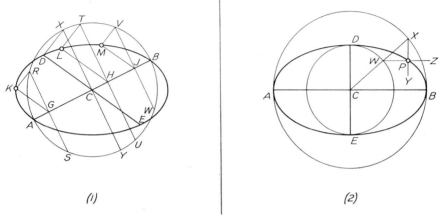

Fig. 8.6. The ellipse—circle methods.

If a pair of conjugate diameters are known, the ellipse may be plotted by using constructions that employ circular shapes. In Fig. 8.6(1), the conjugate diameters AB and DE were given. A circle is drawn with AB as a diameter. The diameter XY and a series of chords (RS, TU, VW, etc.) are drawn perpendicular to AB. Lines through points R, T, and V are drawn parallel to XD. Lines parallel to DE are drawn through points G, H, and J. The intersections K, L, and M are points on the required ellipse.

Whenever the given conjugate pair are the major and minor diameters of the ellipse, two circles whose common center is the center of the ellipse can be advantageously used. The given diameters are respectively equal to the diameters of the circles, as shown in Fig. 8.6(2). Points on the ellipse may be determined by drawing lines that radiate from point C (for example, CWX). Line XY is then drawn parallel to DE, and WZ is drawn parallel to AB. Point P is a point of the ellipse. The construction may be repeated for as many points of the curve as may be required.

8.6. Circle in an Oblique Position. The student has seen that geometric figures have distinct appearances when viewed from different locations. Thus, a circle will appear in one of three ways: as a circle in a normal view of the plane of the circle, as a straight line in an edge view of the plane of the circle, or as an ellipse. In a normal view of the plane of the circle all diameters are shown in true length, whereas in any other view only *one* of the diameters of the circle will be in true length. It will be realized, therefore, that in an elliptical view of a circle the major diameter of the ellipse will be the diameter that is true length in that view; all other diameters will be foreshortened. Since an ellipse can be drawn if the major diameter and another point on the curve are known, the drawing of the principal views of an obliquely positioned circle requires the following steps: (1) Establish the plane of the circle; (2) determine the true-length diameters of the given views, and project the extremities of those diameters to the other views; and (3) use applied geometrical constructions to draw the elliptical representations of the circle.

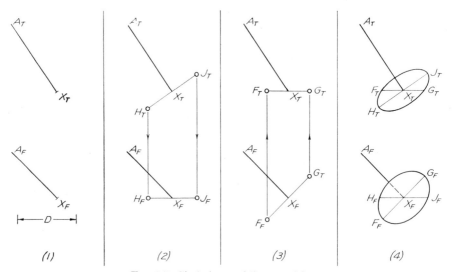

Fig. 8.7. Circle in an oblique position.

In a typical problem that requires the drawing of a circle in an oblique position, the axis, center, and diameter of the circle may be as presented in Fig. 8.7(1), where AX is the axis, X the center, and D a distance equal in length to the diameter of a circle. In (2), the horizontal diameter HJ is established, the top view showing the perpendicular relationship between AX and HJ. The frontal diameter FG is drawn in (3), with the perpendicular relationship of FG and AX being shown in the front view, a normal view of FG. The two views of the circle are shown in (4) after a trammel or other means had been employed to determine the elliptical curves. It should be noted that the proportions of the two elliptical representations of the circle are not the same, owing to the difference of foreshortening in the two views.

This problem can also be solved by securing an end view of the axis of the circle, since such a view will be a normal view of the circle. The difficulty with this solution lies in the lack of practical accuracy that may be expected by projecting points of the curve back through the several views. If the original problem did *not* require the drawing of the circle in the principal views, this latter method may be preferred.

8.7. Ellipse in Auxiliary and Oblique Positions. An ellipse may appear in its true size and shape (normal view), as an ellipse of different size and/or proportion from its normal view, as a straight line, or as a circle.

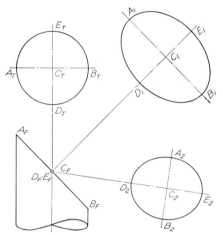

FIG. 8.8. Ellipse in an auxiliary position.

Several views of a truncated right-circular cylinder are shown in Fig. 8.8. The truncating, frontal-receding plane cuts an ellipse on the cylindrical surface. The front view shows the ellipse appearing as a straight line, since it is an edge view of the truncating plane. The top view shows the ellipse appearing as a circle. The true size and shape of the ellipse are seen in its normal view, but the other auxiliary view shows the ellipse appearing as a curve which is differently proportioned and sized. In each of the three curved views, the true length of the minor diameter *DE* is seen. Where either the major or minor diameter appears in true length, it will be the major or minor diameter of the elliptical representations. The second auxiliary of Fig. 8.8 uses the actual minor diameter as the major diameter of that representation.

The intersection of an oblique surface with a right-circular cylindrical feature, such as a drilled hole, will often be required in representation drawing. This problem is presented in Fig. 8.9(1). The oblique surface is *ABCD*. The end view of a vertical hole is seen in the top view.

Any pair of the conjugate diameters of an ellipse will *appear* perpendicular to each other in a circular representation of the ellipse. The diameters *WX* and *YZ* are so established in the top view of (2), and their lines extended to intersect the edges of surface *ABCD*. The front view of these diameter lines is then drawn. *W*, *X*, *Y*, and *Z* are established in the front view, and

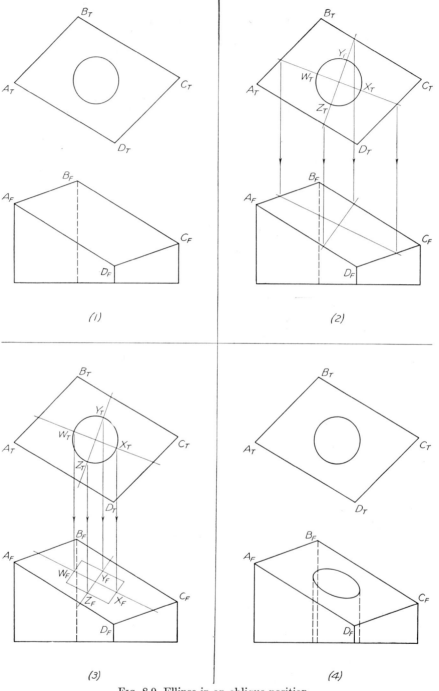

(1)

(2)

(3)

(4)

Fig. 8.9. Ellipse in an oblique position.

106

the sides of the parallelogram are drawn through these points, as shown in (3). In (4), the front view is completed, showing the foreshortened projection of the ellipse.

8.8. The Parabola. A parabola is a plane curve generated by a point moving so that its distance from a fixed point, the *focus*, is constantly equal to its distance from a fixed straight line, the *directrix*. Among its practical applications are certain bridge arches, road sections, and reflectors.

In Fig. 8.10, a parabola is shown and the method of drawing it, based upon the preceding definition, is indicated. *F* is the focus, and *AB* the directrix. Line *CD* is drawn parallel to the directrix. The distance between this line and the directrix is then used as the radius of an arc whose center is the focus of the parabola. Points of the parabola are located where this arc intersects *CD*. The construction is repeated for as many points as may be required.

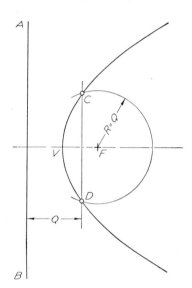

FIG. 8.10. Parabola nomenclature and construction.

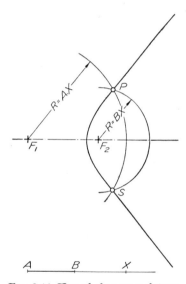

FIG. 8.11. Hyperbola nomenclature and construction.

It will be noted that the *axis* of symmetry of the curve is the line through the focus that is perpendicular to the directrix. The intersection of this axis with the curve is the *vertex* of the curve; it is a point midway between the focus and the directrix.

8.9. The Hyperbola. A hyperbola is a two-branched plane curve generated by a point moving so that the difference of its distances from two fixed points, the *foci*, is constant. One branch of a hyperbola is shown in Fig. 8.11; F_1 and F_2 are the foci, and the constant difference is equal to *AB*. The procedure for determining points of a hyperbola is indicated by the construction shown for points P and S: X, on line AB extended, is arbitrarily selected. An arc centered at F_1 with a radius equal to AX is drawn. A second arc whose radius equals BX and whose center is at F_2 intersects the first arc at points P and S, points of the curve. This construction is repeated for as many points of the curve as may be required.

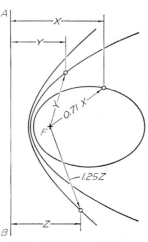

FIG. 8.12. Eccentricity.

8.10. Eccentricity of the Conic Curves. The definition of a parabola given in Sec. 8.8 is based upon the eccentricity of all parabolas. Eccentricity is the ratio of the distances from any point of a conic to a focus and the corresponding directrix. For a parabola this ratio is 1. The eccentricity for an ellipse is less than 1, and for a hyperbola it is greater than 1.

In Fig. 8.12, the ellipse whose eccentricity is 0.71, the parabola, and the hyperbolic branch having an eccentricity of 1.25 are drawn, using the given focal point F and directrix AB.

8.11. Roulettes. Roulettes are a class of plane curves that are generated by the movement of a point having a fixed relationship to one given curve when that given curve rolls, without sliding, along another given curve.

8.12. Cycloidal Curves. A *cycloid* is a curve generated by a point on the line of the radius (extended, if necessary) of a circle when that circle is rolled in its plane along a straight line of the plane. The curve will be a *common cycloid* if the generating point is on the circumference of the rolling circle; it will be a *curtate cycloid* if the point is outside the rolling circle, and it will be a *prolate cycloid* if the generating point is within the rolling circle (Fig. 8.13).

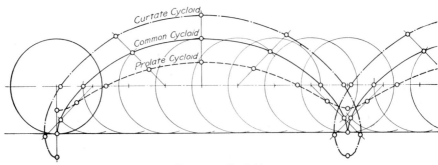

FIG. 8.13. Cycloids.

Should the circle of the generating point be rolled on the outside of another circle, the curve generated will be an *epicycloid* (if the generating point is on the circumference of the rolling circle) or an *epitrochoid* (if the generating

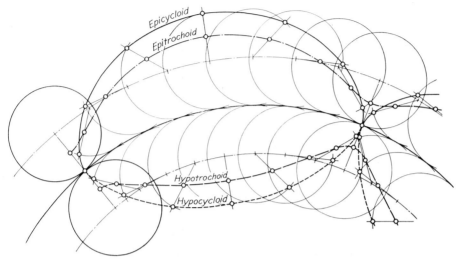

FIG. 8.14. Cycloidal curves.

point is within or without the rolling circle). If the circle of the generating point is rolled on the inside of another circle, the curve generated will be either a *hypocycloid* or a *hypotrochoid* depending upon whether the generating point is on or off the circumference of the rolling circle (see Fig. 8.14). Curves of this group are roulettes.

An example of how to draw a cycloidal curve is given in Fig. 8.15. The rolling circle and straight line AB are given in (1), and the common cycloid is required. The circle is divided into a convenient number of equal parts, and these divisions are used to lay off the length of the circumference on AB. A line parallel to AB is drawn through the center of the circle. Centers of the rolling circle, for each position to be used, are located on this line of centers. Circles that represent different positions of the rolling circle are drawn about these centers. The tracing point P is identified for each position, as shown in (2), and the cycloid is drawn through this series of points.

Knowledge of cycloidal curves is required in the study of *kinematics* (a science that treats of motion) and the application of that science to the study and design of mechanisms.

8.13. Involutes. An involute is a plane curve generated by the movement of a point on a straight-line tangent when that tangent rolls, without sliding, on its curve. (The involute may be considered as a roulette generated by a point on a circle of infinite radius rolling on another curve.)

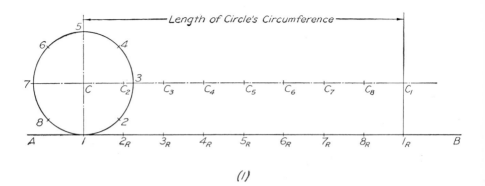

(1)

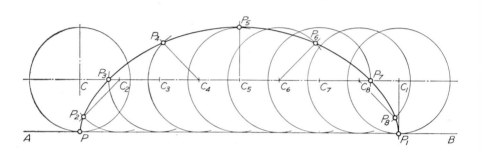

(2)

Fig. 8.15. Cycloid construction.

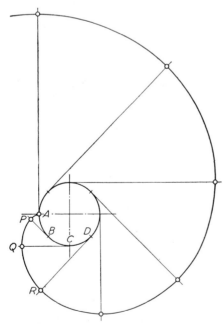

Fig. 8.16. Involute of a circle.

8.14. Involute of a Circle. The involute of a circle is the most important of the involute curves. It is primarily useful in the design of gear teeth. Although of lesser importance than its use in gear design, the intersection between a helical convolute and a plane perpendicular to the axis of the convolute is an involute of a circle (Fig. 9.13).

The procedure for drawing an involute of a circle is shown in Fig. 8.16. The circle is divided into a convenient number of parts, and tangents to the circle are drawn through these points. The length of the arcs from the various points of tangency to the starting point of the involute is laid off on the tangents. For example, BP = arc AB, CQ = arc AC, DR = arc AD, etc.

110

8.15. There are many other classified plane curves. Limitations of space prevent their discussion in this text. Their construction and applications will be covered as needed in other courses of study of the various engineering curricula.

8.16. Space Curves. A space curve is a curved line having no four consecutive points common to one plane. Such curves appear curved in all

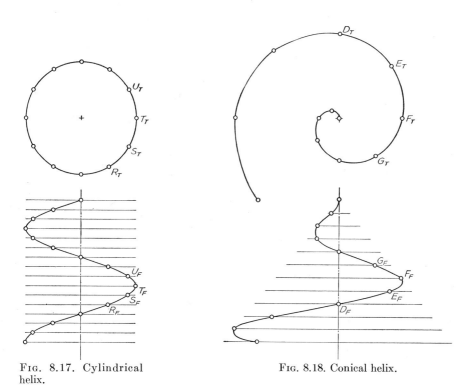

FIG. 8.17. Cylindrical helix.

FIG. 8.18. Conical helix.

orthographic views, and therefore it is impossible to obtain a normal view of a space curve.

The only space curve that occurs frequently enough in structures to merit consideration here is the *helix*. Most others, it will be found, are primarily useful in mathematical studies. A helix, however, can probably be found in every mechanical device, since both screw threads and coil springs are helical in form.

8.17. Helixes (Figs. 8.17 and 8.18). A helix is a space curve generated by a point moving at a uniform rate along a straight line while the line revolves at a uniform rate about another line as an axis. If the moving line is parallel to the axis it will generate a cylinder. The word *helix* alone always means a cylindrical helix.   If the moving line intersects the axis at an angle less than 90°, it will generate a cone and the curve traced by the moving point will be a conical helix.   The distance parallel to the axis through which the point advances in one revolution is called the *lead* of the helix.   When the angle between the axis and the moving line is 90°, the helix degenerates into a plane curve known as the Archimedean spiral.

Helixes are either right or left hand.   The hand of a helix may be readily visualized by observing the helical screw threads of any threaded fastener, such as a bolt or machine screw.   If the screw advances into engagement in a clockwise direction when viewed axially from the head end of the fastener, it has a right-hand helix.

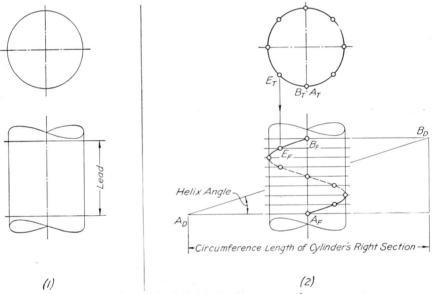

Fɪɢ. 8.19. Cylindrical-helix construction.

8.18. The Cylindrical Helix.

Two views of the cylinder of a right-hand helix and the lead of that helix are drawn in Fig. 8.19(1).   Eight equally spaced points of one turn of the curve are identified in the end view of the axis of the cylinder, as shown in (2).   These points are located in the normal view of the axis by projecting from the circular view to the respective divisions of the lead in that normal view.   If point A is the lower extremity of the helix, the procedure indicated for point E may be followed for all other points of the curve.

A straight-line tangent to the helix makes the *helix angle* with all planes perpendicular to the axis.   This angle is the angle of a right triangle whose adjacent leg is equal in length to the circumference of the right section of the cylinder and whose opposite leg is equal to the lead of the helix.   The hypotenuse of the triangle is the rectified helix in the development of the helix cylinder.

8.19. Tangent Lines to Curves. A tangent to a curve is a line containing two consecutive points of the curve. The tangent may be either straight or curved; however, unless specifically designated otherwise, it will be customary to consider the tangent as a straight line. Of special importance is the fact that *the tangent must lie in the plane of the curve at the point of tangency.* From these definitive statements, it will be understood that the tangent has the same direction as the curve at the point of tangency.

A tangent to a curve will appear tangent in all views. Therefore, it should not be presumed that a tangent condition actually exists if only one orthographic view shows an appearance of tangency.

In the several paragraphs that follow, a review is given of the applied geometry principles governing the construction of straight-line tangents to the most commonly used curved lines.

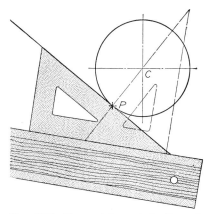

FIG. 8.20. Tangent to a circle through a point on the circle—draftsman's method.

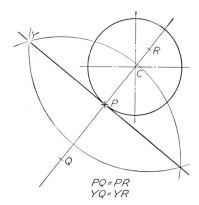

FIG. 8.21. Tangent to a circle through a point on the circle—geometer's method.

8.20. Tangents to Circles. A tangent to a circle is perpendicular to the radius of the circle at the point of tangency. If it is required to draw a tangent to the circle of Fig. 8.20 through point P, it may be accomplished by arranging a triangle in combination with the T square (or another triangle) so that the hypotenuse of the triangle passes through the center of the circle and point P. If the T square is held firmly in place and the triangle turned about its right-angled corner, the triangle may then be moved until the hypotenuse passes through point P. The required tangent is then drawn along the hypotenuse. A geometer's method is shown in Fig. 8.21.

In both Figs. 8.22 and 8.23, a tangent to the circle through point P, a point not on the circle, is required. The draftsman can approximate the tangent by positioning a triangle with one of its legs through point P. Holding another triangle (or T square) against the hypotenuse of the first triangle permits sliding that triangle so that the tangent point B can be

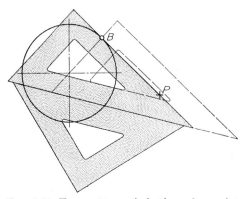

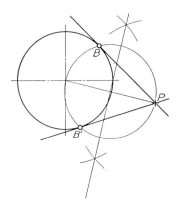

Fig. 8.22. Tangent to a circle through a point outside the circle—draftsman's method.

Fig. 8.23. Tangents to a circle through a point outside the circle—geometer's method.

marked on the circle. The triangle can then be brought back to its original position, and the tangent drawn from P to B. This procedure is then repeated for the second tangent if both are required. Figure 8.21 shows the geometric solution of the problem. Both tangents are shown in the geometric solution.

One of the many problems requiring the application of tangent lines is presented in Fig. 8.24. A mechanism employing a belt drive has two pulleys whose axes are AB and CD, respectively. A guide or idler pulley is necessary to direct the belt, since it must be led off one pulley in the plane of that pulley and onto the other in the plane of this second pulley.

The exact location of the guide pulley is not fixed, but regardless of its actual location the plane of the guide will be determined by two intersecting lines, each of which is tangent to a given pulley. [For the purposes of this solution the pulleys are reduced to their center planes and so shown in (1), where their directions of rotation are also indicated.] An arbitrary point is selected on the line of intersection between the planes of the given pulleys. This point X is identified as the intersection of the tangents XY and XZ, previously described. Since the circle of the guide pulley will be tangent to both XY and XZ, the axis of the guide will be perpendicular to plane XYZ. The predetermined size pulley is positioned in (4). Constructions leading to this solution are shown in (2) and (3). Point M is the center of the guide pulley.

8.21. Tangents to Ellipses. The construction of a tangent to an ellipse is based upon the principle that such tangents bisect the exterior angles

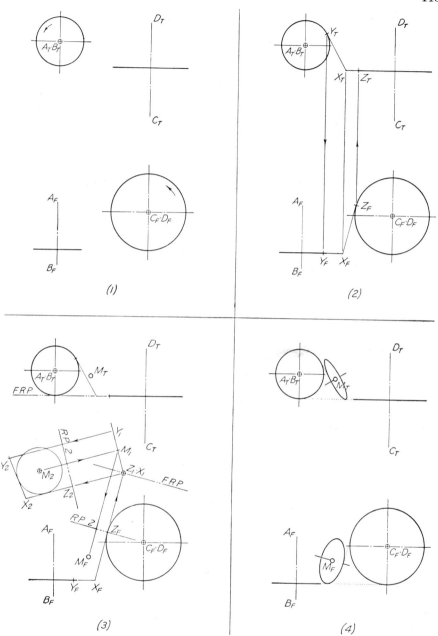

FIG. 8.24. Belt drive.

between the focal radii. In Fig. 8.25, the tangent to the ellipse through the given point P is the bisector of angle XPF_1.

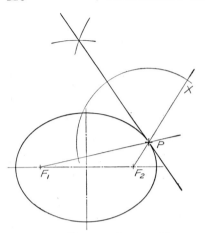

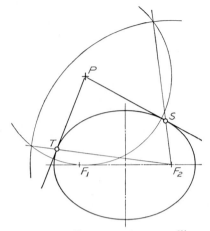

FIG. 8.25. Tangent to an ellipse through a point on the ellipse.

FIG. 8.26. Tangents to an ellipse through a point outside the ellipse.

Construction for tangents through points outside the ellipse is shown in Fig. 8.26. An arc centered at the given point P (through which the required tangents must pass) is drawn to contain the focal point F_1. Another arc, centered at F_2 and with a radius equal to the length of the major diameter, is drawn to intersect the first arc. Lines drawn from the arc intersections to the last used focal point (F_2, in this instance) cut the ellipse at the tangent points. Tangents PS and PT are then drawn.

8.22. Tangents to a Parabola (Fig. 8.27). The tangent to a parabola is drawn through a point P of the parabola by first drawing PQ parallel to the axis and then bisecting the angle FPQ.

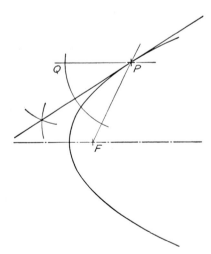

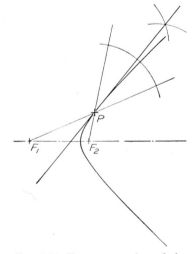

FIG. 8.27. Tangent to a parabola.

FIG. 8.28. Tangent to a hyperbola.

8.23. Tangent to a Hyperbola (Fig. 8.28). The tangent to a hyperbola is drawn through any point P of the curve by bisecting the angle F_1PF_2.

8.24. Tangent to a Helix. This tangent is particularly important as the generatrix of the helical convolute, a single-curved surface described in Sec. 9.8.

Since a tangent to a curve contains two consecutive points of the curve, the tangent to a helix will make an angle with the base of the cylinder equal to the helix angle. The top view of AB, in Fig. 8.29, shows that tangent to the helix appearing tangent to the circular right section of the cylinder. Since AB is frontal, and since the front view is an edge view of the base of the cylinder, the true size of the angle between AB and the base is seen in the front view.

If the problem required a nonfrontal tangent to the helix, such as CD, the construction of a frontal element would shorten the solution. Points A and D are located on their respective tangents an equal distance from the respective tangent points. The top view shows

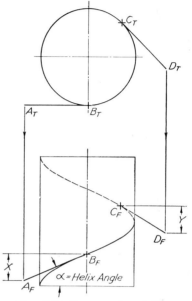

FIG. 8.29. Tangents to a helix.

both AB and CD equally foreshortened; however, the front view shows AB in true length and CD foreshortened. Since both tangents make the same angle with the axis, the distances X and Y appear equal in the front view. The front view of point D is located in this manner.

8.25. Conic-curve Constructions—Projective-geometry Viewpoint. The many admirable properties of conic curves suit them for extensive use in lofting and design in general. Equations fix these curves exactly for correlative and record purposes, and they may readily be drawn by graphic procedures. Some of the most useful of these procedures are applications of two analogous theorems, Pascal's and Brianchon's, from projective geometry (a geometry dealing with those properties of a figure that remain unchanged in projection).

From the viewpoint of projective geometry, conics may be classified as point conics and line conics—point conics being determined by points and line conics by lines. Pascal's and Brianchon's theorems are dual theorems dealing, respectively, with point conics and line conics and constitute bases for graphic constructions of the conics.

The theorems make use of the generalized concept of a hexagon in which a hexagon is a plane figure formed by joining, in any order, six points of which

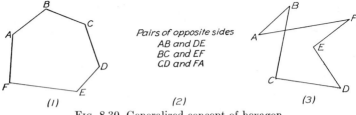

Pairs of opposite sides
AB and DE
BC and EF
CD and FA

(1)   (2)   (3)

FIG. 8.30. Generalized concept of hexagon.

no four are in a straight line (Fig. 8.30). The theorems refer to opposite sides and opposite vertexes of a hexagon. Such "opposites" are obvious in the open construction of Fig. 8.30(1) but not so apparent in (3). *By lettering the vertexes consecutively in the order connected*, the pairs of opposite sides will be AB and DE, BC and EF, and CD and FA. Since the pairing of opposite sides of a hexagon is important in applications of Pascal's theorem, observe carefully that indicated in Fig. 8.30(2). The order, of course, follows the lettering sequence used with the hexagons at (1) and (3) and is also the order consistently used in the ensuing discussions to avoid confusion.

8.26. Pascal's Theorem. This theorem states that *the pairs of opposite sides of a hexagon inscribed in a conic meet in collinear points.* As an example,

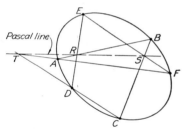

FIG. 8.31. Pascal's theorem.

the inscribed hexagon of the ellipse in Fig. 8.31 has opposite sides AB and DE meeting at R, BC and EF meeting at S, and CD and FA meeting at T. Points R, S, and T are collinear, and their line is called the *Pascal line* for the hexagon.

Any particular conic curve is determined by five known conditions which may be either five points of the curve, four points and the slope of the curve at one of the points, or three points and the slope of the curve at two of the points. A point for which the slope is known is called a *slope point* and is equivalent to two of the five required conditions.

In constructions for a conic using Pascal's theorem, the five known conditions are utilized and the theorem applied in reverse, so to speak, to obtain additional points on the curve. In addition, the theorem is useful in constructing a tangent to a given conic at a specified point.

8.27. Conic Determined by Five Points. In Fig. 8.32(1), a conic is determined by the five given points A, B, C, D, and E. It is required to find an additional point F on the curve. The hexagon used in applying Pascal's theorem is $ABCDEF$; hence, the pairs of opposite sides are AB and DE, BC and EF, and CD and FA.

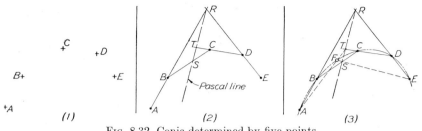

Fig. 8.32. Conic determined by five points.

In (2), the intersection R of opposite sides AB and DE is first found. Then through R a line is drawn at random direction as the Pascal line for the hexagon. Sides BC and CD are drawn to intersect the Pascal line establishing the respective points S and T. Opposite sides BC and EF must meet on the Pascal line at point S, so line ES, drawn in (3), contains point F. Similarly, opposite sides CD and FA must meet on the Pascal line at T; hence, TA is drawn and also contains point F. The intersection of lines ES and TA locates F, a point on the curve as required.

Additional points on the curve may be obtained by utilizing different positions for the Pascal line, each passing through point R. Note that it is necessary to draw only three lines to obtain each new point: (1) the new Pascal line, (2) the line from E to the intersection of BC with the new Pascal line, and (3) the line from A to the intersection of CD with the new Pascal line.

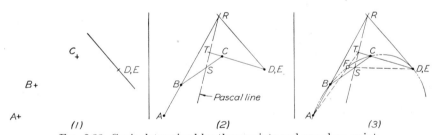

Fig. 8.33. Conic determined by three points and one slope point.

8.28. Conic Determined by Three Points and One Slope Point (Fig. 8.33). Points A, B, and C and slope point DE of a conic are given in (1). An additional point F on the curve is required. The conditions are identical with the preceding case except that points D and E have been moved along the curve to coincide and constitute a slope point (a tangent to the curve and its point of tangency). The construction is the same as that followed in Fig. 8.32 with the tangent DE taking the place of chord DE as that side of the hexagon.

8.29. Conic Determined by One Point and Two Slope Points. In Fig. 8.34(1), slope points AB and DE and point C determine a conic. An additional point F on the curve is required. This is the most commonly occurring case where Pascal's theorem may be applied—it frequently being necessary to pass a curve tangent to two given lines at fixed points on them and through an intermediate fixed point often called the *control point*.

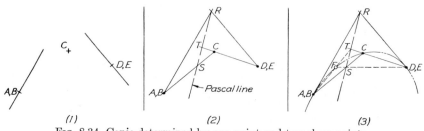

Fig. 8.34. Conic determined by one point and two slope points.

The conditions and construction in Fig. 8.34 are similar to the two preceding examples. In (2), the slope-point tangents AB and DE (opposite sides of the hexagon $ABCDEF$) intersect at R. Sides BC and CD are drawn to intersect a Pascal line (drawn through R with random direction) at S and T, respectively. Lines ES and TA are drawn in (3) as the sides respectively opposite BC and CD. Their intersection F is a point on the curve as required. Additional points are obtained as described in Sec. 8.27 using new positions for the Pascal line.

8.30. Tangent to a Conic. Five points of a conic, A, B, C, P, and F, are given in Fig. 8.35(1). The tangent to the curve at point P is required.

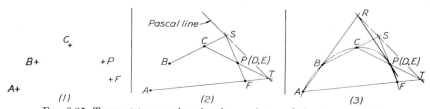

Fig. 8.35. Tangent to a conic using four points and the tangent point.

In applying Pascal's theorem to the solution, point P is considered a slope point (the slope of which is to be determined) equivalent to DE of the hexagon $ABCDEF$. The situation is analogous to that described in Sec. 8.28.

In (2), point S, the intersection of the opposite sides BC and EF of the hexagon, and point T, the intersection of opposite sides CD and FA, are located. Points S and T determine the Pascal line for the hexagon, and in (3), this line yields point R at its intersection with side AB. Since opposite sides AB and DE must intersect at R, and because the required tangent is collinear with DE (slope point P), RP is the required tangent.

In the problem of drawing a tangent to a conic using Pascal's theorem, the given conditions determining the conic may be (1) five points including the point of tangency, (2) three points including the point of tangency and a slope point, or (3) the point of tangency and two slope points. The conditions in the first case are those specified in the above example (Fig. 8.35), and this, as noted before, is analogous to that of Sec. 8.28. The second case is analogous to that of Sec. 8.29, and the construction will be similar to

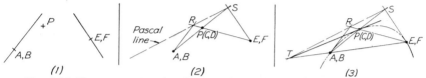

FIG. 8.36. Tangent to a conic using two slope points and the tangent point.

Fig. 8.34(3). For the conditions of the third case, the construction is illustrated in Fig. 8.36 where given slope points AB and EF are used to find the slope of the curve at given point P.

8.31. Brianchon's Theorem. This theorem may be stated: *If the sides of a hexagon are tangents of a conic, the lines joining opposite pairs of vertexes meet in a point.* The point is often called the *Brianchon point* for the hexagon [see Fig. 8.37(1)].

A specific conic is determined by five known conditions which may be either five tangents of the curve, four tangents and the point of tangency of one (a slope point), or three tangents and the point of tangency of

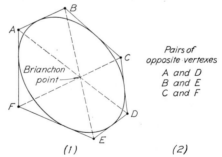

Pairs of opposite vertexes

A and D
B and E
C and F

(1)   (2)

FIG. 8.37. Brianchon's theorem.

two. The five known conditions may be utilized to determine a sixth condition by, figuratively speaking, applying Brianchon's theorem backward. So used, the theorem is helpful in establishing tangents for conic curves, hence in drawing the curves by using an envelope of such tangents. The theorem is also of value in establishing points of tangency for tangents to conics.

Pairs of opposite vertexes of a hexagon play an important part in applications of Brianchon's theorem. The opposite vertexes of Fig. 8.37(1) are readily recognized but would be difficult to discern with more irregularly appearing hexagons. To avoid difficulty, a system of lettering the vertexes *consecutively in the order connected* should be used. That shown in Fig. 83.7(1) and the accompanying table of the pairs of opposite vertexes in (2) is followed in subsequent discussions.

8.32. Conic Determined by Five Tangents. In Fig. 8.38(1), a conic is determined by the five given tangent lines XA, AB, BC, CD, and DY. Another tangent to the curve is required. In applying Brianchon's theorem, the five given tangents plus a tangent being sought constitute a hexagon which envelops the conic. The hexagon is $ABCDEF$ in the lettering system used below; hence, the pairs of opposite vertexes are A and D, B and E, and C and F.

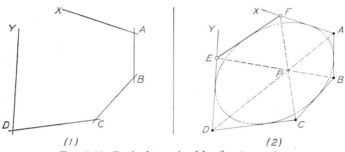

FIG. 8.38. Conic determined by five tangents.

In (2), opposite vertexes A and D are first connected. Any line is then drawn through vertex B cutting tangent DY at E and line AD at P. Thus E, the vertex opposite B, is located for the hexagon determined by point P serving as the Brianchon point. Line CP, produced, intersects tangent XA at F; thus F, the vertex opposite C, is located. Line EF is the sixth side of the hexagon and a tangent of the conic as required. Additional tangents may be obtained by varying the position of point P on line AD.

8.33. Conic Determined by Three Tangents and a Slope Point [Fig. 8.39(1)]. Tangents XA, AB, and DY and slope point C of a conic are given.

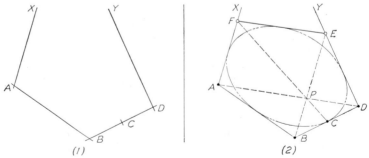

FIG. 8.39. Conic determined by three tangents and a slope point.

An additional tangent to the curve is required. The tangent at slope point C is considered as two collinear sides (BC and CD) of the hexagon, point C thus being a vertex.

In (2), opposite vertexes A and D are connected and point P arbitrarily selected on this line to serve as the Brianchon point. Line CP, drawn to intersect tangent AX, yields point F, the vertex opposite C, and line BP, drawn to intersect tangent DY, yields E, the vertex opposite B. Line EF is a tangent as required.

Additional tangents may be found by altering the position of point P on AD.

8.34. Conic Determined by One Tangent and Two Slope Points. Tangent AX and slope points B and D of a conic are given in Fig. 8.40(1). An additional tangent is required. The tangents at slope points B and D are each considered as two collinear sides of the hexagon; hence, points B and D are vertexes.

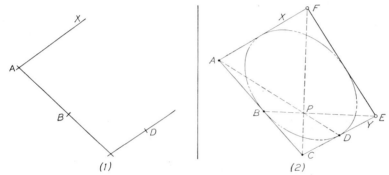

Fig. 8.40. Conic determined by one tangent and two slope points.

Opposite vertexes A and D are joined in (2), and the Brianchon point P is arbitrarily selected on their line AD. Line BP intersects tangent DY, and line CP intersects tangent AX, thereby establishing vertexes E and F whose line is a tangent as required. Additional tangents are had by altering the position of point P on AD.

Figure 8.41 shows the construction for this case where the conic is not an ellipse. The above description applies. Observe that the intersection of tangents BZ and DY is the location of vertex C. It will be well to note that *two sides of a hexagon may be collinear but not three.*

8.35. Points of Tangency to Conics (Fig. 8.42). Five lines tangent to a conic are given in (1). The point of tangency F for tangent AE is required.

The required tangent point F may be regarded as a slope point, and its tangent line considered as two collinear sides (EF and FA) of the hexagon; hence, point F is a vertex (opposite vertex C) of the hexagon.

Opposite vertexes A and D are connected in (2), as are opposite vertexes

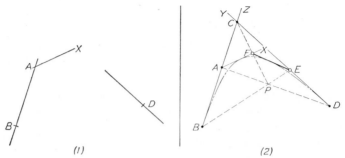

FIG. 8.41. Conic determined by one tangent and two slope points.

E and *B*.   The intersection of these lines is the Brianchon point *P*.   Line *CP* intersects *AE* at the required tangent point *F*.   The similarity of this construction with that of Fig. 8.39(2) will be noted. ·

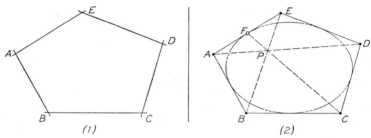

FIG. 8.42. Tangent point for a conic using five line tangents.

The above construction for finding the point of contact for a tangent to a conic may be varied if the given data include three tangents and one slope point or one tangent and two slope points rather than the five tangents of the curve as described.   In the first instance the construction will be similar to that of Fig. 8.40(2) and in the second will follow that of Fig. 8.43.

In Fig. 8.43(1), the given slope points *B* and *D* and the required tangent

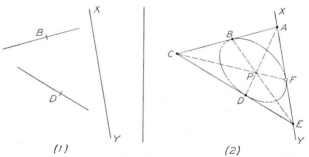

FIG. 8.43. Tangent point for a conic using two slope points and one line tangent.

point F of given tangent XY serve as vertexes of the hexagon. In (2), the remaining vertexes A, C, and E are identified. The Brianchon point P is determined by the intersection of AD and BE. Line CP intersects XY at the required tangent point F.

8.36. To Determine the Type for a Given Conic (Fig. 8.44). Draw tangents to the curve at two points, Q and R, and find A, the intersection of the tangents. Draw chord QR, and locate its mid-point K. Draw line AK. If AK is cut at its mid-point M by the curve, the curve is a parabola. A curve cutting AK between K and M is an ellipse, while a curve cutting AK between M and A is a hyperbola.

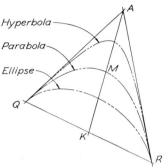

Fig. 8.44. Determining type of conic.

PROBLEMS

Group I. Circles

8.1. In Fig. 8.45 point C is the center of a 4-in.-diameter circular reflector. The ray RC is reflected as ray CS. Draw the top, front, edge, and normal views of the reflector. (The angle of incidence equals the angle of reflection.)

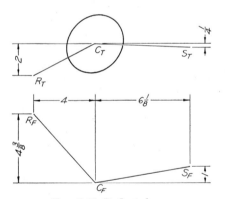

Fig. 8.45. Reflected ray.

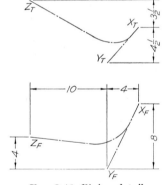

Fig. 8.46. Piping detail.

8.2. In Fig. 8.46 line XY is the centerline of a straight length of pipe in a heating system. The centerline of another straight length of pipe passes through point Z. These two lengths of pipe are connected by a 4-in.-radius 90° elbow. Flow is from X to Z. Draw the top and front views of the elbow centerline. Determine the lengths of each straight pipe from points X and Z, respectively, to their points of tangency with the elbow.

8.3. Line $A(2,0\frac{1}{2},7)$ $B(6,4\frac{1}{2},6)$ is the axis and point $C(3\frac{1}{2},X,X)$ is the center of a 4-in.-diameter circle. *Scale:* full size. Draw the top and front views of the circle.

8.4. Wire $A(3,1,8)$ $B(5\frac{1}{2},3,6\frac{1}{4})$ is the axis of a circular disk. Point $P(4\frac{1}{2},3,8\frac{3}{4})$ is a point on the rim of the disk. Draw the top and front views of the disk and wire.

8.5. A 4-in.-diameter circle lies in plane $A(1,1\frac{1}{2},7)$ $B(3,5,8)$ $C(5,2\frac{1}{2},5\frac{1}{2})$. Point C is the center of this circle. *Scale:* full size. Draw the top and front views of the lower half of this circle.

8.6. The preliminary design of a mechanism has a wheel, with point $P(5,2,7\frac{1}{2})$ on its rim, revolving about axis $A(3,1,8)$ $L(4,4,6)$. Determine the amount of clearance or interference between the housing plane $R(1,2,6)$ $S(2,3,7)$ $T(1,3,7)$ and the circular path of the rotation of point P. *Scale:* half size.

8.7. Draw the top and front views of a 20-ft-radius bend that joins pipe $MN(5,2,6)$ to pipe $OP(3,0\frac{1}{2},8\frac{1}{2})$. The pipe centerlines, if extended, intersect at point $K(0\frac{1}{2},3,7)$. *Scale:* $1'' = 20'$. Determine the included angle of the bend.

8.8. Lines $A(6,1,6)$ $B(4\frac{1}{2},1\frac{1}{4},5\frac{1}{2})$ and $C(6,4\frac{3}{4},8\frac{1}{2})$ $D(4\frac{1}{2},3\frac{1}{2},X)$ are the intersecting centerlines of a cable that runs on a 4-in.-diameter pulley. *Scale:* half size. Draw the top and front views of the circle of the pulley.

Group II. Ellipses

8.9. In Fig. 8.47 the parallelogram plate, having point A as one of its corners, must be cut to permit passage of the cylindrical portion of the combination (round-square) bar. Draw the top, front, edge, and normal views of this elliptical cut.

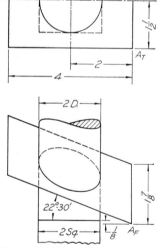

FIG. 8.47. Rod-plate assembly.

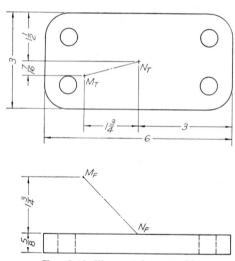

FIG. 8.48. Flange-tube assembly.

8.10. In Fig. 8.48 line MN is the centerline of a 1 OD tube. This tube is to be welded to the flange shown after the flange has been prepared to accept entry of the tube. Draw the top and front views of the hole cut through the flange for this acceptance. Determine the angle with the centerline that the tube must be cut in order to line up with the bottom surface of the flange after assembly.

8.11. In each problem in Fig. 8.49, a pair of conjugate diameters is given. Draw the ellipses.

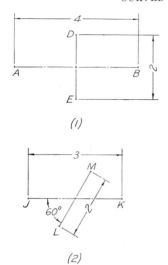

(1)

(2)

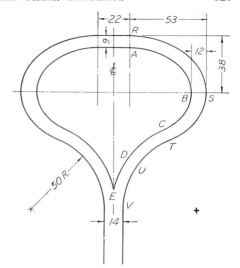

Fig. 8.49. Ellipses.　　　　　　　Fig. 8.50. Elliptical driveway.

8.12. An elliptical driveway is shown in Fig. 8.50. *RST* and *ABC* are elliptical arcs. *CDE* and *TUV* are concentric-circle arcs, respectively tangent to *ABC* and *RST*. Draw the top view of the curb lines.

8.13. *a.* Points $F(2\frac{1}{2},X,6\frac{1}{2})$ and $S(5\frac{1}{2},X,6\frac{1}{2})$ are the foci of a horizontal ellipse whose major diameter is 4 in. long. *Scale:* full size. Draw the top view of this ellipse.

b. Point $S(2,2,X)$ is a light source. Light rays from this source are to be reflected for a concentration at point $R(6,2,X)$. (An elliptical reflector reflects light rays from one focal point to the other focal point.) The minor diameter of the reflector is $3\frac{1}{2}$ in. long. *Scale:* full size. Draw the front view of the semielliptical frontal element of the reflector.

8.14. Points $A(1,2,7)$ and $B(5,2\frac{1}{2},5)$ are the ends of a slack-line cableway. The slack in the cable allows for a bucket discharge at a point 50 ft directly below point B. *Scale:* $1'' = 100'$. Consider all positions of the bucket to be on the cable, and disregard sag of the cable. Determine the height of the loading point that is directly under point A. Draw a normal view of the path of the bucket.

8.15. Draw the true size and shape of the hole that must be cut in a thin flat plate to permit passage of a 3-in.-diameter right-circular cylindrical duct whose axis makes an angle of 30° with the plane of the plate.

8.16. A parabolic reflector throws a 2-ft-diameter shaft of light along an axis $S(1,4,5)$ $L(4,2,6\frac{1}{2})$. Draw the top and front views of the outline of the area illuminated by this shaft of light on the inclined surface $A(2,2\frac{1}{2},8)$ $B(2,1,5\frac{1}{2})$ $C(6,1,5\frac{1}{2})$ $D(6,2\frac{1}{2},8)$. *Scale:* $1'' = 1'-0''$.

8.17. A $1\frac{1}{2}$-in.-diameter vertical hole is to be drilled through surface $R(1,5,8\frac{1}{2})$ $S(3\frac{1}{4},5,6)$ $T(6\frac{1}{4},1,6)$ $U(4,1,8\frac{1}{2})$. The axis of the hole passes through point $A(3\frac{1}{2},X,7\frac{1}{4})$. *Scale:* full size. Draw the top and front views of the elliptical edge cut on surface *RSTU* by this drilling operation.

Group III. Parabolas

8.18. Point $S(3,4\frac{1}{2},X)$ is a light source. The generatrix of a reflector has its vertex at point $V(2,4\frac{1}{2},X)$. The reflector is to be designed so that all reflected light rays are parallel to the axis *VS*. (Light rays from the focal point reflect from a parabola parallel to its axis.) The reflector has a 5-in. diameter at its open end. *Scale:* full size. Draw the front view of the parabolic reflector.

8.19. In Fig. 8.51 lines *AB* and *CD* are the axes of two horizontal straight lengths of pipe. These pipes are to be connected by a reverse curve that is comprised of two circle arcs having point *X* as their point of tangency. The *AB* axis is tangent to the curve at *B*. The end of the pipe having *CD* as its axis has not been determined. Draw the front view of *CD*, and find the point of tangency between the reverse curve and *CD*, the radii of the two arcs, and the bend angle for each of the arcs. (*Suggestion:* Use point *X* as the focal point of a parabola that has *CD* as its directrix.)

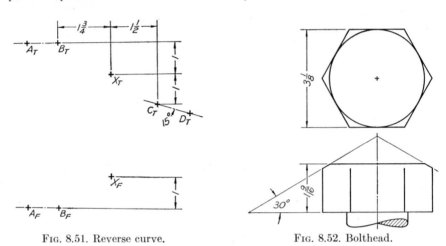

Fig. 8.51. Reverse curve.

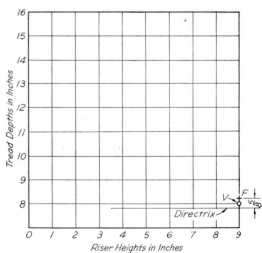

Fig. 8.52. Bolthead.

Group IV.   Hyperbolas

8.20. Complete the front view of the bolthead shown in Fig. 8.52. The lateral faces of the head intersect a right-circular cone in a series of identical hyperbolic curves.

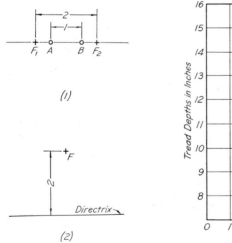

Fig. 8.53. Hyperbolas.

Fig. 8.54. Riser-tread diagram.

8.21. In Fig. 8.53(1), points A and B are the vertexes of a hyperbola, points F_1 and F_2 are the foci of the curve. Draw both branches of the curve.

In Fig. 8.53(2), point F is the focal point of a hyperbolic branch. The eccentricity of the curve is 1.20. Draw the branch curve.

8.22. In Fig. 8.54 dimensions of stair treads and risers can be properly proportioned by using a hyperbolic diagram. The vertex V of the hyperbola has been fixed by previously determining that a tread of 8 in. width requires a riser of 9 in. height. The curve has an eccentricity of 1.105. The directrix, focal point, and hyperbolic curve are required.

8.23. Points $F(3,4\frac{1}{2},X)$ and $S(5,4\frac{1}{2},X)$ are the foci of a frontal hyperbola. The eccentricity of the curve is 1.50. Draw the front view of both branches of the hyperbola to the limits of the drawing sheet.

8.24. Line $A(1,1,X)$ $B(7,1,X)$ is the directrix and point $F(4,3,X)$ is the focal point of a series of frontal conic sections. Draw the parabola, the ellipse whose eccentricity is $\frac{1}{2}$, and the hyperbola whose eccentricity is 2 of this series of curves.

Group V. Cycloidal Curves

8.25. *a.* Point $C(1\frac{1}{2},7,X)$ is the center of a 4-ft-diameter frontal driver on a locomotive. The connecting rod is secured to the driver at point $P(1\frac{1}{2},6\frac{1}{2},X)$. *Scale:* $\frac{1}{2}'' = 1'\text{-}0''$. Draw the path of movement of point P as the locomotive proceeds to the right along a horizontal track.

b. Point $S(4,9,X)$ is the center of an 18-in.-diameter frontal circle. Point $T(0,2\frac{1}{2},X)$ is a point on the circumference of a $1\frac{1}{2}$-in.-diameter frontal circle that rolls, without sliding, within the larger circle. Draw the front view of the path of movement of point T within the limits of the drawing sheet. *Scale:* full size.

8.26. A radial hypocycloid is generated by a point on a circle whose diameter is one-half the diameter of the directrix circle. Draw the radial hypocycloid that is generated by a 3-in. frontal circle rolling within a 6-in. frontal circle. The center of the 6-in. circle is at point $C(4,5,X)$, and one point on the radial hypocycloid is at point $P(1,5,X)$. *Scale:* full size.

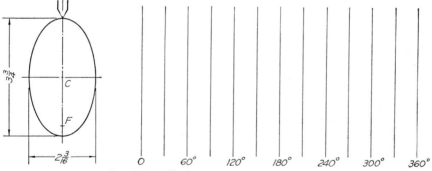

FIG. 8.55. Elliptical cam and knife follower.

8.27. In Fig. 8.55 the elliptical cam is rotated about an axis through point F; the axis is perpendicular to the plane of the ellipse. A knife follower moves vertically in following the cam. Plot the curve of the follower on a grid that is uniformly divided for angles of rotation.

Group VI. Involutes

8.28. *a.* Starting with corner A of square $A(2,X,5)$ $B(2,X,6)$ $C(3,X,6)$ $D(3,X,5)$ and unwinding in a clockwise direction, draw that part of the first turn of the involute of the square that lies behind point A.

b. Point $S(2\frac{1}{2},1,X)$ is the center of a 1-in.-diameter frontal circle. Starting with point $P(2,X,X)$ of this circle and unwinding in a clockwise direction, draw as much of the first turn of the involute of this circle as lies above point P.

Group VII. Helixes

8.29. A helical spring is made of $\frac{1}{2}$-in.-diameter round wire. The outside diameter of the spring is 3 in., and the helix lead is $2\frac{1}{2}$ in. Draw the top and front views of two turns of the right-hand helical centerline of the spring. *Scale:* full size.

8.30. Line $A(4,0,7)$ $B(4,4\frac{1}{2},7)$ is the axis of a 4-in.-diameter right-circular cylinder. A left-hand helix, containing point $P(4,0\frac{1}{2},X)$, is wrapped around this cylinder. The lead of the helix is $3\frac{1}{2}$ in. *Scale:* full size. Draw the top and front views of one turn of this helix.

8.31. Point $C(4,0\frac{1}{2},6\frac{1}{2})$ is the center of a 4-in.-diameter horizontal circle. This circle is the base of a right-circular cone whose altitude is $3\frac{1}{2}$ in. long. Point $P(2,0\frac{1}{2},X)$ is a point on this conical surface. A right-hand helix of this cone contains point P. The helical lead is 3 in. *Scale:* full size. Draw the top and front views of the helix from point P to the vertex of the cone.

8.32. The axis of a cone contains points $A(1,1,8)$ and $B(1,3\frac{1}{2},8)$. The right section of this cone through point A is a 4-in.-diameter circle. The right section through point B is an 8-in.-diameter circle. *Scale:* full size. The right, front fourth of the conic surface between the planes of these two right sections has a helix running from the most forward point of the lower circle to the farthest right point of the upper circle. This helix is generated by a point moving at a uniform rotation rate and at a uniform rate along the generatrix of the cone. Draw the top and front views of this quarter turn of the helix. Determine the slope angle of this limited helix curve at both its lower and upper limits.

8.33. Point $C(1,0\frac{1}{2},6)$ is the center of a 4-in.-diameter horizontal circle. Point $L(1,2\frac{1}{2},6)$ is the center of a 6-in.-diameter horizontal circle. These circles are right sections of a cone. Point $H(1,0\frac{1}{2},4)$ is on a helical type curve. This curve turns 135° radially in a counterclockwise direction when viewed from above from point H to its intersection with the upper circle. The slope of this helix is constant. *Scale:* full size. Draw the top and front views of the helix, and determine its slope.

Group VIII. Tangents

8.34. *a.* Point $C(4,X,7)$ is the center of a $2\frac{3}{4}$-in.-diameter horizontal circle. Point $P(1\frac{1}{2},X,6)$ is a point in the plane of the circle. Point $Q(5,X,X)$ is a point on the rear half of the circle. *Scale:* full size. Draw the top view of all possible tangents to the circle that could be drawn through points P and Q.

b. Point $M(4,2\frac{3}{4},X)$ is the center of a frontal ellipse whose horizontal major diameter is 3 in. long and whose minor diameter is $2\frac{1}{4}$ in. long. Point $S(5\frac{1}{4},X,X)$ is on the upper half of the ellipse. Point $R(1\frac{1}{2},2,X)$ is in the plane of the ellipse. *Scale:* full size. Draw the front view of all possible tangents to the ellipse that could be drawn through points R and S.

8.35. *a.* The foci of a horizontal ellipse are points $F(3,X,6)$ and $P(7,X,6)$. Line $T(1\frac{1}{2},X,6\frac{1}{4})$ $G(5\frac{1}{2},X,8\frac{1}{2})$ is tangent to this ellipse. Locate the top view of the point of tangency.

b. The major diameter of a frontal ellipse is the line segment $A(2,1,X)$ $B(7,1,X)$. Line $R(1,1\frac{1}{4},X)$ $S(5,3\frac{1}{2},X)$ is tangent to this ellipse. Draw the front view of the minor diameter of this ellipse.

8.36. Point $A(1\frac{1}{2},2\frac{1}{2},7\frac{1}{2})$ is the center of a 3-in.-diameter horizontal pulley. Point

$B(4\frac{1}{2},2,5\frac{1}{4})$ is the center of a frontal pulley that is to run at three-fourths the rpm of the first pulley. The pulley drive is reversible. The horizontal pulley runs counterclockwise (as noted in the top view) during the forward motion, and the frontal pulley runs clockwise (as seen in the front view). While operating in the forward direction, the belt leaves the horizontal pulley on a horizontal-profile line, and it leaves the frontal pulley on a frontal line that is inclined 60° to the horizontal. The belt is guided off one pulley and onto the other by means of $1\frac{1}{2}$-in.-diameter idler pulleys. *Scale:* half size. Locate the centers of the idler pulleys, and draw the top and front views of their outlines.

Group IX. Pascal's and Brianchon's Theorems

Note: The problems of this group do not require the drawing of a top view since the planes of the several curves are frontal. The coordinates, therefore, are in a two-numeral sequence rather than the usual three-numeral sequence. The given points are located in the front view only.

8.37. Construct the conic curve passing through the five points $A(6\frac{1}{2},0\frac{1}{2})$, $B(5\frac{1}{4},1\frac{1}{4})$, $C(4\frac{1}{4},3\frac{3}{4})$, $D(5\frac{1}{4},7\frac{3}{4})$, and $E(6\frac{1}{2},9)$.

8.38. The leading edge of the vertical fin of an airplane is a straight line passing through point $A(6\frac{3}{4},7)$ and has a slope of 1 to 5. Construct the conic fillet curve that is tangent to the leading edge of the fin at point A and passes through points $C(4\frac{1}{2},4)$, $D(2\frac{1}{2},3\frac{1}{4})$, and $E(1,3\frac{1}{4})$. The curve meets the top of the fuselage at E.

8.39. Construct the conic curve, for an electric-fan pedestal, that has a slope of 1 to 6 at point $A(1,8)$, is horizontal at point $E(7,1)$, and passes through point $C(3,3\frac{1}{4})$.

8.40. On a large sheet, construct the upper conic curve for the fuselage nose (Fig. 8.56). The curve is vertical at point $A(0,0)$, has a slope of 8 to 1 at point $E(16,10)$, and the control point is $C(5,7)$. The coordinates are in inches. The equation for the curve is

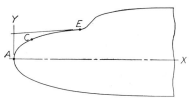

FIG. 8.56. Fuselage nose curve.

$$y = -0.298x + (-0.0712x^2 + 14.8x)^{\frac{1}{2}}$$

Calculate y for $x = 2$ and $x = 12$, and check the values against your layout.

8.41. Construct the conic curve that is tangent to the five lines $X(2,2)$ $A(2,8\frac{1}{4})$, $AB(5\frac{1}{2},7\frac{1}{2})$, $BC(6\frac{3}{4},3\frac{1}{2})$, $CD(4\frac{1}{2},1\frac{1}{2})$, and $DY(1\frac{1}{4},4)$.

8.42. Line $Z(2,0)$ $B(2\frac{1}{2},3)$ is the trailing edge and line $Y(6,0)$ $D(5\frac{1}{4},3)$ the leading edge of an airplane wing. Construct the conic curve, for the wing tip, that is tangent to the leading edge at point D, tangent to the trailing edge at point B, and tangent to line $W(0,4)$ $X(6,4\frac{1}{4})$.

CHAPTER 9

SINGLE-CURVED SURFACES

9.1. Single-curved surfaces are generated by the motion of a straight line moving so as to maintain contact with a stationary plane curve and either be parallel to or intersect the line of its previous position. The moving line is the *generatrix*, and the stationary curve is the *directrix* for the surface. The various positions of the generatrix are straight-line *elements*, and since all surfaces of this classification are curved, no three consecutive elements will be in one plane.

Cylinder   Cone Convolute Transition Helical Convolute

Fɪɢ. 9.1. Examples of single-curved surfaces.

Cylinders, cones, and convolutes are the three types of single-curved surfaces. In Fig. 9.1, pictorial illustrations of such surfaces are shown.

9.2. Cylinders. A cylinder is generated by the motion of a straight line that always intersects a given plane curve and is always parallel to its original position in space. There are many types of cylinders, as many as there are plane curves; however, in applications the majority of cylindrical surfaces will be found to have either circular or elliptical *right sections*. For the purposes of this text no consideration will be given, unless so noted, to the bases of cylinders. Even though common usage requires that a right-circular cylinder have bases at right angles to the axis of the cylinder, the cylindrical surface, *not necessarily terminated in length by base planes*, is our primary concern. Identifying names are assigned with reference to the section at right angles to the axis, regardless of the angle a base may have with that axis.

9.3. Representation of Cylinders. Cylindrical surfaces are represented in orthographic projection drawings by their outline elements and one or more curves cut on the cylinder by other surfaces. The preferred views show the true length or end views of the elements. In Fig. 9.2, several

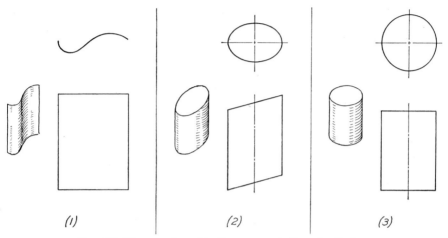

Fig. 9.2. Views preferred in the representation of cylinders.

cylindrical surfaces are drawn. The front views show the elements in true length, and the top views show the elements appearing as points. A general-type cylinder, in which the directrix is an open curve, is drawn in (1). In (2), an elliptical cylinder is presented. The bases of this cylinder are inclined to the elements of the cylinder. A right-circular cylinder limited by bases that are perpendicular to its elements is drawn in (3).

If the cylinder of Fig. 9.2(3) is positioned with its axis parallel to only one of the principal planes of projections, a slightly more difficult presentation is required, as shown in Fig. 9.3(1). The bases, although actually circles, appear as ellipses in the top view. If the top view is not required, this cylinder can be represented more easily by the front and auxiliary views of (2). Whenever the top and front views are required, the limitless cylindrical surface may be shown by the procedures indicated in (3). The frontal receding plane that contains points B and D cuts an ellipse on the cylinder, whose top view appears as a circle. This presentation is accomplished by first drawing the circular shape, with a diameter equal to the diameter of the cylinder and centered at any point on the axis. The intersections of elements AB and CD with the curve are projected to the front view, where the plane of the ellipse appears as a straight line. It should be noted that the view showing the curve as a circle is not a normal view of the axis of the cylinder. The view that is a normal view of the axis shows the curve as a straight line.

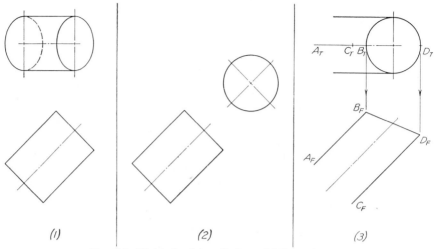

FIG. 9.3. Right-circular cylinders with frontal axes.

The views drawn in Figs. 9.2 and 9.3 permit ready determination of visibility for points and lines of the cylindrical surface. When one of two adjacent views is a normal view of the axis of a right-circular cylinder, the outline elements of one view appear coincidental with the axis in the adjacent view.

Right-circular cylinders in oblique positions require additional consideration. Their outline elements will be a true radius distance from the axis in all views; however, the outline elements of one principal view will not appear coincidental with the axis in any other principal view. In Fig.

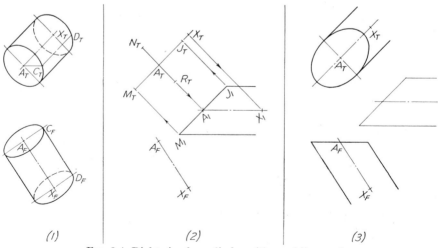

FIG. 9.4. Right-circular cylinder with an oblique axis.

9.4(1), the top and front views of an obliquely positioned right-circular cylinder are drawn. The outline element *CD* of the front view is positioned in the top view by recognizing that *AC* is a frontal radius.

If specifications for the cylinder of Fig. 9.4(1) had been presented to an engineering draftsman with only the axis and diameter size, the representation of the *unlimited* curved surface could be more simply accomplished by using a base whose plane will appear as a straight line in one of the given views and normal in the other given view. A horizontal base is used in the current example. This elliptical base will have a minor diameter equal to the diameter of the cylinder. The minor diameter *NR* is positioned perpendicular to the axis of the cylinder in the normal view of the base, as shown in (2). Extremities of the major diameter are determined by drawing an auxiliary view that is both a normal view of the axis of the cylinder and an edge view of the base plane. In this auxiliary view the intersections of the outline elements with the base plane are the extremities *M* and *J* of the major diameter of the elliptical base. The top and front views of the cylinder are drawn in (3).

9.4. Development of a Cylinder (Fig. 9.5). Since a cylinder can be considered as a many-sided prism, the student is referred to Sec. 4.14 for comparison with the material that follows. The stretch-out of the pattern

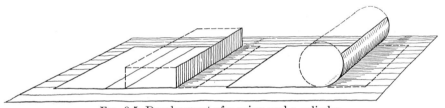

Fig. 9.5. Development of a prism and a cylinder.

of a cylinder is equal in length to its rectified right section. This may be determined equationally (πD for a right-circular cylinder) or graphically. The graphical method will serve for all cylinders and is effected by identifying a convenient number of the elements of the cylinder and totaling the distances between them. Element extremities, measured from the stretch-out right section, will permit completion of the pattern.

In Fig. 9.6(1), the cylindrical surface of the lowest member of a three-piece elbow is developed. The middle member is developed in (2). The orthographic views used are normal and end views of the elements. Speed is gained in transferring element lengths by positioning the developments so that these lengths can be projected from their normal views.

A comparison of the patterns will show that the several members of any elbow could be cut from a single sheet of material, without waste, if the seams are alternated on the long and short elements.

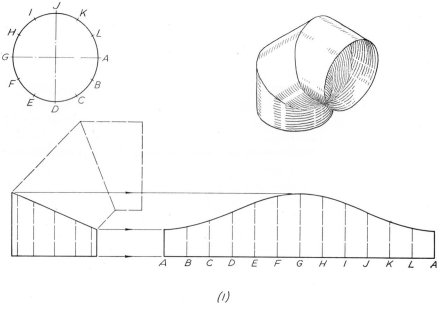

(1)

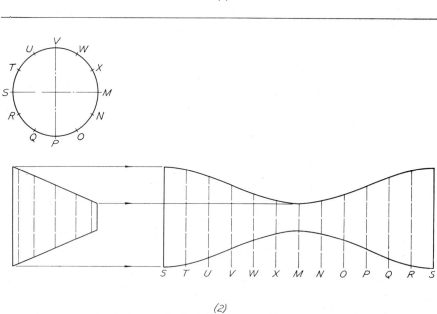

(2)

Fig. 9.6. Development of a right-circular cylinder.

9.5. Cones (Fig. 9.7). A cone is a surface generated by the motion of a straight line that contains a fixed point and always intersects a given plane curve. Since the generating line is not limited by the fixed *vertex* point, cones have two nappes. From a practical standpoint, however, the majority of engineering problems limit our consideration of conical surfaces to but one nappe each. Thus, the term *cone* is commonly used to mean one nappe of the theoretical cone.

The variety of cones is unlimited. Cones whose right sections are circles or ellipses predominate. For the purposes of this text the names of cones will be descriptive of the *right section* of the cone and will not necessarily refer to the angle that the base of the cone may have with the axis. A right-circular cone, therefore, may have a base that is either inclined or perpendicular to the axis of the cone.

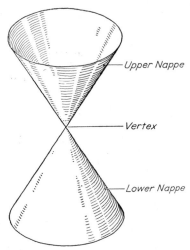

Fig. 9.7. A theoretical cone.

9.6. Representation of Cones. Cones are represented in orthographic projection drawings by the vertex, the outline elements, and a curve cut on the cone by some other surface. Not all views have outline elements to show, but where they do exist, the outline elements limit the visible and hidden portions of the conic surface. In views having no outline elements, the entire surface is either visible or hidden.

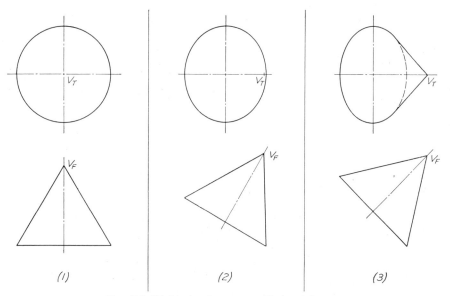

Fig. 9.8. Right-circular cones with frontal axes.

Several representations of a right-circular cone are shown in Fig. 9.8. The axis of the cone is vertical in (1). In (2), the axis is frontal but inclined to the other two principal planes of projection. The top views of both (1) and (2) show the vertex appearing inside the base curve. In (3), the axis is inclined so far as to cause the vertex to appear outside the base curve in the top view. Outline elements, therefore, are shown in both views of (3). It should be noted that whenever outline elements are drawn they will appear tangent to the base curve, except in edge views of that curve.

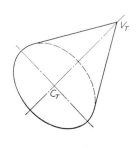

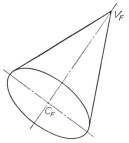

If it is necessary to draw the principal views of a right-circular cone in an oblique position, the procedures of Sec. 8.6 can be advantageously used in determining any right section of the cone. The problem becomes one involving a circle in an oblique position, plus the drawing of the outline elements as tangents to the elliptical representations of the circular right section of the cone, as shown in Fig. 9.9.

Solutions to many problems use right-circular cones as loci of straight lines meeting angular specifications (see Chap. 11). Complete representation of such a cone is usually not required. The views preferred in these solutions will be end and normal views of the axis of the cone.

The representation of cones whose right sections are not circular will be similar to those described above. In almost all cases, however, it will be desirable to work with normal and edge views of the given base curve.

9.7. Development of a Cone. Figure 9.10 illustrates the fact that a cone will develop on a curved stretch-out line. The stretch-out length is usually approximated by the graphical summation of chordal distances between conveniently selected points of the base curve of the cone, although the included angle of the pattern can be equationally determined. (This latter solution is particularly applicable in the development of right-circular cones.)

Views that show the base of a cone appearing in true shape or as a line are most useful in developing the conical surface. Element lengths are usually determined by the cone method described in Sec. 3.9 or the true-length diagram variation of that method. Distances between plotted points of the stretch-out are obtained from the normal view of the base of the cone. If the base of a right-circular cone is perpendicular to its axis, the stretch-out is an arc whose radius is equal to the length of the elements of the cone.

In Fig. 9.10, the radius of the stretch-out arc is equal to VA. Since VA

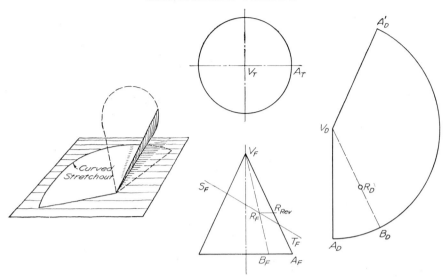

Fig. 9.10. Development of a right-circular cone.

is frontal, its true length is shown in the front view. The angle AVA' of the pattern is determined equationally (see Fig. 9.11). If the cone had been truncated by plane RST, the true length of each element could be determined by rotation, as shown for element RB. These lengths could then be transferred to the pattern.

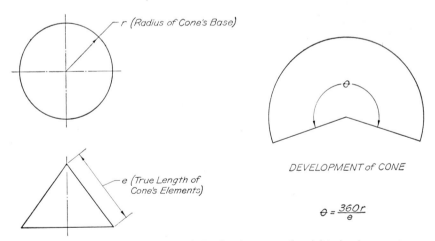

Fig. 9.11. The included angle of the development of a right-circular cone.

All cones can be approximated with a series of narrow triangles whose long sides are closely spaced elements of the cone and whose short sides are

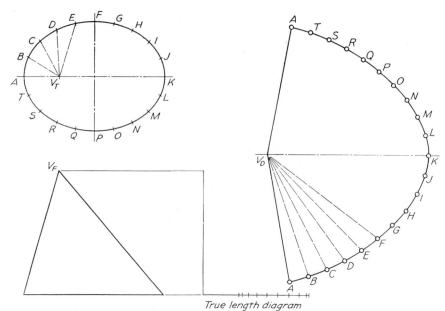

True length diagram

FIG. 9.12. Development of an oblique cone.

chords of the base curve. The development of cones other than right-circular is particularly adapted to this procedure. In Fig. 9.12, it will be

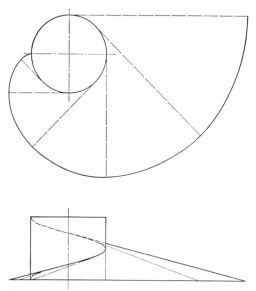

FIG. 9.13. Helical convolute extended to a base plane.

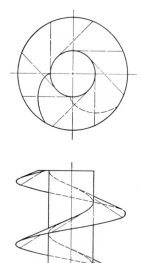

FIG. 9.14. Helical convolute limited by an outer cylinder.

140

seen that the triangles VAB, VBC, etc., closely approximate the conical surface. The development of this series of triangles is actually the pattern of a many-sided pyramid. Here, however, a smooth curve is drawn through the points of the stretch-out, while in the development of a pyramid the stretch-out is compounded of several straight lines, each equal to one of the base edges of the pyramid (see Sec. 4.15).

9.8. Convolutes. A convolute is a surface generated by the motion of a straight line moving so as to remain tangent to a space curve. The surface is theoretically unlimited in extent, but in practical work it will usually be limited by cylinders and bases. In Fig. 9.13, a helical convolute is extended to a horizontal base plane. The intersection of this base plane with the convolute is the involute of the circular base of the helix cylinder. In Fig. 9.14, a second helical convolute is shown; in this case the surface is further limited by an outer cylinder.

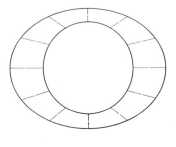

Convolute surfaces are often used for transitions between two curved plane sections, as shown in Fig. 9.15. These transitions may be conceived with the motion of a plane that remains tangent to both of the given curved sections. An element of the convolute is determined for each position of the moving plane by connecting the tangent points of the plane with the curves.

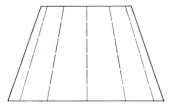

FIG. 9.15. Convolute transition piece.

9.9. Representation of a Convolute Generated by the Motion of a Line Tangent to a Space Curve. The representation of convolutes of this type requires the drawing of the space curve, several positions of the tangent generatrix, and the limits of the surface, if any. In this group the helical convolute is predominant, so the following will describe such a surface.

A helix of specified diameter and lead is shown in Fig. 9.16(1). A helical convolute, having this space curve as its directrix, is to be employed in the design of a screw conveyor blade. The over-all diameter of the blade is indicated by the larger limiting cylinder of the convolute, as shown in (2). All elements of the convolute make an angle with the base plane of the helix cylinder equal to the helix angle, since they are tangent to that space curve. Therefore, the horizontal element AB is drawn tangent to the curve, using the helix angle for the top view positioning of that element, as shown

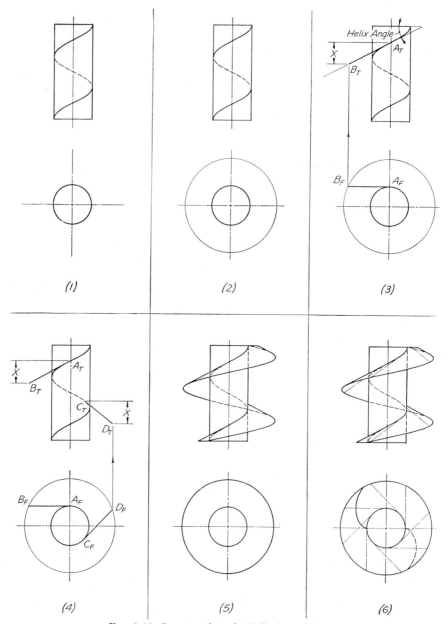

FIG. 9.16. Construction of a helical convolute.

in (3).   Point B, the intersection of element AB with the outer limiting cylinder, is then projected from the front view to the top view.   Since all elements of this convolute are the same length and all make the helix angle with the base plane, the distance between the extremities of any one element, measured parallel to the axis, is equal to X. As many elements as are necessary can be drawn by this procedure. In (4), CD was so positioned.

The intersection of the convolute with the outer cylinder is a second helix. The given and outer helixes have equal leads. In (5), the curves are shown. The subsequent presentation, in (6), shows a series of elements and the involute intersections of the base planes with the convolute surface.

9.10. Development of a Helical Convolute. The development of a helical convolute is limited, owing to the overlapping nature of the surface. The amount of surface that can be laid out in a single pattern is controlled by the size of the inner helix angle. This quantity is usually expressed by the number of turns that can be developed in one piece, as indicated in the following equation: $N = 1/\cos \alpha$, where N is the number of turns and α is the inner helix angle.

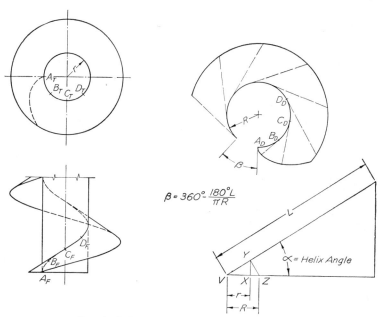

$$\beta = 360° \frac{180°L}{\pi R}$$

$\alpha = $ Helix Angle

FIG. 9.17. Development of a helical convolute.

While it is possible to approximate the development of this convolute with a series of adjacent triangles (similar to the development of an oblique cone), the use of a few selected equations provides an easier and more accurate method. In this development, the inner helix becomes a circle, whose radius R may be found by using the following equation: $R = r/\cos^2 \alpha$, where r is the radius of the inner helix cylinder and α is the inner helix angle. This equation may be graphically solved, as shown in Fig. 9.17, by the following constructions: Locate point X on one side of the inner helix angle, the distance r from V; erect XY perpendicular to VX; erect YZ perpendicular to VY. Distance VZ equals radius R.

Conveniently placed elements are drawn tangent to this circular development of the helix. Their true lengths, when transferred to the pattern, establish points on the outer limit of the surface. The intersection of the base plane with the convolute plots as an involute of the circular pattern of the inner helix. The outer helix plots as a circle, concentric with the inner helix development. Only one turn of the convolute has been developed in Fig. 9.17, but it may be seen that only a small amount of another turn could be added before an overlapping would result.

9.11. Representation of a Convolute Transition. Convolutes of this type allow for a smoothly changing right section between two sections of dissimilar shape and/or size. The given curved sections may lie in either parallel or nonparallel planes. The representation of the surface is accomplished by showing both of the given curves and a series of the elements of the convolute.

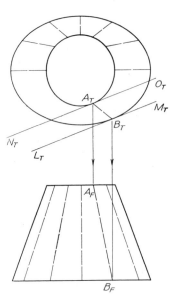

Fig. 9.18. Convolute transition with parallel bases.

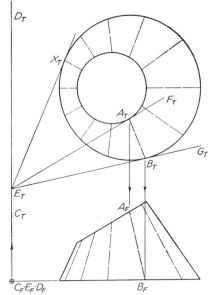

Fig. 9.19. Convolute transition with nonparallel bases.

If the planes of the curves are parallel, the elements are positioned through the realization that the parallel planes of the curves will intersect the moving plane along parallel lines of intersection for any one position of that moving plane. Such lines of intersection will be respectively tangent to the curves, and a line between these points of tangency is an element of the convolute. In Fig. 9.18, several elements of the convolute are shown, together with the construction used to locate element AB. In this construction, LM is drawn tangent to the elliptical curve. Line NO is then drawn parallel to LM and tangent to the circular curve. The points of tangency are identified, and the element AB is drawn between them.

When the curves are in nonparallel planes, the construction is more complex. This complication occurs because the nonparallel planes of the curves intersect the moving plane on nonparallel lines, for each position of the moving plane. However, such lines intersect at a point on the line of intersection between the planes of the given curves. In Fig. 9.19, the construction for element AB is shown. The planes of the two curved lines intersect on line CD. Line AF, intersecting CD at E, is drawn tangent to the smaller curve at A. Line EG is drawn tangent to the larger curve, the point of tangency being point B. Line AB is the element of tangency between the convolute and the moving plane for the ABE position of that moving plane. (Care must be taken that the tangent to each curve lies on the same side of the convolute. It will be obvious that plane EFX is not tangent to the convolute, even though EX is tangent to the lower curve; AX, therefore, could not be an element of the convolute.)

9.12. Development of a Convolute Transition (Fig. 9.20). The pattern of a convolute transition may be developed by approximating its surface

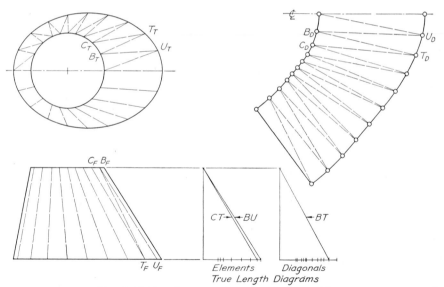

FIG. 9.20. Development of a convolute transition.

with a series of adjacent triangles. This solution requires that a convenient number of the elements of the convolute be first established, such as BU and CT. The resulting quadrilaterals, for example, $BCTU$, are then

divided in each instance by one of their diagonals.   The pattern is drawn
by consecutively positioning the true shape of these triangles, as shown by
BUT and *BTC*.

The development may also be accomplished through the use of a mock-up
of the surface. (The shape of both openings and a sufficient number of
ribs to hold those shapes in their respective positions are required.)   The
pattern is obtained by either rolling the mock-up on a plane or by rolling a
sheet of easily bent material around the mock-up.

PROBLEMS

Group I. Cylinders

9.1. Line $A(3,4,7)$ $B(5,1,8\frac{1}{4})$ is the axis of a 3-in.-diameter right-circular cylinder
whose base planes contain points A and B, respectively, and are perpendicular to the
axis.   A hole is bored through this cylinder, leaving the wall $\frac{1}{2}$ in. thick.   *Scale:* full
size.   Draw the top and front views of the resulting sleeve.

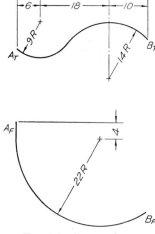

Fig. 9.21. Bent rod.

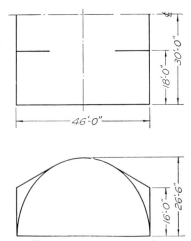

Fig. 9.22. Quonset-type barn.

9.2. In Fig. 9.21 a steel rod has been bent so that its centerline conforms to the double-
curved line AB.   Determine the true length of the centerline from A to B.

9.3. In Fig. 9.22 a quonset-type barn has a semielliptical cross section.   Lay out the
pattern for a model of this barn.   *Scale:* $\frac{1}{8}'' = 1'-0''$.

9.4. Develop the transition elbow shown in Fig. 9.23.

9.5. Develop the twisted elbow shown in Fig. 9.24.

Group II. Cones

9.6. A warehouse storage room has a rectangular floor that is $80'-0''$ by $40'-0''$.   The
ceiling height of the room is $15'-0''$.   Sprinklers are to be installed at the ceiling level.
Coverage for each sprinkler is considered as a right-circular cone whose base angle is
$45°$.   Show the location, in a reflected ceiling plan, of the sprinklers that must be installed
to ensure coverage over the entire floor area of the room.

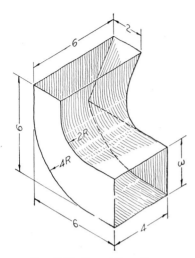

FIG. 9.23. Transition elbow.

FIG. 9.24. Twisted elbow.

9.7. Lines $A(2\frac{1}{2},3\frac{1}{2},5\frac{1}{2})$ $B(3\frac{3}{4},1\frac{1}{4},8\frac{1}{2})$ and $AC(0\frac{1}{2},0\frac{1}{2},7\frac{1}{4})$ are the axes of two shafts. Torque is transmitted from shaft AB to shaft AC by means of two tangent right-circular cones rolling against each other. The base planes of the cones are perpendicular to their respective axes, and their element lengths are the same. The AB axis cone has a 5-in. altitude and a 3-in.-diameter base. *Scale:* half size. Show the top and front views of the base centers.

9.8. Point $A(5\frac{1}{2},1,5)$ is the center of a 2-in.-diameter circle, and point $B(3,3,6\frac{1}{2})$ is the center of a 3-in.-diameter circle. These circles are coaxial, and they are the base curves of a cone frustum. A $1\frac{1}{4}$-in.-diameter hole is bored coaxially through the frustum. *Scale:* full size. Draw the top and front views of the resulting tapered sleeve.

9.9. The axis of a right-circular cone is $V(2,0\frac{1}{2},5)$ $T(5,3,8)$. The true length of all elements of the cone is 4 in. Point V is the vertex of the cone. The cone lies on the horizontal surface that contains point V. *Scale:* full size. Draw the top and front views of the cone.

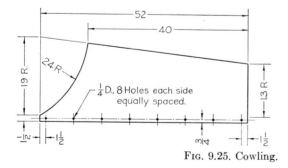

FIG. 9.25. Cowling.

9.10. Develop the cowling section shown in Fig. 9.25.
9.11. Develop the conical connection shown in Fig. 9.26.

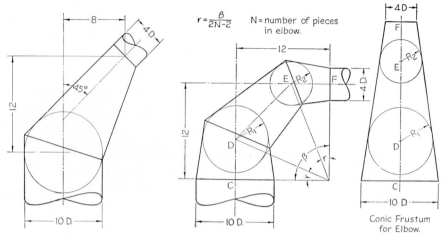

$$r = \frac{\beta}{2N-2}$$ N = number of pieces in elbow.

Conic Frustum for Elbow.

FIG. 9.26. Conical connection.   FIG. 9.27. Reducing elbow.

9.12. Develop the three pieces of the reducing elbow shown in Fig. 9.27.

9.13. In Fig. 9.28 the ventilator transition is made up of alternating plane and conical surfaces. Develop the transition.

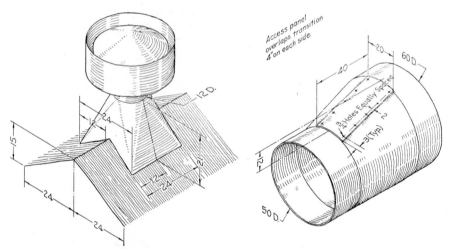

Access panel overlaps transition 4" on each side.

FIG. 9.28. Ventilator transition.   FIG. 9.29. Boiler transition and access panel.

9.14. Develop the boiler transition and the cover panel shown in Fig. 9.29.

Group III.   Convolutes

9.15. Line $A(2\frac{1}{4},2,4\frac{1}{2})$ $B(2\frac{1}{4},2,9)$ is the axis of a helical convolute whose lead is 4 in. This convolute is limited by an inner cylinder of $1\frac{1}{2}$ in. diameter and by an outer cylinder of $3\frac{1}{2}$ in. diameter. A frontal plane through point A further limits the surface. Point $S(1\frac{1}{2},2,4\frac{1}{2})$ is on the inner helix. The helixes are right hand. *Scale:* full size.

Draw the top and front views of at least one turn of the convolute, and show 12 equally spaced elements of the surface per turn. (The elements are to run forward from their points of tangency with the inner helix.) Develop one turn of this convolute surface, and show the intersection between the convolute and the frontal plane through point A.

9.16. A department-store chute has been designed with its bottom turn being banked. The outer edge of the chute floor follows the straight line $A(7\frac{1}{2},6\frac{1}{4},8)$ $C(3,3\frac{1}{2},8)$ and makes the 90° turn with a left-hand helix. The angle of this helix equals the slope angle of line AC. The cylinder of this helix is 4'-0'' in diameter. The inner edge of the chute floor follows the straight line $M(7\frac{1}{2},6\frac{1}{4},7)$ N(a line parallel to AC), then a conic curve to point $O(3,X,7)$, and makes the turn on a helix that is tangent to the conic curve NO. The chute floor changes surface classification from plane $ABNM$ to conoid $BCON$ to cone CPO (with point C as its vertex) to helical convolute $CDQP$ to cone $Q(2,X,6)$ $D(2,X,X)$ $E(1,X,6)$, whose vertex is point Q, to a second conoid, etc. These surfaces are tangent to their adjacent surfaces. *Scale:* $1'' = 2'-0''$. Draw the top and front views of the chute floor at this turn. Develop the cone-convolute-cone sequence of surfaces.

9.17. Point $C(4,2\frac{1}{2},5)$ is the center of a 4-in.-diameter frontal circle. Point $M(5\frac{1}{2},2\frac{1}{2},6\frac{1}{2})$ is the center of a 2-in.-diameter vertical circle whose plane is inclined to the frontal plane of projection at a 30° angle. These circles are the openings of a convolute transition. Develop one-half of this symmetrical piece. *Scale:* full size.

9.18. Point $R(3,2,4)$ is the center of a frontal ellipse whose $3\frac{1}{2}$-in. major diameter is horizontal and whose minor diameter is 2 in. long. Point $Q(4\frac{1}{4},2,5)$ is the center of a 2-in.-diameter frontal circle. These curves are the openings of a convolute transition. Develop one-half of this symmetrical transition. *Scale:* full size.

CHAPTER 10

INTERSECTIONS AND TANGENTS OF
SINGLE-CURVED SURFACES

10.1. The constant advances made in the various branches of engineering serve to focus attention upon the designing engineer's need of creative thought and ability to record those thoughts accurately in the graphic language. New products and advanced techniques permit an almost limitless selection for the surfaces of any design. The intersections and tangents of such surfaces must, therefore, be recorded. Conventionalized treatments are often adequate for such a record, but if the surfaces are to be developed, or if they are involved in problems of motion, more accurate representations will be required.

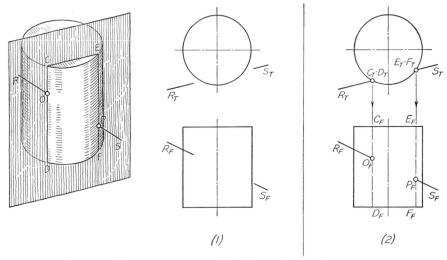

Fig. 10.1. Intersection of an oblique line and a vertical cylinder.

10.2. Intersections of a Line and a Cylinder. If a cutting plane is established that contains the given line, the intersections of that cutting plane and a cylinder will in turn intersect the given line at points where that line intersects the cylinder. Straight-line elements will be cut on the cylinder if the cutting plane is parallel to the axis of the cylinder. Such cutting planes permit the most rapid solution to this type of problem and are recommended.

A vertical right-circular cylinder and the line RS are presented in Fig. 10.1(1); the points of intersection between the line and cylinder are required. Since the axis of the cylinder is vertical, a vertical cutting plane containing line RS is employed, as shown in the pictorial sketch. This plane cuts elements CD and EF on the cylinder. RS intersects CD at point O and EF at point P. Points O and P are the required points of intersection. The construction and solution are drawn in (2).

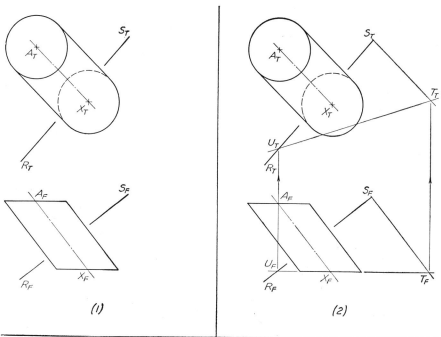

FIG. 10.2. (Parts 1 and 2). Intersection of an oblique line and an oblique cylinder.

In Fig. 10.2, the axis of the given cylinder is AX and the given line is RS. The cutting plane RST is established parallel to AX by drawing ST parallel to AX, as shown in (2). The intersection of this cutting plane with the plane of the lower base of the cylinder is determined as the line TU. In (3), points Y and Z, the intersections of line TU with the base curve, are found. Elements cut on the cylinder by the cutting plane will contain points Y and

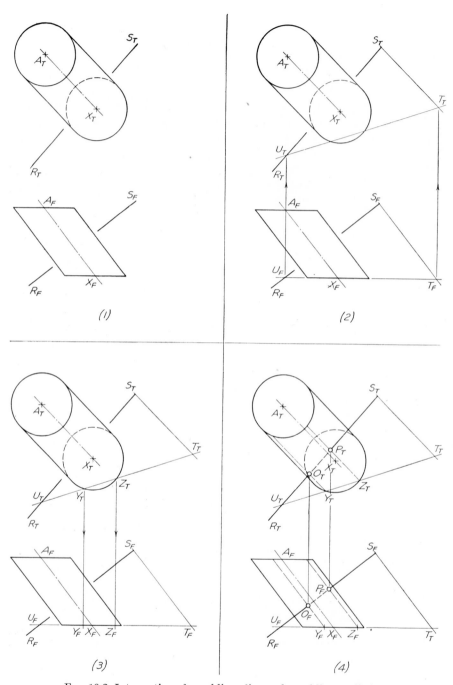

FIG. 10.2. Intersection of an oblique line and an oblique cylinder.

Z, respectively. The intersections of these elements with the given line RS determine the points of intersection between line RS and the cylindrical surface. In (4), those points are identified as points O and P.

10.3. Intersection of a Plane and a Cylinder. The intersection of a plane with a right-circular cylinder will be a circle (if the plane is perpendicular to the axis of the cylinder), straight lines (if the plane is parallel to the axis), or an ellipse. All the ellipses that can be cut on any single right-circular cylinder will have one thing in common: *Their minor diameters will be equal in length to the diameter of the cylinder*.

If the cylinder is other than right-circular, the curves of intersection between the cylinder and a plane can be determined by finding the intersections of the elements of the cylinder with the plane. Knowledge of the right section of the cylinder may be of assistance in more readily finding this intersection. In all instances, however, a plane parallel to the axis of a cylinder will intersect that cylinder on straight-line elements.

10.4. Intersection of a Prism and a Cylinder. Since the surfaces of a prism are planar, the solution to the problem of finding the intersection between a prism and a cylinder is merely one of several planes intersecting the cylinder. In the following, a problem of this type will be discussed, but prior to its study the student is encouraged to review Sec. 5.10, the intersection of two polyhedrons, for the purpose of becoming once again familiar with the sequence followed in the solution of intersection problems.

In Fig. 10.3(1), a spring clip and a right-circular cylinder are shown. The problem requires the intersection of the cylinder with three plane surfaces of the clip. This intersection will be used in the preparation of a pattern for the hole that must be cut into the clip if the cylinder is to enter the clip at the angle shown. The current problem will consider only the determination of the intersection.

Several elements of the cylinder are first spotted in its end view and then located in the top and front views, as shown in (2). Their intersections with surface $ABCD$ are identified in the top view (an edge view of $ABCD$) and then projected to the front view. The elliptical intersection between the cylinder and $ABCD$ is drawn through these points.

Surface $CDEF$ is parallel to the axis of the cylinder and, therefore, will intersect the cylinder along two elements, as shown in (3).

The intersection of surface $EFGH$ and the cylinder is determined in (4), where the complete line of intersection is also drawn. This second elliptical curve might have been found in the manner used for the $ABCD$-cylinder intersection, but greater accuracy is secured by locating a pair of conjugate diameters of the elliptical curve (the actual major and minor diameters, in this instance) and then using these diameters in the parallelogram method of plotting the curve. This routine requires a view that would show both a

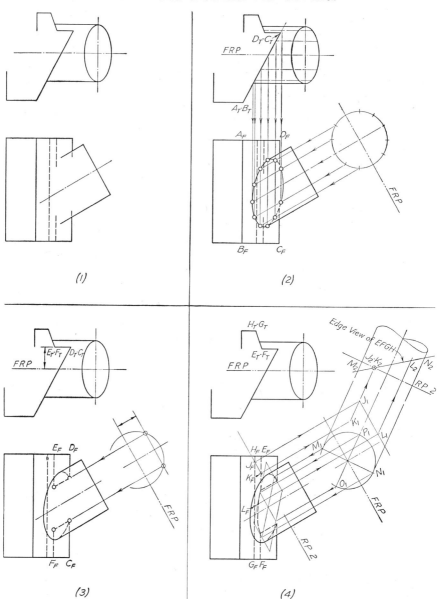

Fig. 10.3. Intersection of a cylinder and several plane surfaces.

normal view of the axis of the cylinder and an edge view of plane *EFGH*. Hence, line *JK* of plane *EFGH* is drawn so as to be normal in the end view of the cylinder. The edge view of *EFGH* is then projected from this normal view of *JK*. The outline elements of the cylinder are also drawn in this last view.   The intersections of the outline elements with plane $EFGH$, as seen in the edge view of $EFGH$, determine MN, the major diameter of the elliptical intersection between the plane and cylinder.   The minor diameter of the ellipse, OP, is normal in the end view of the cylinder.

10.5. Intersection of Two Cylinders.   The intersection of two cylinders may be determined through the use of a system of parallel cutting planes. The intersections of one such plane with the two cylindrical surfaces will, in turn, intersect on the line of intersection between the cylinders.   Cutting planes that are parallel to both the axes of the cylinder will cut straight-line elements on both cylinders and, therefore, are the easiest to work with.

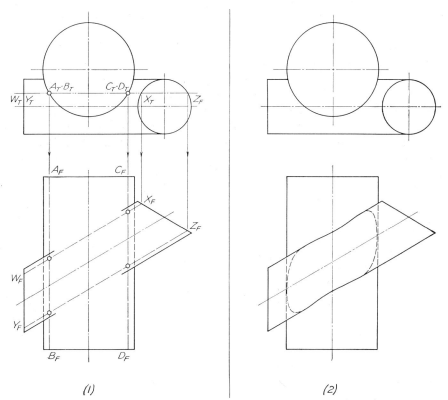

Fig. 10.4. Intersection of two cylinders whose axes are frontal.

Problems which require the accurate line of intersection between two cylinders usually demand the development of the cylindrical surfaces. Since normal and end views of elements are desirable in solving the development of the problem, the intersection is customarily determined through the use of those same views.

In Fig. 10.4, the axes of two cylindrical surfaces are frontal, so a system of frontal cutting planes can be used to advantage. One cutting plane is shown in (1), together with the elements of intersection between the plane and both of the cylinders. The intersections of these elements (AB and CD on the vertical cylinder and WX and YZ on the inclined cylinder) determine points on the intersection of the cylinders. The completed intersection is shown in (2).

Two obliquely positioned cylinders are given in Fig. 10.5(1). Although the given views do not lend themselves toward ready use in developing either cylinder, the *intersection* between the cylinders can be determined without the use of additional views. The solution shown in (4) is achieved by using cutting planes parallel to both AB and CD, the axes of the cylinders. These cutting planes will intersect the cylinders along straight-line elements, and points on the required intersection between the cylinders will be determined at the intersections of the elements cut on the cylinders by one such cutting plane. Plane XYZ is established parallel to the axes of both cylinders, through the arbitrarily selected point X, by drawing XY parallel to AB and XZ parallel to CD, as shown in (2).

The views given in (1) show the curved lines of intersection between a horizontal plane and the cylinders. Line YZ of plane XYZ is drawn parallel to the plane of these curves in (2). Plane XYZ and all planes parallel to XYZ will intersect the plane of these curves on lines parallel to YZ. In (3), therefore, line MN is drawn in the plane of the curves and also parallel to YZ. Thus, MN is actually the intersection of a cutting plane parallel to the axes of both cylinders with the base plane common to those cylinders.

The intersections of line MN with the curves are points on elements of the cylinders cut by the cutting plane that contains MN. Elements GH and JK are drawn parallel to axis AB, and elements PQ and RS are drawn parallel to CD. The intersection of the elements, points T, U, V, and W, are on the intersection of the two cylinders. Additional points of the intersection of the cylinders are found by use of other cutting planes. The complete intersection is shown in (4).

10.6. Lines Tangent to a Curved Surface. A line is tangent to a curved surface if it is tangent to some line of that surface. A review of Sec. 8.18 should be made in this connection.

10.7. Planes Tangent to Curved Surfaces. Any two straight lines tangent to a curved surface at one point of that surface will determine the plane tangent to the surface through that point. In the instance of single-curved surfaces it will be apparent that such a tangent plane will contain the straight-line element of the surface that passes through the point. The tangent plane, therefore, can be defined by the element of tangency and a line tangent to the surface at some point on the element of tangency.

10.8. Plane Tangent to a Cylinder through a Given Point on the Cylinder. The edge view of all planes tangent to a cylinder will be seen in an end view of the cylinder. The tangent planes will be represented by straight lines

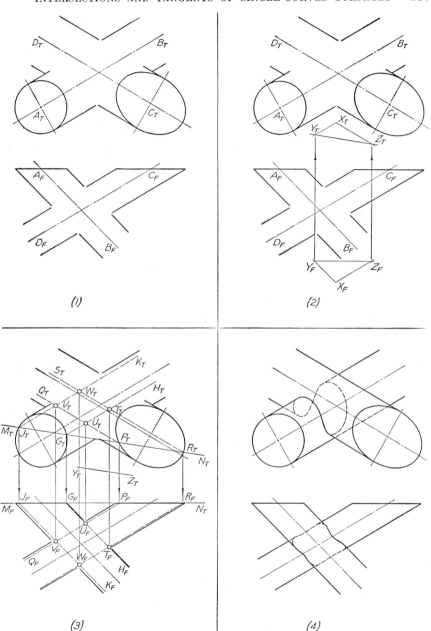

Fig. 10.5. Intersection of two oblique cylinders.

which are drawn tangent to the right section of the cylinder in that view.

If the cylinder is in an oblique position, the determination of a particular tangent plane does not, however, necessitate the drawing of an end view of the cylinder. In Fig. 10.6(1), the problem requires a plane that will contain point P and be tangent to the cylinder. The straight-line element containing point P is drawn in (2) as one line of the required plane. The intersection of this element PR with the upper base of the cylinder is selected as the point through which a second line of the tangent plane will be drawn. Line RS, tangent to the base curve, is drawn in (3). Plane PRS is the required plane.

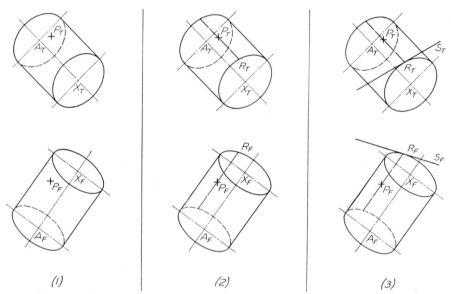

(1)   (2)   (3)

FIG. 10.6. Plane tangent to a cylinder through a given point on the cylinder.

10.9. Plane Tangent to a Cylinder through a Given Point off the Cylinder. All planes tangent to a cylinder are parallel to the axis and elements of the cylinder. In this problem, there are two planes that meet the specified conditions and each can be determined by two lines: one through the given point and parallel to the axis of the cylinder and a second line that intersects the first line and is tangent to a curve of the cylindrical surface.

In Fig. 10.7(1), point P and the cylinder are given. Planes tangent to the cylinder and containing point P are required. Line PL is drawn parallel to the axis of the cylinder in (2). Point M, the intersection of line PL with the plane of the upper base of the cylinder, is found in (3) by drawing the horizontal and frontal diameter lines of the base (AZ and AY, respectively) and using a vertical cutting plane containing PL. Lines MN and MO are drawn tangent to the upper base curve in (4). The required planes are PMN and PMO.

10.10. Intersections of a Line and a Cone (Fig. 10.8). Intersections of

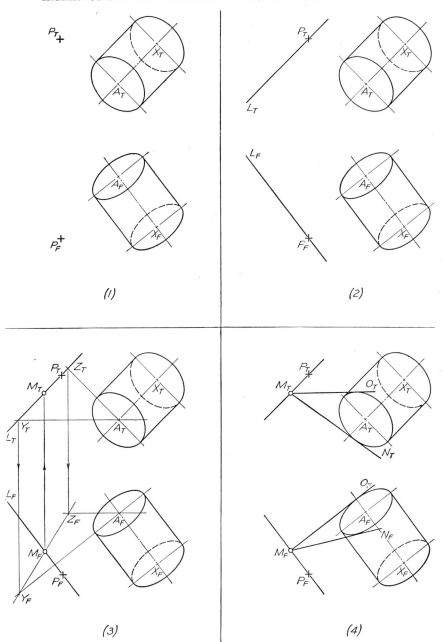

Fig. 10.7. Plane tangent to a cylinder through a given point off the cylinder.

a line and a cone may be determined as points of intersection between the given line and two specific elements of the cone. These elements and the

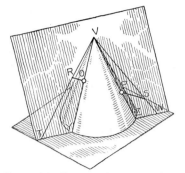

FIG. 10.8. Intersection of a line and a cone.

given line are coplanar—the vertex of the cone and the given line fix the plane of the elements.

In Fig. 10.9, the problem is presented with a cone having a vertical axis; in Fig. 10.10, an obliquely positioned cone is shown. The following discussion is equally applicable to both presentations.

The given data are shown in (1). In (2), the intersection of the plane VRS with the base plane of the cone is determined by finding points T and W, the points of intersection between two lines of plane VRS and the base plane. Points Y and Z, common to the base curve and TW, are on the elements of the cone cut by plane VRS, as shown in (3). The intersections of these elements with the given line RS are points O and P, the points of intersection between the line RS and the cone.

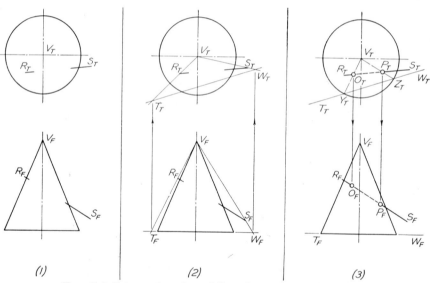

FIG. 10.9. Intersection of an oblique line and a vertical cone.

10.11. Intersection of a Plane and a Cone. The intersection of a plane and a right-circular cone will be either a conic section or a degenerate conic (see Sec. 8.3). If the cone is other than right-circular, the intersection will be a curve (unless the plane contains the vertex of the cone) that can be determined by finding the intersections of the elements of the cone with the plane. This procedure could also be used to solve for the intersection of a

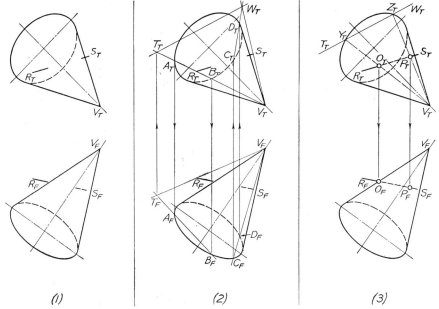

FIG. 10.10. Intersection of an oblique line and an oblique cone.

plane with a right circular cone.   Knowledge of the right section of the cone may be of assistance in deciding what procedure to employ for an accurate and rapid solution to the problem of plane and cone intersections. In all instances, however, *a plane through the vertex of a cone will cut straight-line elements on the cone* provided such a plane makes an angle with the axis of the cone that is no greater than the angle between the elements of the cone and the axis.

10.12. Intersection of a Prism and a Cone.   Problems that require the drawing of intersections between prisms and cones are simply plane and cone intersection problems.

In Fig. 10.11, the complete intersection is determined by finding, in sequence, the intersections of plane surfaces $ABCD$, $CDEF$, and $EFBA$ with the conical surface.   Since this cone is right-circular, its intersection with $ABCD$ will be circular.   The intersection of the outline element of the cone with $ABCD$ may be projected to the top view, and the resultant circle arc intersection drawn concentric with the base of the cone as shown in (1). Surface $CDEF$ makes the same angle with the axis of the cone as do its elements, so the intersection of these surfaces will be a parabola.   In (2), the plane $CDEF$ is extended, so that the vertex of the parabola may be projected from the side view to the front view.   The intersections of the frontal elements of the cone with $CDEF$ are also projected to the front view from the side view.   Additional points of the parabola may be found by using horizontal cutting planes.

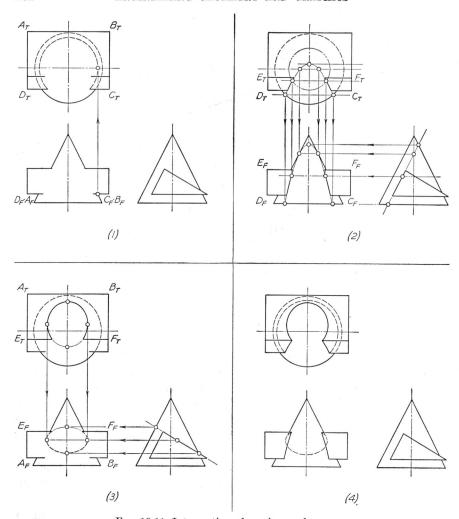

Fig. 10.11. Intersection of a prism and a cone.

The intersection of *EFBA* with the cone is elliptical. This elliptical intersection may be determined through the use of horizontal cutting planes, or it may be drawn by determining the major and minor diameters of the ellipse. The latter procedure is indicated in (3). These three intersections are combined, as shown in (4), for the complete intersection of the prism and the cone.

10.13. Intersection of a Cylinder and a Cone. A series of cutting planes, all of which contain the vertex of the cone and are parallel to the axis of the cylinder, will cut straight-line elements on both surfaces, regardless of the right-sectional shape of those surfaces. The intersections of the elements

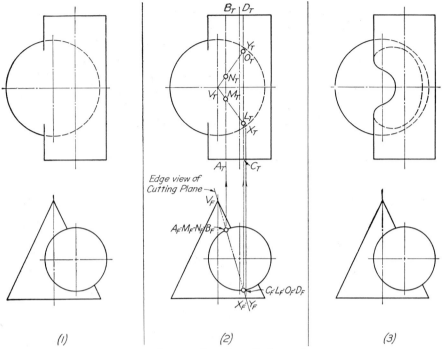

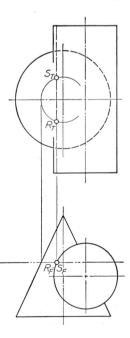

FIG. 10.12. Intersection of a cylinder and a cone.

of one surface with the other surface are points on the intersection between the surfaces. To employ this solution it will be found advantageous to have one view in which an end view of the axis of the cylinder is shown, for in such a view the cutting planes will all appear as straight lines.

In Fig. 10.12, the solution outlined above is followed, with the cylinder and cone being indicated in (1). A typical cutting plane appears as a line in the front view of (2), and in the top view the elements cut on each surface by that plane are shown. The intersections of elements AB and CD (of the cylinder) with elements VX and VY (of the cone) are points on the intersection of the cylinder and cone; these points are identified as points L, M, N, and O. The completed intersection is shown in (3).

FIG. 10.13. Use of a cutting plane perpendicular to the axis of the cone and parallel to the axis of the cylinder.

When the cutting planes of the previous solution approach a profile position, the intersection of the elements cannot be accurately determined if only the top and front views are employed. In such instances, it may be desirable to use cutting planes parallel to the axis of the cylinder and perpendicular to the axis of the cone. The resultant cuts of one such plane on the curved surfaces of Fig. 10.12 are shown in the top view of Fig. 10.13. Points R and S, on the intersection of the surfaces, are determined by the intersection of the circle of the cone and the straight-line element of the cylinder.

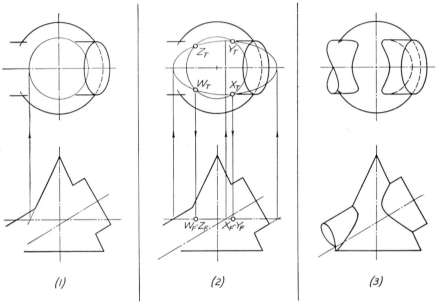

Fig. 10.14. Use of a cutting plane perpendicular to the axis of the cone and inclined to the axis of the cylinder.

In Fig. 10.14, where the axes of the cone and cylinder are not perpendicular, it is expeditious to use cutting planes perpendicular to the axis of the cone. Circles are cut on the cone, and ellipses on the cylinder. Since all the cutting planes are parallel, the several ellipses cut on the cylinder are equal. There is no need to draw an ellipse physically in this solution, for the circle on the cone can be drawn and a trammel used simply to trace the ellipse on the cylinder for any cutting plane. Points on the intersection of the objects are determined wherever the elliptical trace crosses the circle.

The circle cut on the cone by a horizontal cutting plane is shown in (1). The ellipse cut on the cylinder by that same plane is drawn in (2). This ellipse, traced by the trammel, crosses the circle at points W, X, Y, and Z, points on the intersection of the cylinder and cone. The completed intersection is shown in (3).

10.14. Intersection of Two Cones. In any intersection involving a right-circular cone, the use of cutting planes can best be limited to those perpendicular to the axis of the cone or those that contain the vertex of the cone. If the cone is other than right-circular, the cutting planes employed will usually be passed through its vertex.

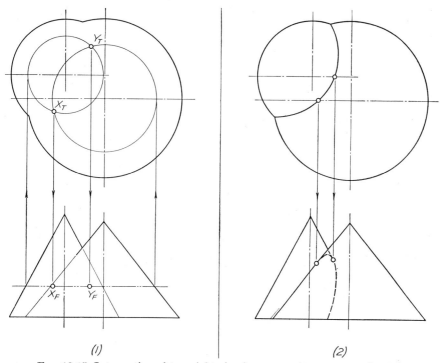

Fig. 10.15. Intersection of two right-circular cones whose axes are frontal.

Figure 10.15 shows two right-circular cones whose axes are parallel. A series of planes perpendicular to the axes will cut circles on the cones and, therefore, can be readily employed. A typical cutting plane is shown in (1). This horizontal plane cuts circles on both cones, as drawn in the top view. Points X and Y, on the intersection of the cones, are located at the intersection of these circles. This procedure is repeated for as many points of the intersection as may be required. After the top view of the intersection has been drawn, the intersection of the frontal element of one cone with the other cone is projected from the top view to the front view, as shown in (2), to determine this limiting point. The front view of the intersection is then drawn.

The general case of a two-cone intersection is shown in Fig. 10.16. Cutting planes containing both vertexes are used. In setting up the several cutting planes to be employed, the line of the vertexes AV is first drawn and its intersections with the base planes (points X and Y) are determined,

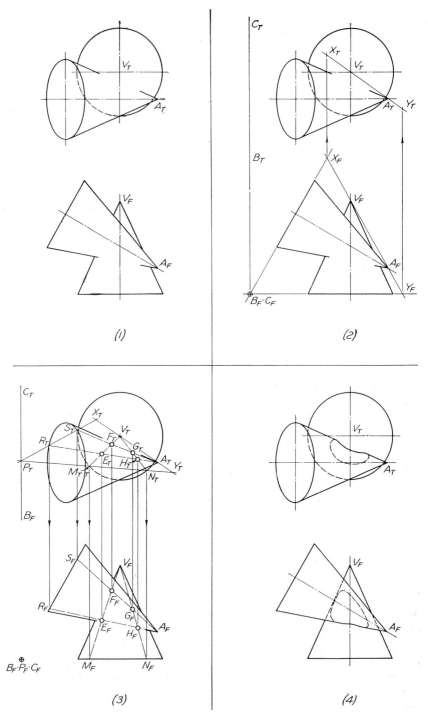

(1)

(2)

(3)

(4)

Fig. 10.16. Intersection of two cones, cutting planes through both vertexes.

as shown in (2).   The intersection BC of the base planes is then established. Any point P on BC is selected to determine a particular cutting plane that also contains points X and Y.   In (3), the intersections of the cutting plane PXY with the respective base planes of the cones are drawn (PX and PY). The intersections M and N of PY with the base curve of the vertical cone and the similar points R and S on the other cone are on elements of those cones cut by plane PXY.   Where VM intersects AR and AS, and where VN intersects AS and AR, points E, F, G, and H on the intersection of the two cones are found.   In (4), the intersection is completely drawn.

10.15. Plane Tangent to a Cone through a Given Point on the Cone. Reference is made to Sec. 10.8, where the surface is cylindrical.   In Fig.

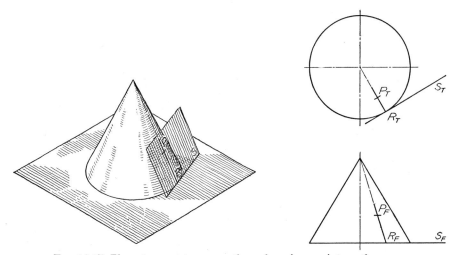

FIG. 10.17. Plane tangent to a cone through a given point on the cone.

10.17, the problem is to establish a plane through point P that will be tangent to the cone.   The element containing point P intersects the base curve at R. RS, a tangent to the base curve, is drawn.   The required plane is PRS.

10.16. Planes Tangent to a Cone through a Given Point off the Cone. The tangent planes will contain the vertex of the cone and the given point. If a line is drawn through these points and its intersection with the plane of the base curve determined, and if tangents to the base curve are drawn through this last determined point, the tangents and the given-point–vertex line determine the required planes.

In Fig. 10.18, the problem is presented in (1).   In (2), the intersection of line VP with the plane of the base curve is found at point M.   Lines MN and MO are drawn tangent to the base curve in (3).   Planes PMN and PMO are the required tangent planes.

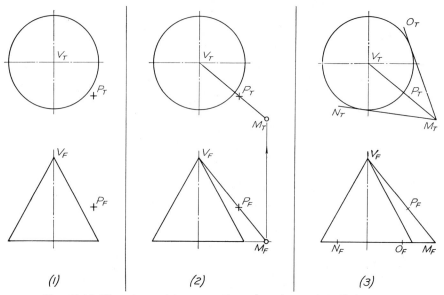

FIG. 10.18. Plane tangent to a cone through a given point off the cone.

10.17. Tangents to a Convolute Transition. The constructions used in Sec. 9.11 for the purpose of locating elements of a convolute transition determine planes tangent to the transition. The elements are the elements of tangency in each instance. In Fig. 10.19, plane $ABCD$ is tangent to the transition surface; BC, an element of the surface, is the element of tangency between the plane and convolute.

The proper design of a transition will often require a combination of several geometric surfaces. In order to effect a smooth change between such surfaces, they are selected so as to be tangent to each other. In Fig. 10.20, the several surface classifications (convolute, cone, and plane) used in the design of the transition are identified. It should be noted that the corners of the upper opening are the respective vertexes of two cones. These cones and the con-

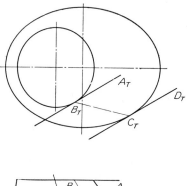

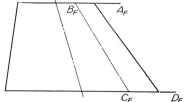

FIG. 10.19. Plane tangent to a convolute transition piece.

volute surface are separated by triangular-shaped plane surfaces whose bases are edges of the upper opening.

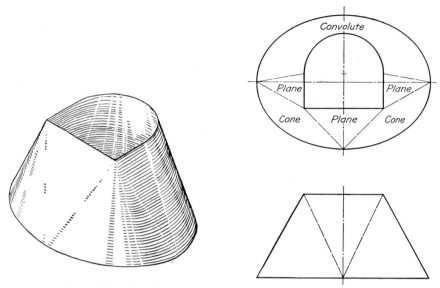

FIG. 10.20. Tangent surfaces of a compound transition piece.

PROBLEMS

Group I. Intersections of Cylinders with Lines and Planes

10.1. Line $J(2,3\frac{1}{2},6)$ $K(6,0\frac{1}{2},8\frac{1}{2})$ is the axis of a 2-in.-diameter right-circular cylinder. *Scale:* full size. Locate the points of intersection between this cylinder and line $M(1\frac{1}{2},2\frac{1}{2},8)$ $N(6\frac{1}{2},3,6\frac{1}{2})$.

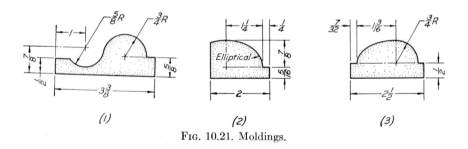

FIG. 10.21. Moldings.

10.2. In Fig. 10.21 determine the outline of a cutting knife for each of the moldings. The knife planes are inclined at an angle of 45° with the plane bed, and the intersection of each knife plane with the plane bed is perpendicular to the direction of cut.

10.3. Line $A(0\frac{1}{2},0\frac{1}{4},5)$ $B(0\frac{1}{2},0\frac{1}{4},9)$ is the axis of a 7-in.-diameter right-circular cylinder. $R(5,5,7)$ $S(5\frac{1}{2},4,5\frac{1}{2})$ $T(6,3,7)$ $U(5\frac{1}{2},4,8\frac{1}{2})$ is a right-section of a duct that intersects the cylinder. *Scale:* full size. Draw the top and front views of this intersection.

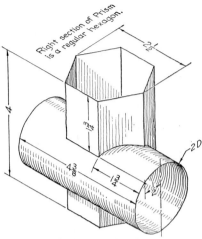

FIG. 10.22. Cylinder-prism intersections.

10.4. In Fig. 10.22 determine the intersection between the cylindrical and prismatic ducts. Develop each surface.

Group II. Intersection of Two Cylinders

10.5. In Fig. 10.23 line AB is the centerline of a 4-ft-OD sewer pipe. Prepare a template for use in making the formwork for the outside surface of the four-centered concrete pipe at the intersection of these two pipes. (Develop a portion of the four-centered pipe, showing the intersection of the pipes.)

10.6. In Fig. 10.24 prepare the template for cutting a hole in the 6½-in.-diameter cylinder that will permit entry of the 4-in.-diameter cylinder.

10.7. Line $J(0\frac{1}{2},4\frac{1}{2},9)$ $K(0\frac{1}{2},0,9)$ is the axis of an 8-in.-diameter right-circular cylinder. Line $L(6,3\frac{1}{2},7)$ $M(3,1\frac{1}{2},7)$ is the axis of a 3-in.-diameter right-circular cylinder. *Scale:* full size. Draw the top and front views of the intersection between these two cylinders.

10.8. Line $R(2,5,7\frac{1}{4})$ $L(2,0,7\frac{1}{4})$ is the axis of a 3-in.-diameter right-circular roof leader. Line $E(2,2,7)$ $T(5,2\frac{1}{2},7)$ is the axis of a 2½-in.-diameter semicircular eaves trough. The straight edges of the trough are in a frontal receding plane. *Scale:* full size. Draw the top and front views of the outline of the hole that must be cut into the roof leader for acceptance of the trough.

10.9. Draw the top and front views of the intersection between the two 3-in.-diame-

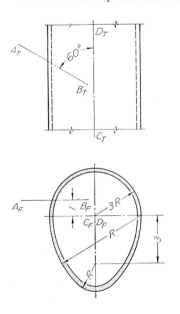

FIG. 10.23. Sewer connection.

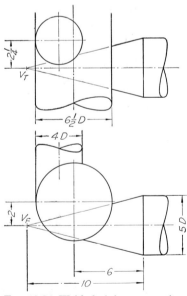

FIG. 10.24. Welded piping connections.

ter right-circular cylinders whose axes are lines $A(2,1,4\frac{1}{4})$ $B(5,1,8)$ and $C(3,1,5\frac{1}{2})$ $D(5\frac{1}{2},2\frac{1}{4},5\frac{1}{2})$, respectively. *Scale:* half size.

10.10. Draw the top and front views of the intersection between the two right-circular cylinders whose axes are lines $V(2,3\frac{1}{2},7)$ $W(6,1\frac{1}{4},7)$ and $Y(3,1\frac{1}{2},7\frac{1}{2})$ $Z(5,3\frac{1}{2},7\frac{1}{2})$ and whose diameters are $1\frac{1}{2}$ and 2 in., respectively. *Scale:* full size.

10.11. Points $L(2,0\frac{1}{4},7\frac{1}{2})$ and $K(6,0\frac{1}{4},6\frac{1}{2})$ are the centers of $2\frac{1}{2}$-in.- and $3\frac{3}{4}$-in.-diameter horizontal circles, respectively. These circles are the lower bases of cylinders whose axes are lines $LM(5,3\frac{1}{2},4)$ and $KJ(0\frac{1}{2},3,4)$. *Scale:* full size. Draw the top and front views of the intersection between these cylinders.

10.12. The axis of a 6-ft-diameter cylindrical boiler is $B(7,2\frac{1}{2},6\frac{1}{2})$ $L(1,2\frac{1}{2},6\frac{1}{2})$. Line $S(4,4\frac{3}{4},6\frac{1}{2})$ $D(4,3\frac{1}{2},6\frac{1}{2})$ is the axis of a cylindrical steam dome that is 3 ft in diameter. *Scale:* $1'' = 2'\text{-}0''$. Prepare a pattern for the hole that must be cut into the boiler plate to permit passage of the steam-dome cylinder.

Group III.   Planes Tangent to Cylinders

10.13. Line $A(1,4,7)$ $B(3,2\frac{1}{4},8)$ is the axis of a $1\frac{1}{2}$-in.-diameter right-circular cylinder. *Scale:* full size. Determine the intersections of the profile plane through point B with the planes that make 45° angles with the horizontal and are also tangent to the cylinder.

10.14. A V-shaped ditch has been cut with its sides intersecting on $D(0\frac{1}{2},2,6)$ $T(4,1,7\frac{1}{2})$. Point $P(1\frac{1}{4},3\frac{1}{4},8\frac{1}{4})$ is in the plane of one side of the ditch, and point $R(3\frac{1}{2},3\frac{1}{4},8\frac{1}{4})$ is in the plane of the other side. A 24-in.-diameter pipe is laid into this ditch. *Scale:* $\frac{3}{4}'' = 1'\text{-}0''$. Draw the top and front views of the elements of tangency between the pipe and the sides of the ditch. Identify each element of tangency with distinctive letters.

Group IV.   Intersection of Cones with Lines and Planes

10.15. In Fig. 10.25 determine the points of intersection of lines RS and XY with the conical surface.

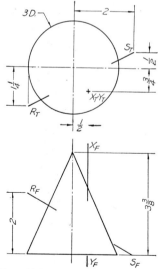

FIG. 10.25. Cone-line intersection.

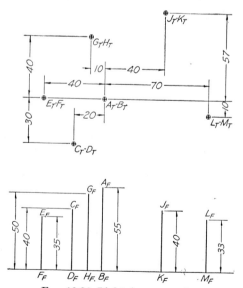

FIG. 10.26. Lightning protection.

10.16. Studies of protection against lightning have shown that a vertical conductor will generally divert to itself all direct hits that might otherwise strike in a right-circular cone space having the top of the conductor as its apex and a base radius four times the height of the conductor. In Fig. 10.26 lines AB, CD, EF, GH, JK, and LM represent the trunks of trees that are growing on a level plot of ground. If the tallest tree is protected with an air terminal at point A, are all the other trees protected? If not, what is the minimum number and where is the location of the additional required protection?

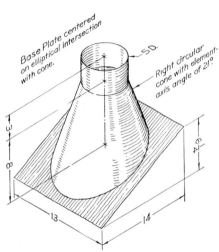

FIG. 10.27. Conical flashing.

10.17. In Fig. 10.27 determine the intersection between the conical and plane surfaces of the flashing. Develop the conical surface.

10.18. A right-circular conical beam of light has an axis $S(0\frac{1}{2},4,6\frac{1}{2})$ $L(4\frac{1}{2},1,6\frac{1}{2})$. The axis-element angle of the cone is 15°. Draw the outline of the area illuminated by this beam of light on the horizontal plane containing point L.

10.19. Rectangle $A(1\frac{1}{2},1,6)$ $B(5,1,6)$ $C(5,2,9)$ $D(1\frac{1}{2},2,9)$ is the top of a working surface. This surface is illuminated by a light placed at point $L(2,5,7)$. The most intense light from this source is inclined 30° from the vertical. Draw the top and front views of the curve of maximum light intensity on the working surface.

Group V. Intersection of Cones with Cylinders

10.20. Determine the cone-cylinder intersection of Fig. 10.24.

10.21. Line $A(4,4\frac{1}{2},7\frac{1}{2})$ $B(4,0\frac{1}{2},7\frac{1}{2})$ is the axis of a $5\frac{1}{2}$-in.-diameter right-circular cylinder. Line $V(7,2\frac{1}{2},6\frac{1}{4})$ $C(2,2\frac{1}{2},6\frac{1}{4})$ is the axis of a cone whose right section through C is a 7-in.-diameter circle. Point V is the vertex of the cone. *Scale:* half size. Draw the top and front views of the intersection between these surfaces.

10.22. Point $V(2\frac{1}{2},0,7\frac{1}{4})$ is the vertex and $C(2\frac{1}{2},5,7\frac{1}{4})$ is the center of the 42-in.-diameter horizontal base of a right-circular conical hopper. Some material enters this hopper via an 18-in.-diameter right-circular cylindrical chute whose axis is $A(2\frac{1}{2},3\frac{1}{2},7)$ $B(5\frac{1}{2},4,8\frac{1}{2})$. *Scale:* $1'' = 1'\text{-}0''$. Draw the top and front views of the intersection between the hopper and the chute.

10.23. The axis of a 2-in.-diameter right-circular cylinder is $A(4,1,6)$ $B(4,4,6)$. The vertex of a right-circular cone is $V(4,4,6\frac{1}{2})$; the base of the cone is a 3-in.-diameter horizontal circle whose center is $C(4,1,6\frac{1}{2})$. *Scale:* full size. Draw the top and front views of the intersection between these single-curved surfaces.

Group VI. Intersection of Two Cones

10.24. In Fig. 10.28 the double conical offset connects three vertical ducts. Determine the intersection between the cones, and develop each of the conical surfaces of this offset.

10.25. Point $A(4\frac{1}{2},2\frac{1}{4},5\frac{1}{2})$ is the vertex and $B(4\frac{1}{2},2\frac{1}{4},8\frac{1}{2})$ is the center of the 4-in.-diameter base of a right-circular cone. The vertex of an oblique cone is $V(6\frac{1}{2},4\frac{1}{2},4\frac{3}{4})$; the base of this cone is a $3\frac{1}{4}$-in.-diameter frontal circle, centered at $C(2\frac{1}{2},2\frac{1}{2},8\frac{1}{2})$.

Scale: full size.   Draw the top and front views of the intersection between these surfaces, and complete the views of this combined figure.

10.26. The vertex of a right-circular cone is point $R(4,3\frac{1}{4},6\frac{1}{4})$, and its base is a 3-in.-diameter circle centered at $S(4,0\frac{1}{2},6\frac{1}{4})$.   The vertex of an oblique cone is at $T(6,5,7\frac{1}{2})$.   The base of this second cone is a horizontal ellipse whose frontal major diameter is $4\frac{1}{2}$ in. long and whose minor diameter is 3 in. in length; the center of this ellipse is $W(5\frac{1}{2},0\frac{1}{2},7)$.   *Scale:* full size.   Draw the top and front views of the intersection between these cones, and complete the views of the combined figure.

10.27. Point $A(3,4\frac{1}{2},6\frac{1}{2})$ is the vertex and $B(4,1\frac{1}{2},6\frac{1}{2})$ is the center of the $2\frac{1}{4}$-in.-diameter base of a right-circular cone.   Point $C(4\frac{1}{4},4,7)$ is the vertex and $D(1\frac{3}{4},2\frac{3}{4},7)$ is the center of the $3\frac{1}{2}$-in.-diameter base of a second right-circular cone.   *Scale:* full size. Draw the top and front views of the line of intersection between these cones, and complete the views of the combined figure.

10.28. Lines $A(3,4,7)$ $B(5,1,7)$ and $AC(X, 1,X)$ are elements of a vertical right-circular cone.   Angle BAC is 30°.   Point C is in front of point B.   Draw the top and front views of AC.

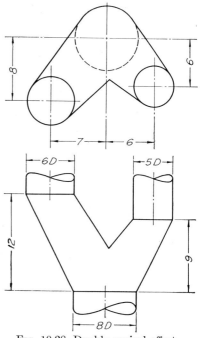

FIG. 10.28. Double conical offset.

Group VII.   Planes Tangent to Cones

10.29. The dihedral angle between plane $L(4,X,4\frac{1}{2})$ $M(2\frac{1}{2},4,7)$ $N(5,2,8)$ and the horizontal is 45°.   Complete the front view of triangle LMN.

10.30. Point $C(3,4,6\frac{1}{2})$ is the center of a 5-in.-diameter circular opening.   *Scale:* half size.   The rectangular opening $J(1\frac{1}{4},0\frac{1}{2},4\frac{1}{2})$ $K(6,0\frac{1}{2},4\frac{1}{2})$ $L(6,0\frac{1}{2},8\frac{1}{2})$ $M(1\frac{1}{4},0\frac{1}{2},8\frac{1}{2})$ is to be connected to the circular one by means of a transition piece.   The transition is to be designed with conical and plane surfaces only, and adjacent surfaces are to be tangent to each other.   Draw the top and front views of the several elements of tangency between the plane and cone surfaces.

10.31. Point $S(4\frac{1}{4},0\frac{1}{2},7)$ is the center of a 4-in.-diameter horizontal circular opening. *Scale:* full size.   The triangular opening $N(3,4,7)$ $O(1\frac{1}{2},3,6)$ $P(1\frac{1}{2},3,8)$ is to be connected to the circular one by means of a transition piece.   The transition is to be designed with conical and plane surfaces only, and adjacent surfaces are to be tangent to each other. Draw the top and front views of the several elements of tangency between the plane and conic surfaces.

10.32. Point $C(3,1,7)$ is the center of the 3-in.-diameter base of a right-circular cone. Point $V(3,4,7)$ is the vertex of this cone.   *Scale:* full size.   Determine the planes that are tangent to this cone and also parallel to line $R(6,4,7)$ $S(8,3,6)$.

CHAPTER 11

ANGULAR RELATIONSHIPS

11.1. The determination of the angle between two intersecting lines requires simply that the angle be measured in a normal view of the plane of those lines. The angle between two planes can be measured in a view that shows an end view of the line of intersection between the planes. Beyond these elementary problems of angular relationships it will usually be found desirable to establish right-circular cones whose base or vertex angles are such as to permit direct measurement of existing conditions or the accomplishment of required angular specifications.

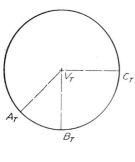

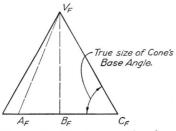

Fig. 11.1. The base angle of a right-circular cone.

11.2. Angle between a Line and a Plane. The true size of the angle between a line and a plane will be seen in a view that is a *normal view of the line and an edge view of the plane.* This may be observed in Fig. 11.1, where two views of a right-circular cone are drawn. All elements of this cone make the same angle with its base, but in the front view the elements VA, VB, and VC appear to make different-sized angles with the horizontal base plane. Since VC is frontal, the true size of the angle that all elements make with the base may be measured between VC and the base plane in the front view.

11.3. Lines through a Given Point and Making a Specified Angle with a Given Plane. All lines passed through a given point that make a specified angle with a given plane are elements of a right-circular cone whose base lies in the given plane and whose base angle equals the specified angle. The given point is the vertex of the cone.

In Fig. 11.2(1), the front view of line AB is given. The problem specifications require that AB make an angle of 30° with the horizontal and that point B lie generally to the rear of point A. AB may be considered as an element of a right-circular cone whose base is horizontal and whose base

174

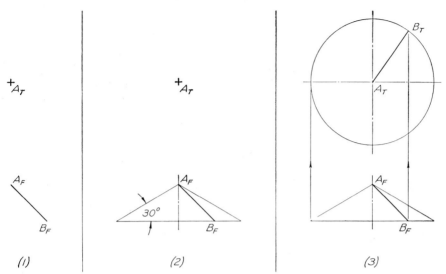

Fig. 11.2. Line making a specified angle with a given plane.

angle is 30°. The front view of the cone (a view that will show the true size of its base angle) is drawn in (2), with point B in the plane of the base of the cone. In (3), the circle of that base is drawn in the top view. Point B is projected from the front view to the top view, where AB is then drawn.

11.4. Grade. The *slope angle* of any line is the angle between that line and the horizontal. The tangent of this slope angle, usually expressed per-

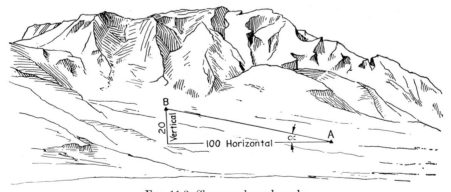

Fig. 11.3. Slope angle and grade.

centagewise, is the grade of the line. In Fig. 11.3, points A and B in the pass between two mountains are shown. These points, located during the survey for a highway through the pass, are connected by a straight line that has a slope angle α of slightly less than 11°-19′ and a grade of 20 per

cent.   (The relationship that exists between the slope angle and the grade
will be seen if the student will refer to his trigonometric tables for the angle
whose tangent is 0.20000.)

11.5. Lines Making Specified Grades.   Many practical problems of
roadbed constructions require the establishment of lines having specified
grades on hillsides.   Such problems usually involve some earth-moving
projects, as in cuts and fills, but the following problem is presented in its
simplest form, as though the hillside were a plane surface.   For the purpose
of clarifying the principle involved, the specified grade will be larger than
what might ordinarily be encountered.

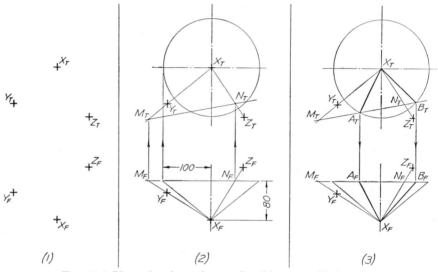

Fig. 11.4. Lines of a given plane and making a specified grade.

A hillside is represented by three points X, Y, and Z, as shown in Fig.
11.4(1).   Lines having an 80 per cent upgrade from point X are to be
established on that hillside.   In (2), a right-circular cone whose elements all
make the required grade is positioned with its vertex at point X.   The
required lines will be elements of this cone as well as lines of the given plane
XYZ.   The problem thus becomes one of a plane and cone intersection.

The base plane of the cone intersects plane XYZ along line MN.   Points
A and B are common to the base circle and plane XYZ, as shown in (3).
The required lines are elements XA and XB, the lines of intersection between
plane XYZ and the cone.

11.6. Angle between a Line and an Oblique Plane.   This problem was
previously presented in Sec. 4.12, where the solution required the drawing of
three auxiliary views.   This paragraph offers a more rapid procedure if the
introduction of a right-circular cone as a tool does not unduly complicate
the problem for the student.

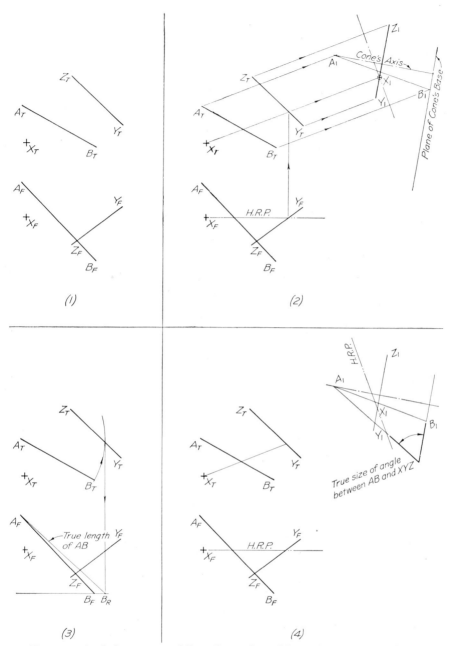

FIG. 11.5. Angle between an oblique line and an oblique plane—cone method.

The angle between a line and a plane is equal to the base angle of a right-circular cone having the given line as an element and its circular base parallel to the given plane. Line AB and plane XYZ are given in Fig. 11.5(1). Line AB is considered as an element of a right-circular cone.

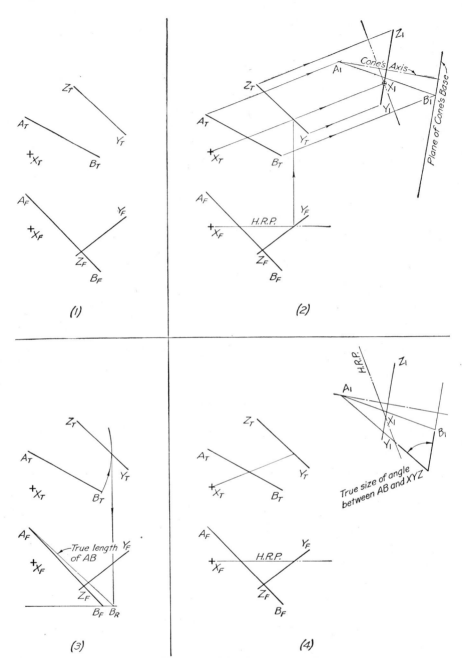

FIG. 11.5. (*Repeated.*) Angle between an oblique line and an oblique plane—cone method.

Point A is arbitrarily established as the vertex of the cone. Its base contains point B and is parallel to plane XYZ. In (2), an edge view of XYZ (and of the base of the cone) is secured. The true length of AB is found in (3), and that true length used as the outline element length of the cone in the edge view of its base, as shown in (4). The angle between the line AB and the plane XYZ is identified as equal to the true size of the base angle of the cone.

11.7. Lines through a Given Point and Making Specified Angles with Two of the Principal Planes of Projection. A study of the possibilities of this problem shows that the sum of the acute angles between any line and any two *perpendicular* planes will range between 0 and 90°. The sum of the angles between a horizontal-frontal line and the horizontal and frontal planes of projection is 0°; however, the sum of the angles between that line and the horizontal and profile planes is 90°. Any horizontal line will make angles with the frontal and profile planes of projection that are complementary, and any frontal line will make angles with the horizontal and profile planes that also total 90°. The angles between an oblique line and any two principal planes of projection will total somewhere between 0 and 90°.

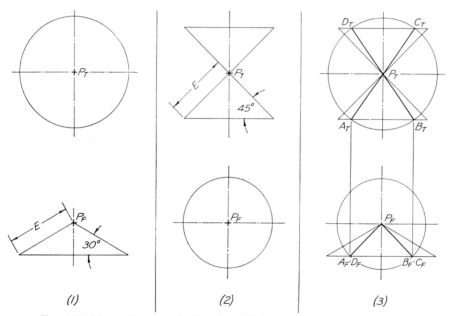

(1) (2) (3)

FIG. 11.6. Line making specified angles with horizontal and frontal planes.

In the problem of Fig. 11.6, lines that make angles of 30° with all horizontal planes, 45° with all frontal planes and contain point P are required. If the given point P is the common vertex of two cones, each of which has elements that comply with one of the angular requirements, the problem is solved by finding the intersection of these cones. In (1), a cone whose elements all make an angle of 30° with the horizontal is established with point P as its vertex. Both nappes of a second cone, whose elements all make 45° with frontal planes, are drawn in (2). Point P is the vertex of the second cone as well as the first. By establishing these cones with equal-length elements, the circles of their bases intersect. The cones are both drawn in (3), where their bases intersect at points A, B, C, and D. Lines PA, PB, PC, and PD are the lines of intersection of the two cones, hence the required lines. If the upper nappe of the first cone had been drawn, its base intersections would be points on the common elements already determined.

11.8. Planes through a Given Point and Making Specified Angles with Two of the Principal Planes of Projection (Fig. 11.7). A line that is per-

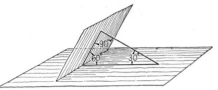

pendicular to one plane will make an angle with a second plane that is the complement of the angle between the two planes. This principle can be employed in establishing a plane to make specified angles with other planes.

FIG. 11.7. Angle between planes and the use of a line perpendicular to one plane.

The problem of Fig. 11.8 requires a plane through point P that dips rearward and to the left, makes an angle of 60° with all horizontal planes and 50° with all frontal planes. A line that would be perpendicular to the required plane would rise to the left

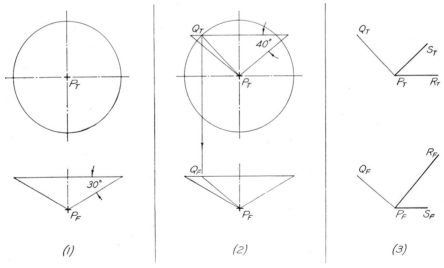

FIG. 11.8. Plane making specified angles with horizontal and frontal planes.

rear, make 30° with the horizontal and 40° with the frontal planes. Line PQ meets these conditions. [The student should note that the construction shown in (1) and (2) is similar to that used in Fig. 11.6; however, the front view of the second cone is not required to solve for the line.] The required plane PRS is drawn perpendicular to line PQ, as shown in (3).

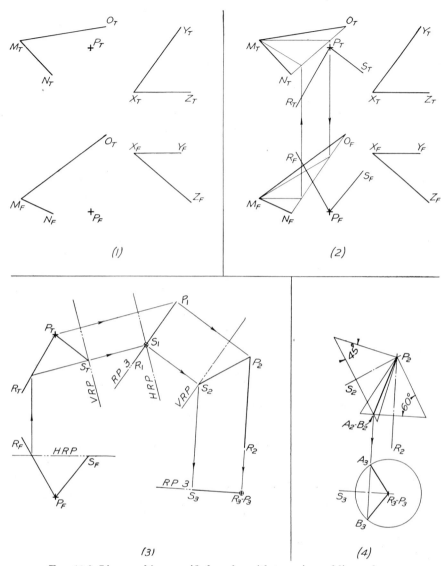

FIG. 11.9. Lines making specified angles with two given oblique planes.

11.9. Lines through a Given Point and Making Specified Angles with Two Given Oblique Planes. The problem in Fig. 11.9 requires the lines containing point P that make a 60° angle with plane MNO and a 45° angle with plane XYZ. In (2), line PR is drawn perpendicular to plane MNO, and line PS is drawn perpendicular to plane XYZ. These lines may be considered as the axes of two cones, each meeting one of the angular specifications.

The required lines can be determined through the use of a normal view of plane PRS and an end view of either PR or PS. Such views are drawn in (3). Both base angles of the cone appear in true size in the normal view

181

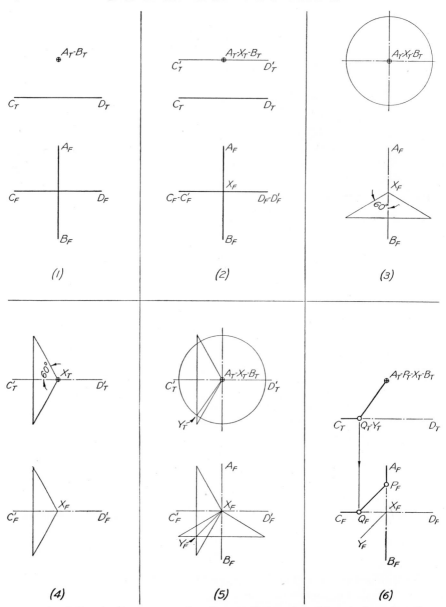

FIG. 11.10. A line that intersects and makes specified angles with two given skew lines.

of PRS, as shown in (4). The cone whose axis is PR has a base angle of 60°, since PR is perpendicular to plane MNO and the required lines must make 60° with MNO. Similarly, the cone having PS as its axis has a 45°

base angle. The cones are established with equal-length elements, and the base curves intersect at points A and B. The end view of RP permits a rapid and accurate location of A and B, since the base curve shown appears in its true circular shape in that view. The top, front, and auxiliary elevation views are omitted in (4); if the required lines PA and PB must be shown in the principal views, they can be so located by the usual projection procedures.

11.10. Lines Making Specified Angles with Two Given Skew Lines and Intersecting Both Skew Lines. The problem of Sec. 11.7 was solved through the use of cones whose base angles met the given specifications. Problems of this section differ from the preceding ones in that the angular specifications will require the use of cones whose element-axis angles fulfill the requirements of the problems.

The problem of Fig. 11.10 presents AB and CD as the centerlines of two straight lengths of pipe. A third straight length of pipe is to connect the given two, using 60° elbows. The flow through the piping is from A toward C, thereby restricting the solution to only one possible answer. The required line is a common element of two cones, one with AB as its axis and the other having CD as its axis. Since AB and CD do not intersect, no common vertex for these particular cones is available, and the problem is most readily solved by first directionalizing the required line.

Line $C'D'$ is drawn parallel to CD and intersecting line AB, as shown in (2). Point X, the intersection of $C'D'$ and AB, can be used as a common vertex for two cones, with AB and $C'D'$ being the respective axes of the cones. The element-axis angles of both cones are 60°. The cones are shown individually in (3) and (4) and combined in (5). Point Y is one of the points of intersection between the base curves, and the line XY is a common element of the cones. The centerline of the required connecting pipe is parallel to XY.

Since the top view is an end view of AB, the required centerline will appear coincidental with XY in that view. Point Q, the intersection of CD with the required line, is projected from the top view to the front view, as shown in (6). The front view of the required line PQ is drawn through Q parallel to XY.

A similar problem is presented in Fig. 11.11, where the given lines are again identified as AB and CD. It is required to locate a line that makes an angle of 30° with AB and an angle of 45° with CD. In addition, the required line must intersect the given lines and be the nearest to horizontal of the possible solutions. In (2), a sequence of views that presents an end view of CD and a normal view of both AB and CD is drawn. The original views and first auxiliary view are omitted in (3) through (6), where the construction employed to determine XY, the direction of the required line RP, is shown. In (7), line RP is drawn parallel to XY and projected back to the original views.

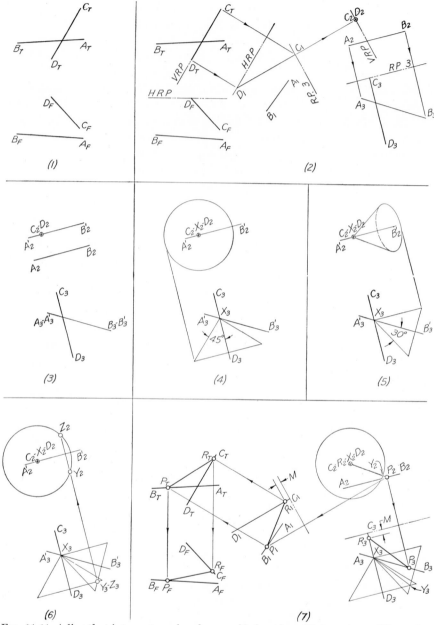

Fig. 11.11. A line that intersects and makes specified angles with two given oblique skew lines.

The angles used in the above problems were selected arbitrarily. Actual angles of standard pipe fittings are shown in the catalogues of various manufacturers. (The factor of cost will usually require the use of standard, rather than custom-made, fittings.)

PROBLEMS

Group I. Angles between Lines and Principal Planes of Projection

11.1. Determine the true size of the angles between line $A(1,4,7)$ $B(3,1,8)$ and the horizontal, frontal, and profile planes of projection.

11.2. Line $S(1,4,6)$ $L(3,1,8)$ is the axis of a straight length of pipe. One end of the pipe is to be cut off by a frontal plane through point L; the other end is to be cut off by a horizontal plane through point S. Determine the angles between the pipe axis and the plane of each cut, and determine the angle of twist between the two end cuts.

11.3. The compound centerline of a penstock is $A(1,5,6)$ $B(1\frac{1}{2},X,7)$ $C(4\frac{1}{4},X,7)$ $D(6,1,8\frac{1}{2})$. All segments of the penstock make the same angle with the horizontal plane of projection. Draw the front view of $ABCD$.

Group II. Grade

11.4. Draw the top and front views of lines $BK(0,X,X)$ and $BL(8,X,X)$ of plane $A(0,5,7)$ $B(4,0,4)$ $C(8,3,9)$ which have a plus grade of 25 per cent.

11.5. A survey party is camped on a mountainside at point $S(4,0\frac{1}{2},8\frac{1}{2})$. The mountainside is considered as plane $M(7,2\frac{1}{2},4\frac{1}{2})$ $T(1,4,6)$ S for the purposes of this problem. Draw the top and front views of the two routes from S, each having a plus 30 per cent grade, that could be taken on this mountain.

11.6. A survey party, having previously located points $M(3,1,6)$ $N(1\frac{1}{2},4\frac{1}{2},9)$, and $P(5,3,7\frac{1}{2})$ on Mt. Bagana, is now stationed at a point on line MN that is one-third of the distance from M to N. The present problem requires the running of a line in plane MNP that will have an upgrade of 30 per cent and a bearing generally to the east. Draw the top and front views of the required line.

11.7. Points $A(2,3\frac{1}{2},5)$, $B(6,2\frac{1}{2},4)$, $C(7,0\frac{1}{2},8)$, and $D(3,0\frac{1}{2},8\frac{3}{4})$ are the four corners of a mining property. The inclination of this property is uniform within the limits of the triangle ABC but falls off at a steeper rate from there to point D. The owner has purchased 250 ft of narrow-gauge track and desires to have this track laid along a straight centerline so that mine cars can be run by gravity from the mine mouth $J(5,X,5)$ to a tipple at the other end of the track. A downgrade of 25 per cent has been established for the track. A minimum of trestlework is desired. Trucks will transport the mined material to its destination, and the highway entrance to the property is at point D. A minimum of roadway from point D is desired. In view of the above, a decision has been reached to run the track on the ground from the mine mouth, within the limits of the triangular area ABC, and to carry the remainder of the track to the tipple by trestlework. *Scale:* 1 in. = 100 ft. Draw the top and front views of the track centerline.

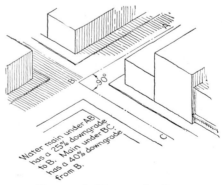

FIG. 11.12. Water-main elbow.

11.8. In Fig. 11.12 the street centerlines AB and BC are horizontal. Determine the true size of the water-main elbow angle that is required to turn this corner.

Group III. Angles between Lines and Oblique Planes

11.9. In Fig. 11.13 the tripod legs *AB*, *AD*, and *AC* all make the same angle with the horizontal. Draw the top and front views of the tripod.

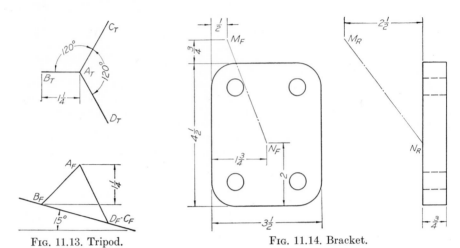

FIG. 11.13. Tripod.   FIG. 11.14. Bracket.

11.10. In Fig. 11.14 line *MN* is the centerline of a tube that is to be welded to the plate shown. Determine the angle with *MN* that the tube must be cut to fit against the face of the plate.

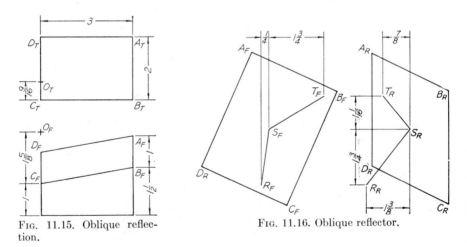

FIG. 11.15. Oblique reflection.   FIG. 11.16. Oblique reflector.

11.11. In Fig. 11.15 a light ray through point *O* strikes the reflector *ABCD* at its center. Draw the top and front views of the reflected ray. (The angle of incidence equals the angle of reflection.)

11.12. In Fig. 11.16 point *S* is the center of the square-shaped reflector *ABCD* whose area is 16 sq in. Sides *AD* and *BC* are frontal. The ray *RS* is reflected as ray *ST*. Draw the front and right-side views of the reflector.

11.13. In Fig. 11.17 determine the true size of the angles between each of the three lettered edges of the corner seal with the planes of the other two lettered edges.

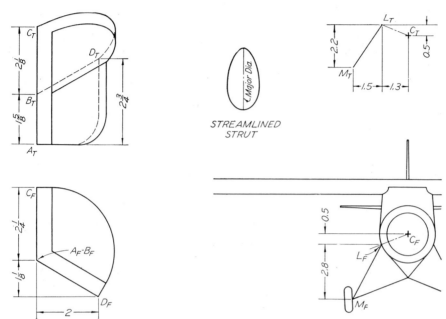

Fig. 11.17. Corner seal.　　　　　　　Fig. 11.18. Landing-gear strut.

11.14. Tubing is often egg-shaped to streamline exposed aircraft struts. The plane of the major diameters must be parallel to the line of flight. In Fig. 11.18 line LM is the axis of such a strut. The axis of an attaching bolt is line LC. Determine the true size of the angle between the plane of the major diameters of the strut and the axis of the attaching bolt.

11.15. Determine the true size of the angle between line $J(4,2\frac{1}{2},5)$ $K(2\frac{1}{2},3,7)$ and plane $L(6,3\frac{1}{2},8)$ $M(4\frac{1}{2},2,6\frac{1}{2})$ $N(7\frac{1}{4},2\frac{1}{2},4\frac{1}{2})$.

11.16. Determine the true size of the angle between line $A(2,4,7)$ $B(2,0\frac{1}{2},4\frac{1}{2})$ and plane $R(1,1,7)$ $S(5,2\frac{1}{2},8\frac{1}{2})$ $T(3,4\frac{1}{2},6)$.

11.17. Points $A(2,0,5)$, $B(5,3,5)$, $C(5,3,9)$, and $D(2,0,9)$ lie in the plane of a roof surface. Line $BR(0,4,9)$ is the centerline of a strut. Preliminary to the design of the strut anchor at B, it is necessary to determine the angle between RB and plane $ABCD$. Find the true size of this angle.

11.18. A light ray passing through point $P(2,5,8)$ is to be reflected by a horizontal mirror whose plane contains point $M(4,2,7)$ so that its reflected ray will pass through point $R(6,5,6)$. Determine the point at which the ray is reflected.

11.19. A light ray is to pass through point $L(1,3,7)$ and be reflected by a mirror in plane $S(1,1,6)$ $T(4,3,8)$ $V(4\frac{1}{2},2,5\frac{1}{2})$. The reflected ray is to pass through point $R(5\frac{1}{2},3,4\frac{1}{2})$. Determine the point at which the ray is reflected.

Group IV. Lines Making Specified Angles

11.20. Draw the top and front views of all lines through point $R(4,3,7)$ that make an angle of 30° with all frontal planes and an angle of 45° with all horizontal planes. Identify each line by locating and lettering a second point on each one.

11.21. Wire $A(4,1\frac{1}{2},8)$ $B(2\frac{1}{2},X,6)$ makes an angle of 30° with all frontal planes. Point B is higher than point A. Draw the front view of AB. *Scale: $1'' = 20'-0''$.* How long is wire AB?

11.22. Rod $P(5,2,8)$ Q is 16'-0'' long. It makes an angle of 30° with all horizontal planes and an angle of $22\frac{1}{2}°$ with all frontal planes. Point Q is above, to the left, and in front of point P. *Scale: $\frac{1}{4}'' = 1'-0''$.* Draw the top and front views of PQ.

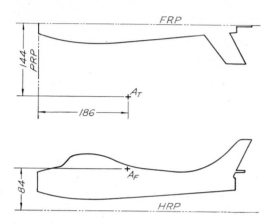

FIG. 11.19. Wing relocation.

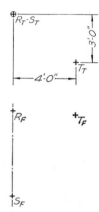

FIG. 11.20. Stack-trap connection.

11.23. Preliminary design determined that the wing centerlines on an experimental aircraft were to make 15° angles with the horizontal reference plane HRP and 60° angles with the frontal reference plane FRP. In Fig. 11.19 point A is on the left-wing centerline that meets these angular conditions. In studying the aerodynamics of this design, it has been further determined that the wings must be rotated from their preliminary design position. The intersection of the wing centerlines with FRP and the length from this point to the rotated position of point A will not be changed. The new position of the wings will cause their centerlines to make 10° angles with HRP and 60° angles with FRP. Show the new position of point A in both the top and front views.

11.24. In Fig. 11.20 a trap at point T is to be connected to the soil stack RS by means of a straight length of pipe and a 45° Y branch. How far below point T is the intersection of the stack and the centerlines of the connecting pipe?

11.25. In Fig. 11.21 a discharge pipe is to be connected to the tank by means of the nipple flange and the 30° elbow shown. Locate the centers of the four holes to be drilled in the elbow flange so that they will mate with the holes shown in the nipple flange. The discharge pipe is to have a downgrade of 50 per cent to the right.

11.26. In Fig. 11.22 drainage line DN is to be connected to the vertical stack ST by use of a $67\frac{1}{2}°$ elbow fitting on DN, a straight length of pipe, and a 45° Y branch. Locate the points of intersection between the centerline of the connecting pipe and the drain and stack centerlines.

11.27. Lines $A(2,2\frac{1}{2},7)$ $B(4\frac{3}{4},4,7)$ and $C(1\frac{3}{4},2\frac{1}{4},8\frac{1}{2})$ $D(4\frac{1}{2},0\frac{3}{4},6\frac{1}{2})$ are the respective centerlines of two lengths of pipe. Line RS is the centerline of a straight length of pipe that connects the other two. This connecting pipe makes an angle of 45° with AB and an angle of 60° with CD. Draw the top and front views of RS.

11.28. Line $C(5\frac{1}{2},5,8)$ $D(5\frac{1}{2},1,8)$ is the vertical centerline of a $112\frac{1}{2}°$ trap. The main centerline of a 135° Y branch is $A(1\frac{1}{2},0\frac{1}{2},6\frac{1}{2})$ $B(6\frac{1}{2},2,6\frac{1}{2})$. The trap and

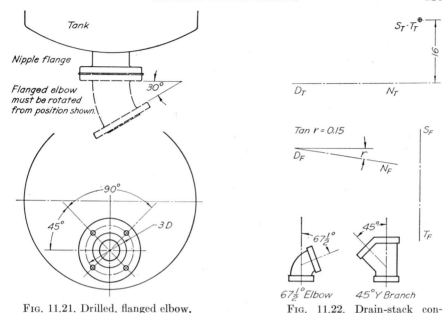

FIG. 11.21. Drilled, flanged elbow.

FIG. 11.22. Drain-stack connections.

branch are positioned on their respective centerlines so that the stack, centered on CD, may be connected to the sewer, centered on AB, by a straight length of pipe between the trap and branch. Flow is from C to A. Draw the top and front views of the centerline of the connecting length of pipe.

Group V. Planes Making Specified Angles

11.29. In Fig. 11.23 the dihedral angle between surfaces LMN and MNO is 60°. Draw the top, front, and right-side views of the block.

11.30. In Fig. 11.24 the angle between surfaces $ABCD$ and CDE of the symmetrical inclined mortise is 75°. Draw the top, front, and side views of the block.

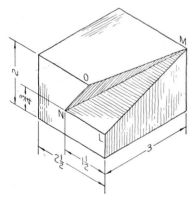

FIG. 11.23. Undercut block.

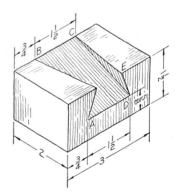

FIG. 11.24. Inclined mortise.

11.31. Draw the top and front views of the rectangular-duct–rectangular-plate assembly shown in Fig. 11.25.

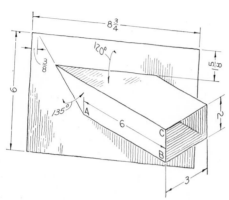

Fig. 11.25. Rectangular-duct–rectangular-plate assembly.

Fig. 11.26. Clip angle.

11.32. Draw the top and front views of the clip angle shown in Fig. 11.26.

11.33. Planes $B(4,4,8)$ $C(3,X,6)$ $D(2,3,7\frac{1}{2})$ and $BDF(3,X,6)$ make 45° angles with all horizontal planes. Draw the front view of triangles BCD and BDF.

11.34. Plane $A(4,2,8)$ $B(5,X,8)$ $C(3,2,X)$ dips 60° to the left rear and makes an angle of 75° with the frontal plane of projection. Draw the top and front views of triangle ABC.

11.35. Plane $M(3,3,6)$ $N(3\frac{1}{2},X,7\frac{1}{2})$ $O(1,X,6\frac{1}{2})$ makes a 45° angle with all horizontal planes and a 60° angle with all frontal planes. This plane dips to the left rear. Draw the front view of triangle MNO.

11.36. Plane $R(3,3,6)$ $S(4,1,X)$ $T(1\frac{1}{2},2,X)$ makes a $67\frac{1}{2}$° angle with all horizontal planes and an angle of 30° with all frontal planes. Plane RST dips to the left front. Draw the top view of triangle RST.

11.37. Point $A(5,3\frac{1}{2},7)$ is the center of a 4-in.-diameter circular disk. The plane of this disk makes an angle of 60° with the horizontal and 60° with the frontal plane of projection. The axle of this disk is the 3-in.-long rod AB. Point B is below, to the rear of, and to the right of point A. *Scale:* full size. Draw the top and front views of AB and the circular outline of the disk.

11.38. The upper part of a bridge pier is a 7-ft-high frustum of a pyramid whose horizontal base is a rhombus. The sides of the rhombus are 20 ft long. Point $P(3\frac{1}{2},1,6\frac{1}{2})$ is the most westerly corner of the rhombus (north is to the rear). The lateral surfaces of the pyramid make 45° angles with the base plane and 60° angles with all frontal planes. The top of the frustum is horizontal. *Scale:* $\frac{1}{8}'' = 1'-0''$. Draw the top and front views of the pyramidal frustum.

11.39. Lines $A(1,2,7)$ $B(3\frac{1}{2},1,4\frac{1}{2})$ and $BC(7,2,4\frac{1}{2})$ are property lines of a building lot. The lot is to be leveled off at the elevation of point A. The sloping banks are to make 45° angles with the horizontal and are to intersect the natural ground surface on the property lines. Draw, in the top view, the limits of the horizontal part of the lot near lines AB and BC.

CHAPTER 12

WARPED SURFACES

12.1. Warped surfaces are ruled surfaces whose consecutive rectilinear elements are skew lines. Such a surface is orthographically represented by one or more curves of the surface and the principal elements or by the surface outline. Surfaces of this classification are not developable but may be approximated by triangulation procedures.

There are several types of warped surfaces. All may be generated by the motion of a straight line moved in accordance with a law peculiar to each type of surface. The following paragraphs will be limited to the more common surfaces of this group.

12.2. Warped Surfaces with Two Linear Directrixes and a Plane Director. One type of warped surface is generated by the straight-line generatrix moving so as to touch two linear directrixes while remaining parallel to a plane director.

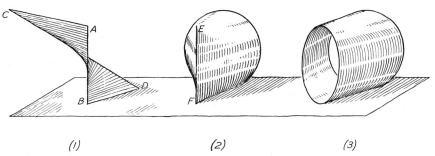

(1)   (2)   (3)

Fig. 12.1. Warped surfaces with two linear directrixes and a plane director.

A *hyperbolic paraboloid* is generated if the linear directrixes are both straight lines. In Fig. 12.1(1), the lines AB and CD are the directrixes and the horizontal plane the director of the surface.

A *conoid* is generated when one of the linear directrixes is straight and the other curved. Figure 12.1(2) shows a conoid whose directrixes are line EF and the curved lines. The plane director is again horizontal.

When both linear directrixes are plane curves, the resultant surface is a *cylindroid*. A horizontal-plane director is employed in Fig. 12.1(3). The

191

linear directrixes will be recognized as the two curved limits of the surface.

12.3. Warped Surfaces with Three Linear Directrixes. Certain warped surfaces may be generated by moving the straight-line generatrix so as to touch three linear directrixes.

A hyperbolic paraboloid may be generated by this method as well as by that described in the preceding section. In Fig. 12.2(1), the lines AB, CD, and EF are three linear directrixes of the surface. All three directrixes are straight lines in this instance, but curved lines of the surface would serve equally as well.

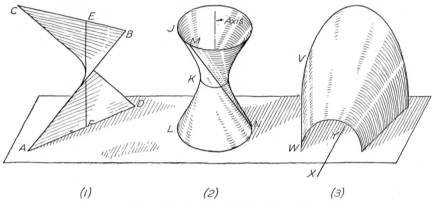

FIG. 12.2. Warped surfaces with three linear directrixes.

A *hyperboloid of revolution of one nappe* is generated if the linear directrixes are three coaxial circles. In Fig. 12.2(2), the circles J, K, and L are directrixes of the surface shown.

A *warped cone*, or a *corne de vache* (cow's horn), results when two of the directrixes are curved and one is straight. An example of a warped cone is shown in Fig. 12.2(3). The straight line XY and the curves W and V are the directrixes of the surface.

12.4. Warped Surface of Revolution. The only surface of revolution that is also a warped surface is the hyperboloid of revolution of one nappe. Although it may be generated by the use of three linear directrixes, its generation is more usually effected by rotating one straight line about another, the two being skew lines.

In Fig. 12.2(2) the element MN and the axis of revolution are shown.

12.5. Warped Surfaces with Two Linear Directrixes and a Constant Angle between One Directrix and the Generatrix. The common surfaces of this type are the *helicoids*. They are usually generated with one helical directrix and with the second directrix being the axis of the first. If the generatrix is perpendicular to the axis, the surface is a right helicoid; the resultant surface is an oblique helicoid if the constant angle is other than 90°. Examples of both are shown in Fig. 12.3(1) and (2), respectively.

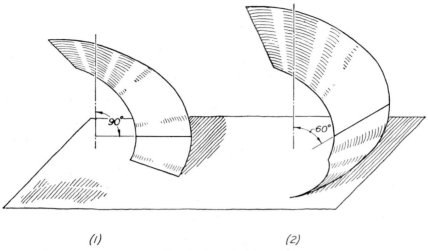

(1)   (2)

FIG. 12.3. Helicoids.

The generation of warped surfaces by this method is not restricted to
helicoids. If both directrixes are straight and if the constant angle is 90°,
the surface generated will be a hyperbolic paraboloid. Other warped
surfaces result when the generatrix is not perpendicular to either directrix
and when the directrixes are other than the types mentioned above.

12.6. Double-ruled Warped Surfaces. Hyperbolic paraboloids and
hyperboloids of revolution of one nappe are both capable of being developed
by two *different* straight-line generatrixes. This means that two straight-

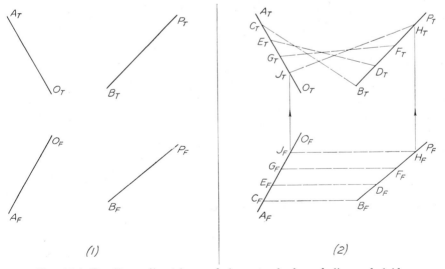

(1)   (2)

FIG. 12.4. Two linear directrixes and elements of a hyperbolic paraboloid.

line elements of such a surface may be drawn through any point on the surface. A more detailed discussion of this property will be given in the paragraphs specifically covering each surface.

12.7. Hyperbolic Paraboloids. A hyperbolic paraboloid may be represented orthographically by a pair of adjacent views which show the linear directrixes and elements of the surface. Lines AO and BP of Fig. 12.4(1) are the linear directrixes of a hyperbolic paraboloid. The plane director of this particular surface is horizontal. Elements BC, DE, FG, and HJ have been drawn parallel to the plane director, as shown in (2).

It should be observed in Fig. 12.4 that the elements of a hyperbolic paraboloid divide the directrixes proportionally. That is, $CE/BD = EG/DF$. Conversely, it may be determined that if two skew lines are divided into any number of proportional parts, the lines joining the corresponding points of division will lie in a system of parallel planes and will be elements of a hyperbolic paraboloid whose plane director is parallel to the dividing lines. This knowledge is particularly useful in the representation of such surfaces when limits on the directrixes are known.

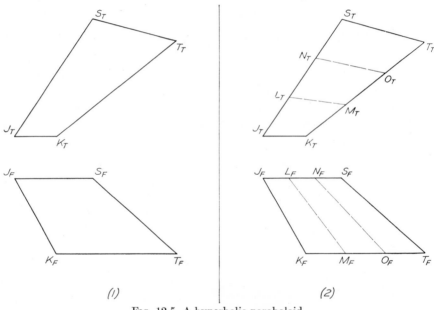

FIG. 12.5. A hyperbolic paraboloid.

The outline of a warped surface is shown in Fig. 12.5(1) as $JSTK$. If JS and KT are the directrixes of the surface, each may be divided into a like number of equal parts, as shown in (2). Elements LM and NO are added to elements JK and ST of the outline presentation. It should be observed that the plane director need not be known to establish elements of the surface.

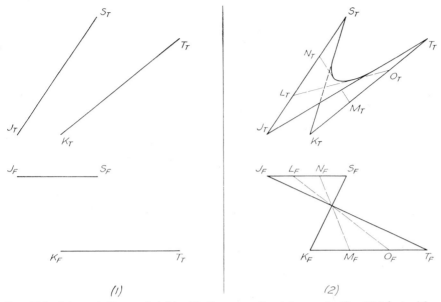

(1)

(2)

FIG. 12.6. A hyperbolic paraboloid with the same directrixes as in Fig. 12.5 but with a different plane director.

The directrixes JS and KT of Fig. 12.5 are repeated in Fig. 12.6(1). In (2), JT, LO, NM, and SK are drawn as elements of the surface. A comparison of Figs. 12.5 and 12.6 shows that the same directrixes may be employed for separate and distinct hyperbolic paraboloids. Use of differing segment lengths of limitless lines JS and KT will allow the generation of an infinite number of hyperbolic paraboloids by use of these directrixes. This will be obvious when it is realized that any plane not parallel to either directrix could be the plane director used with any pair of linear directrixes.

12.8. The Double Ruling of a Hyperbolic Paraboloid. The surface shown in Fig. 12.5 is repeated in Fig. 12.7. In the earlier presentation, lines JS and KT were assumed as the directrixes for the surface. Such an assumption was purely arbitrary, since JK and ST are just as acceptable. If JK and ST are used as the linear directrixes of the surface, then JS, AB, CD, and KT

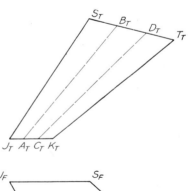

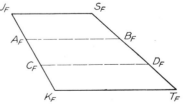

FIG. 12.7. The hyperbolic paraboloid of Fig. 12.5, with different directrixes and plane director.

are elements of this second generation. Consequently, the surface is a *double-ruled* surface.

Proof that a hyperbolic paraboloid is actually a double-ruled surface may be had by proving that any point on an element of one generation is also a point on the surface of the second generation. In Fig. 12.8(1), point

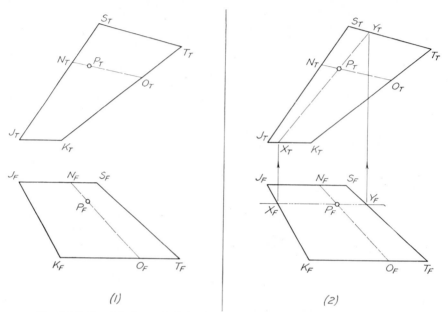

(1)   (2)

Fig. 12.8. Graphical proof of the double ruling of a hyperbolic paraboloid.

P on element NO of the first generation is arbitrarily selected as the point to be so proved. The second generation, with JK and ST as directrixes and with JS and KT as elements, has a horizontal plane director (since both JS and KT are horizontal). In (2), the front view of the horizontal plane containing point P is drawn. This plane intersects the warped surface along element XY. By projecting points X and Y to the top view, it can be proved graphically that XPY is a straight line. Hence, two rectilinear elements can be drawn through any point of a hyperbolic paraboloid.

12.9. Three Linear Directrixes of a Hyperbolic Paraboloid. Since a hyperbolic paraboloid is a double-ruled surface, any pair of elements of one generation could serve as a pair of rectilinear directrixes for the second generation. A third rectilinear directrix can be used to replace the plane director in each instance.

In Fig. 12.9, AB and CD are two directrixes of a hyperbolic paraboloid. Lines AC and BD are elements of that surface. Since other elements of the surface can be determined by proportional division of the directrixes,

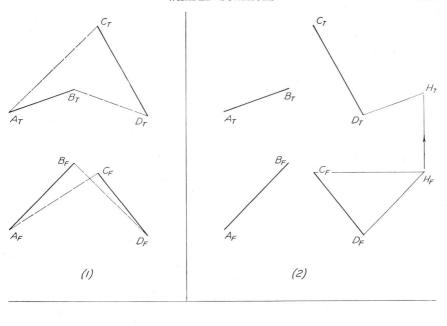

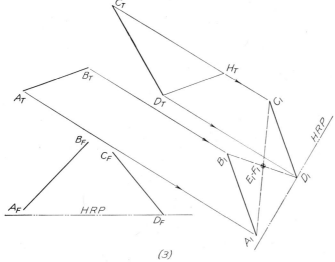

Fig. 12.9. Three rectilinear directrixes of a hyperbolic paraboloid.

a view that shows the directrixes appearing parallel will also show all elements of that generation appearing to intersect at a common point. [In the front view of Fig. 12.6(2), this apparent point of intersection is actually the end view of a third rectilinear directrix for the generation.] Plane *CDH* is established parallel to *AB*, in Fig. 12.9(2), for use in determining a rectilinear directrix that may be used with directrixes AB and CD.   The auxiliary view of (3) shows the end view of EF, this third directrix.

12.10. Hyperbolic Paraboloid Solution to the Problem of Determining the Shortest Line Segment of Specified Angle with a Given Plane That Intersects Both of Two Given Skew Lines.   The given skew lines are two linear directrixes of a particular hyperbolic paraboloid whose plane director is perpendicular to the given plane.   The required line is an element of that surface.   The problem presented in Figs. 7.7 and 7.8, although solved with a simpler approach, have basis for their solutions in this current group of problems.   The student is urged to read again the text material relevant to this reference prior to continuing his study of the following paragraphs.

12.11. Shortest Distance between Two Given Skew Lines.   The problem of Fig. 7.8 is repeated in Fig. 12.10.   The skew lines AB and CD are the

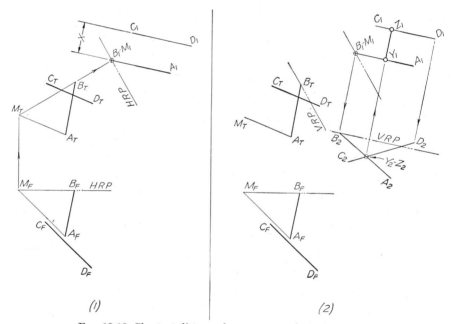

(1)   *(2)*

FIG. 12.10. Shortest distance between two given skew lines.

linear directrixes of a series of hyperbolic paraboloids.   Views that show the directrixes AB and CD appearing parallel will be normal views of the shortest distance between the skew lines.

Plane ABM is established parallel to CD by drawing AM parallel to CD, as shown in (1).   An edge view of plane ABM shows the clearance between lines AB and CD as X.   The location of the line that is perpendicular to both AB and CD and also intersects both AB and CD cannot be fixed in this one view.   To position this line a normal view of plane ABM is drawn in (2).   This last drawn view shows the required line appearing as a point at what

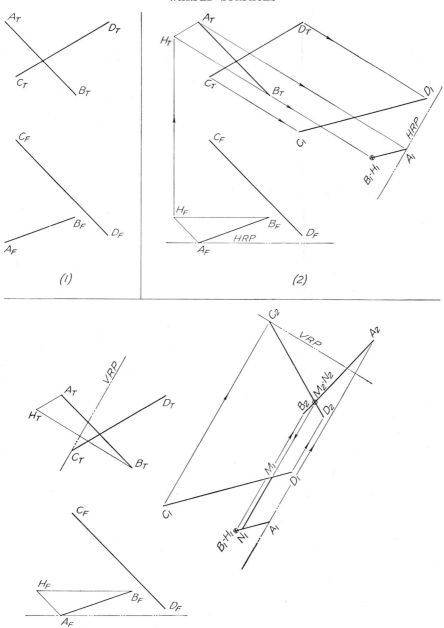

FIG. 12.11. Shortest horizontal line segment between two given skew lines.

appears to be the intersection of AB and CD.   Line YZ, the common perpendicular, can be projected back to the other views if so required.

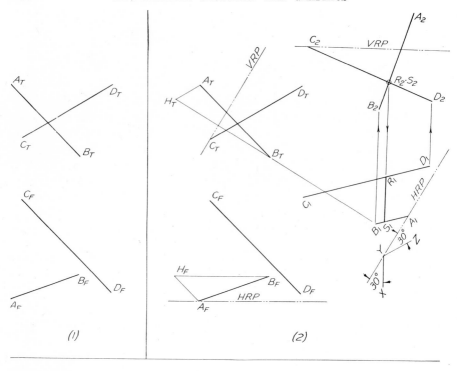

(1)   *(2)*

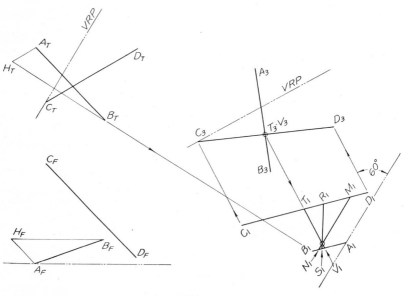

(3)

FIG. 12.12. Shortest line segments, of specified angles with the horizontal, between two given skew lines.

12.12. Shortest Horizontal Line Segment between Two Given Skew Lines. Skew lines AB and CD are given in Fig. 12.11(1). The shortest horizontal line segment that intersects both of these skew lines is required. The true length of the required line will be seen in the auxiliary view of (2), where an edge view of all horizontal planes is shown and the skew lines appear parallel. (This may be deduced from the fact that all horizontal line segments between AB and CD appear equal in length in this auxiliary view but only one of them is normal in that view. A second solution employs AB and CD as linear directrixes of a hyperbolic paraboloid whose plane director is normal in the auxiliary view mentioned.)

The shortest horizontal distance between AB and CD can be measured in the auxiliary view of (2), but the actual line segment required cannot be established without an additional view. Final positioning of the required line is effected by drawing a view that will be an end view of that line. The required line MN is drawn in (3).

12.13. Shortest Line Segment of Specified Angle with the Horizontal between Two Given Skew Lines. The problem of Fig. 12.11 required the shortest horizontal line segment between the given skew lines. In Fig. 12.12, lines AB and CD are given and the shortest line segments between them that, respectively, make 30 and 60° with the horizontal are required. The required lines, together with MN of the previous problem, are elements of the same hyperbolic paraboloid.

The auxiliary view of Fig. 12.11 is repeated in (2). The required line that makes 30° with the horizontal will be parallel to XY rather than YZ. An end view of the required line RS is drawn adjacent to the auxiliary view. Line TV, drawn in (3), meets the 60° requirement. The shortest horizontal line segment between AB and CD (MN of Fig. 12.11) is added to the auxiliary view in (3). It should be noted that RS, TV, and MN appear to intersect at a common point in this auxiliary view. This apparent point of intersection is the end view of the third rectilinear directrix of the hyperboloid.

12.14. Shortest Frontal Line Segment between Two Given Skew Lines. This problem is identical with the one of Sec. 12.12, except that the required line is to be parallel to the frontal plane of projection instead of the horizontal plane. The auxiliary view employed, therefore, is either a right or left auxiliary in which the skew lines appear parallel. The solution is shown in Fig. 12.13, where AB and CD are the given skew lines and GH is the required line.

12.15. Shortest Profile Line Segment between Two Given Skew Lines. Reference is made to the preceding paragraphs for the solution of this problem. The solution requires an auxiliary view that shows the edge view of all profile planes and the skew lines appearing parallel. The end view of the required line can be projected from this auxiliary view.

12.16. Representation of Conoids. Conoids are represented by drawing

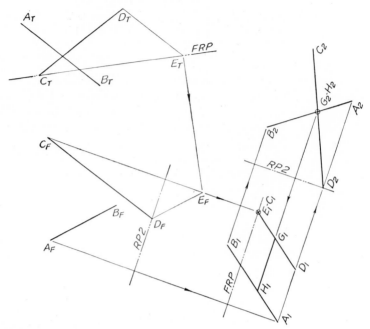

Fig. 12.13. Shortest frontal line segment between two given skew lines.

their linear directrixes and various elements. In Fig. 12.14(1), the horizontal circle and straight line AB are the directrixes of the right conoid

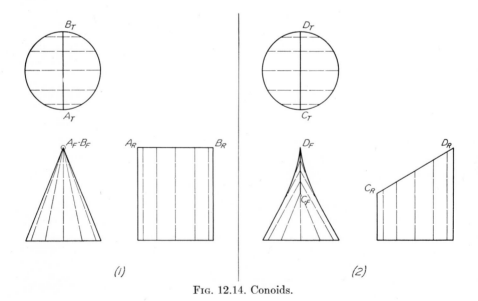

Fig. 12.14. Conoids.

shown. The circle and straight line CD are the directrixes of the oblique conoid shown in (2). In each instance the plane director is frontal; hence, the elements of both surfaces are frontal.

It should be noted that the elements of right conoids are perpendicular to their straight-line directrixes. Elements of an oblique conoid intersect the straight-line directrix at an angle other than 90°.

12.17. Representation of a Cylindroid. A cylindroid is represented orthographically by drawing the two curved-line directrixes and a series of its elements. In Fig. 12.15, the two curves are the directrixes of the surface. The plane director is horizontal, and elements of the surface (for example, AB, CD,

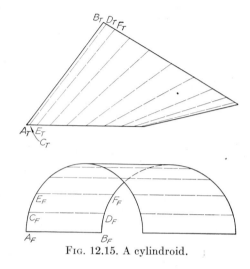

Fig. 12.15. A cylindroid.

and EF) are drawn parallel to the horizontal plane director.

12.18. Representation of a Hyperboloid of Revolution of One Nappe. Hyperboloids of revolution of one nappe are usually generated by revolving

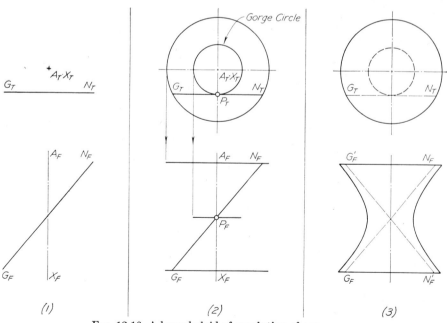

Fig. 12.16. A hyperboloid of revolution of one nappe.

a straight-line generatrix about an axis. The orthographic representation of the surface, however, employs certain features of the three-linear-directrix concept of the generation of the surface.

In Fig. 12.16(1), the line GN is given as the generatrix of a hyperboloid of revolution, and the line AX is given as its axis. If GN is revolved about AX, the circular paths of points G and N will be as drawn in (2). The point of line GN that is nearest the axis (point P) revolves in the small circular path known as the *gorge circle* of the surface. These three circles may be considered as three linear directrixes of the surface if so desired.

Elements of the surface can be determined by: (1) drawing them apparently tangent to the gorge circle in the end view of the axis, (2) finding their intersection with the other two circular directrixes, and (3) projecting these points of intersection to the other view. Two possible positions of such an element will be realized, since this surface is a double-ruled surface. If the three circular directrixes had been given and the front view of GN required, that element could have been either GN or $G'N'$, as shown in the front view of (3).

The representation of the surface is completed by showing the hyperbolic outline. This outline may be readily determined by establishing a series of elements and using them as an envelope.

12.19. Representation of a Warped Cone. The outline of a warped cone, together with a selected series of its elements, is the usual means of representing the surface. The outline normally consists of two curved-line directrixes and two elements. Other elements of the surface can best be determined by securing a view in which the straight-line directrix appears as a point. All elements will radiate from the end view of this directrix.

In Fig. 12.17(1), the curves MS and NT are given as curved-line directrixes of a warped cone whose straight-line directrix is line AC. Elements MN and ST are readily drawn, since they are lines of the horizontal plane that contains directrix AC. Other elements of the surface may be determined by first securing an end view of AC and drawing the curves in this new view. Elements OP and VW are shown in (2), having first been established in the auxiliary view. The line of each element is drawn through the end view of AC, and its intersections with the curves projected to the original views.

12.20. Representation of Helicoids. Helicoids are represented by their inner and outer helixes, elements, and limits in length. If the surface is secured to the cylinder of its inner helix, that cylinder is also shown in the representation.

One turn of a cylindrical helix, its cylinder, and its axis are drawn in Fig. 12.18(1). The helix and axis are the directrixes of a right helicoid. The limiting outer cylinder is shown in the top view of (2), where a series of the elements of the helicoid is also drawn. Since the specifications require that this surface be a right helicoid, all the elements are perpendicular to

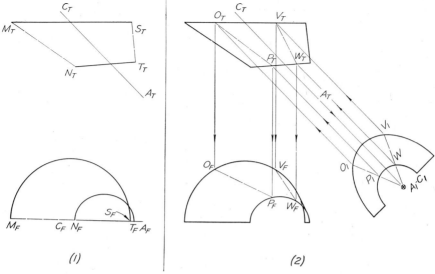

FIG. 12.17. A warped cone.

the axis and will appear so in the front view.   Elements RS, TU, and VW are identified.   The outer and inner helixes have equal leads, and once a point on the outer helix is located, that curve can be plotted.   In (3), the outer helix is drawn.

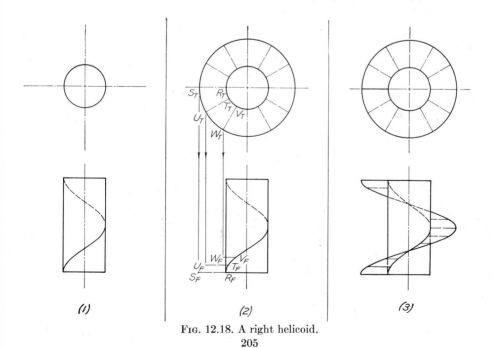

FIG. 12.18. A right helicoid.
205

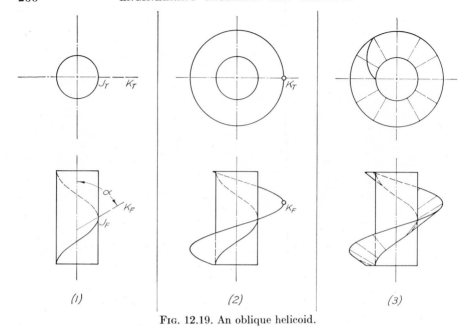

Fig. 12.19. An oblique helicoid.

In Fig. 12.19(1), one turn of a helix, its cylinder, and its axis are presented. The helix and axis are directrixes of an oblique helicoid.   The generatrix

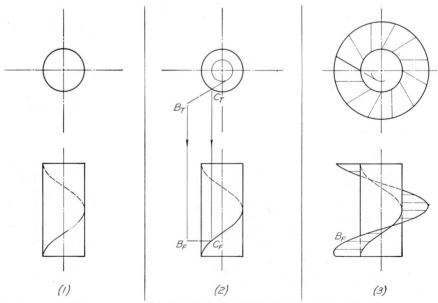

Fig. 12.20. A helicoid whose generatrix does not intersect the axis.

and axis make the constant angle α with each other. This angle can be established between element JK and the axis in the front view, since both are normal in that view. Once point K is determined, the outer helix containing K is drawn, as in (2). In (3), a series of elements are shown, further outlines established, and the representation is completed by determining the intersections of the base planes with the helicoidal surface.

It should be noted that the surface of the preceding problem would be a helical convolute if the specifications had required the generatrix to be tangent to the inner helix (see Sec. 9.9).

A helicoid whose generatrix does not intersect the axis is shown in Fig. 12.20. One turn of the inner helix is drawn in (1). The specifications require a right helicoid with the theoretically limitless generatrix passing the axis at a constant distance equal to one-half the radius of the given helix cylinder. An end view of a cylinder having a radius equal to this constant distance is drawn in the top view of (2). All elements of the required helicoid will be tangent to this smaller cylinder in addition to being perpendicular to the axis. Element BC is shown for illustrative purposes. Further specifications require the outer helix to contain point B. The representation is completed in (3).

12.21. Approximate Development of Warped Surfaces. Since consecutive elements of every warped surface are noncoplanar, those surfaces cannot be developed except by approximate means. An approximation can be effected by establishing a series of conveniently placed elements on the

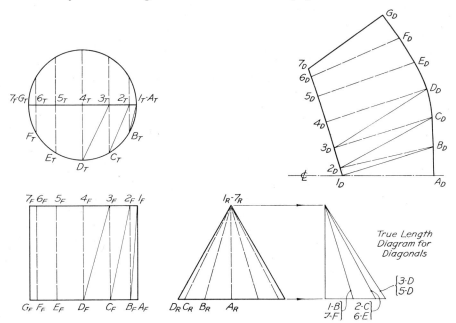

Fig. 12.21. Approximate development of a warped surface.

surface, thus dividing the surface into a sequence of warped quadrilaterals. Each of these quadrilaterals is then divided by one of its diagonals. The triangles so produced can be laid out in the development by determining the true lengths of their sides. The procedure is illustrated in the following example.

Three orthographic views of a conoid are shown in Fig. 12.21. A series of elements are selected so as to intersect the circular directrix at evenly spaced points, a strictly arbitrary but convenient positioning. The warped quadrilaterals are then divided by diagonals. All the elements of the conoid are shown true length in the side view. True lengths of the diagonals are determined in the true-length diagram. The top view shows the true lengths on both the curved- and straight-line directrixes. Only one-half of the pattern is drawn, since the surface is symmetrical.

PROBLEMS

Group I. Hyperbolic Paraboloids

12.1. Lines $A(2,2,6\frac{1}{2})$ $B(5,1,8\frac{1}{2})$ and $C(5\frac{1}{2},2,5\frac{1}{2})$ $D(1,0,8\frac{1}{2})$ represent two tunnels of a mining operation. Locate and determine the length of (a) a vertical shaft between these tunnels, (b) the shortest possible tunnel between the given tunnels, and (c) the shortest horizontal tunnel between the given tunnels.

12.2. Lines $H(1,1,8)$ $Y(5,4,5)$ and $B(6,4,8)$ $L(6,1,6)$ are the linear directrixes of a hyperbolic paraboloid whose limiting elements are YB and HL. Draw the top and front views of five additional elements of the surface, and show the outline of the surface in both views.

12.3. The plane director of a hyperbolic paraboloid makes an angle of 15° with the horizontal, 90° with the frontal plane of projection and dips to the left. The directrixes of this surface are the lines $D(1,3\frac{1}{2},5)$ $R(3,0\frac{1}{2},8)$ and $T(7,5,8\frac{1}{2})$ $C(4\frac{1}{2},0\frac{1}{2},5)$. Draw the top and front views of six elements of this warped surface, equally spaced at their inter-sections with DR. The limiting elements of the surface, for the purposes of this problem, contain points D and R, respectively.

12.4. Line $R(3,3\frac{1}{2},8)$ $G(6,3\frac{1}{2},8)$ is the ridge and line $E(1,1,7)$ $V(6,1,5)$ is the eave of a hyperbolic paraboloid roof surface. Lines RE and GV represent roof rafters. Draw the top and front views of five other rafters, equally spaced between RE and GV.

12.5. The linear directrixes of a hyperbolic paraboloid are $A(2,3\frac{1}{4},5)$ $C(2,3\frac{1}{4},8\frac{1}{2})$ and $B(3\frac{1}{2},0\frac{1}{2},5)$ $L(5\frac{1}{2},0\frac{1}{2},8\frac{1}{2})$. This surface is one-half of the pilot of a locomotive. Lines AB and CL are elements of the surface. Draw the top and front views of six equally spaced elements of this warped surface.

Group II. Conoids

12.6. In Fig. 12.22 the transition shown is made up of two semiconoidal surfaces and two triangles. These surfaces alternate and are tangent to their adjacent surfaces. Draw the top, front, and right-side views of the transition, showing a series of elements of the conoidal surfaces. Develop a half pattern for this transition.

12.7. In Fig. 12.23 the sports arena is roofed with its central bays having a cylindrical roof. The right section of this cylinder is a semiellipse whose major diameter is 100 ft and whose semiminor diameter is 35 ft. The end bays of the arena have identical conoidal roof surfaces. A model of the structure at a scale of $1'' = 32'\text{-}0''$ is required. Develop the roof surfaces for the model.

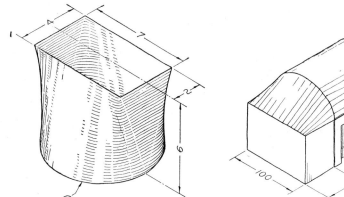

Fig. 12.22. Conoidal transition.

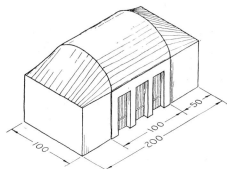

Fig. 12.23. Sports-arena roof.

12.8. Point $M(3,0\frac{1}{2},6\frac{1}{2})$ is the center of a 4-in.-diameter horizontal circle. This circle and the line $A(0,3\frac{1}{2},9)$ $B(6,3\frac{1}{2},4)$ are the linear directrixes of a right conoid. *Scale:* full size. Draw the top and front views of 12 elements of this conoid, equally spaced at their intersections with the circular directrix.

12.9. Point $P(4,0\frac{1}{2},6\frac{1}{2})$ is the center of an 8-in.-diameter horizontal circle. This circle and the line $R(1,3\frac{1}{2},4)$ $S(7,3\frac{1}{2},9)$ are the linear directrixes of a conoid. The plane director of this surface is frontal. *Scale:* half size. Draw the top and front views of 12 elements of this conoid, equally spaced at their intersections with the circular directrix.

12.10. Point $C(2,0\frac{1}{2},6\frac{1}{2})$ is the center of a $3\frac{1}{2}$-in.-diameter horizontal circle. This circle and line $R(0\frac{1}{4},3\frac{1}{2},8\frac{1}{4})$ $S(3\frac{3}{4},3\frac{1}{2},8\frac{1}{4})$ are the linear directrixes of a right conoid. The top of the conoid is removed by a truncating cut made in the horizontal plane containing point $A(2,2\frac{1}{4},X)$. *Scale:* full size. Draw the top, front, right-side, and one-half developed views of the resulting surface.

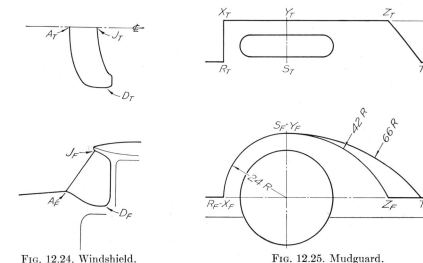

Fig. 12.24. Windshield.

Fig. 12.25. Mudguard.

Group III.   Cylindroids

12.11. In Fig. 12.24 one-half of an automobile windshield is limited by a curve that contains points $A(1\frac{1}{2},2\frac{1}{2},7\frac{1}{2})$, $B(1\frac{5}{8},2\frac{7}{16},6\frac{1}{2})$, $C(2,2\frac{1}{4},5\frac{13}{16})$, $D(2\frac{3}{4},2\frac{1}{8},5\frac{11}{16})$, $E(2\frac{7}{8},2\frac{3}{8},5\frac{13}{16})$, $F(2\frac{7}{8},3\frac{3}{8},6)$, $G(2\frac{3}{4},3\frac{5}{8},6\frac{1}{8})$, $H(2\frac{1}{2},3\frac{11}{16},6\frac{3}{4})$, and $J(2\frac{3}{8},3\frac{3}{4},7\frac{1}{2})$. The windshield is a warped surface whose plane director is frontal.   Draw the top and front views of a series of elements of this surface, and develop one-half of the windshield.

12.12. In Fig. 12.25 the fully exposed rear wheel of an experimental sports car has a mudguard composed of a cylinder and a cylindroid.   (The cylindroid has a horizontal plane director.)   Develop this composite surface.

12.13. Point $C(2,1,8\frac{1}{2})$ is the center of a frontal ellipse whose vertical major diameter is 6 in. long and whose minor diameter is 3 in. in length.   Point $M(4\frac{1}{2},1,5)$ is the center of a 6-in.-diameter frontal circle.   These curves are the linear directrixes of a cylindroid. *Scale:* full size.   Draw the top and front views of 12 elements, equally spaced at their intersections with the circular directrix, on the upper half of the cylindroid.

12.14. Point $M(2,1,7\frac{1}{2})$ is the center of a semicircle, the upper half of a circle of 16'-0'' diameter having $MN(4,1,5\frac{1}{2})$ as its axis.   Point $R(5,0\frac{1}{2},5)$ is the center of a 20'-0'' diameter circle arc whose axis is $RS(5,0\frac{1}{2},7)$.   These curves are the directrixes of a cylindroidal soffit whose plane director is horizontal.   *Scale:* $\frac{1}{4}'' = 1'$-0''.   Draw the top and front views of the soffit, showing 12 elements of the surface that are equally spaced at their intersections with the larger diameter arc.

Group IV.   Hyperboloids of Revolution of One Nappe

12.15. A hyperboloid of revolution of one nappe is generated by revolving line segment $R(3\frac{1}{2},4,6)$ $L(3\frac{1}{2},1,8)$ about axis $A(4,5,7)$ $B(4,0,7)$.   Draw the top and front views of 12 equally spaced elements of this surface.   Draw the outline of the hyperboloid in the front view.

12.16. Skew gears are used when two noncoplanar shafts are to be directly geared together.   The "pitch" surfaces of such gears are hyperboloids of revolution.   Lines $A(3,1,7)$ $B(3,5,7)$ and $C(1,2,6)$ $D(5,4,6)$ are the axes of shafts.   The gore circles of the mating hyperboloids are of equal diameter.   The gears measure 3 in. in length, parallel to their respective axes, and their axial lengths are centered on the planes of their respective gore circles.   *Scale:* full size.   Draw the top and front views of 12 equally spaced elements of the hyperboloid whose axis is AB.

Group V.   Warped Cones and Cow's Horns

12.17. The center of a 4-in.-diameter circle is point $P(4,1\frac{1}{2},6\frac{1}{2})$.   The plane of this circle is frontal-receding, inclined to the horizontal at an angle of 30°, and dips to the left. Point $R(4,4,6\frac{1}{2})$ is the center of a 2-in.-diameter horizontal circle.   These circles and the line joining their centers are the directrixes of a warped cone.   *Scale:* full size.   Draw the top and front views of 12 elements of this surface, equally spaced at their intersections with the smaller circle.

12.18. A stone arch has been designed with a cow's-horn surface.   The straight-line directrix of this surface is $A(3,0\frac{1}{2},8\frac{1}{2})$ $B(4,0\frac{1}{2},6\frac{1}{2})$.   Point A is the center of a 15-ft-diameter frontal semicircle, and point $C(4\frac{1}{4},0\frac{1}{2},6\frac{1}{2})$ is the center of a 10-ft-diameter frontal semicircle.   These semicircles are the other linear directrixes of the cow's horn. *Scale:* $1'' = 5'$-0''.   Draw the top and front views of six elements of the warped surface, equally spaced at their intersections with the larger curved-line directrix.

Group VI.   Helicoids

12.19. In Fig. 12.26 the nosings (tread-riser intersections) of a circular stairway are elements of a right helicoid.   Tread depths, measured on a walking line that is 16 in.

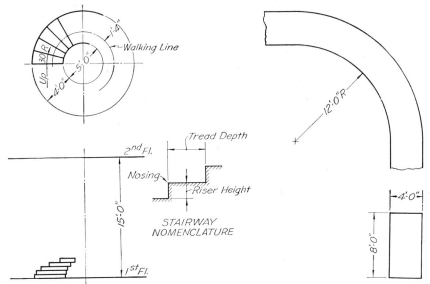

FIG. 12.26. Circular stairway.

FIG. 12.27. Ramped passageway turn.

from the inner handrail, are $12^{11}/_{16}$ in. Draw the top and front views of all the nosings of this stairway.

12.20. In Fig. 12.27 the vertical sections through the ramped passageway are 4'-0'' by 8'-0'' rectangles. The passageway turns through a 90° angle. A 10 per cent grade is maintained on the floor centerline. Prepare patterns of the floor, ceiling, and walls for a model of this passageway, to be made at a scale of $\frac{1}{4}'' = 1'-0''$.

12.21. The diameter of a right-hand square thread is 5 in.; its lead is $1\frac{3}{4}$ in. In a normal view of its axis, draw the true projection of several turns of this thread. Omit hidden features.

12.22. Line $A(4,2,4)$ $B(4,2,9)$ is the axis of a 9-in.-diameter shaft. Welded to this shaft is a right-helicoidal blade whose outer limit is a 36-in.-diameter cylinder, coaxial with the shaft. The directrix for the blade is a left-hand helix having a 36-in. lead. *Scale:* $1'' = 1'-0''$. Draw the top and front views of the blade-shaft assembly.

12.23. Line $C(4,5,7)$ $H(4,0,7)$ is the axis of two coaxial cylinders, one 3 ft in diameter and the other 9 ft in diameter. These cylinders are the inner and outer limits of a right-helicoidal fire-escape chute. Line CH is a directrix of the chute as well as its axis. A vertical clearance of 8 ft between successive turns of the chute is required. The intersection of the chute surface with the second-floor level of a school building is along the horizontal-profile line through point C. Floor-to-floor distance is 12 ft. *Scale:* $\frac{3}{8}'' = 1'-0''$. Draw the top and front views of the helical directrixes of the chute surface; the terminal of this surface is 24 in. above the first-floor level.

12.24. The axis of a 12-in.-diameter pipe is $S(4,2,5)$ $T(4,2,9)$. The surface of the pipe is the cylinder of a right-hand helix having a 44-in. lead and containing point $P(3\frac{1}{2},2,5)$. This helix and ST are the linear directrixes of a helicoidal blade whose outer edge is the intersection of the helicoid with a 48-in.-diameter cylinder having ST as its axis. Elements of the blade surface make an angle of 60° with ST and run forward from their intersection with the inner helix. Draw the top and front views of the inner and outer helixes, 12 equally spaced elements of one turn of the blade, and the intersection of the blade surface with the frontal plane containing point S.

CHAPTER 13

DOUBLE-CURVED SURFACES

13.1. Double-curved surfaces have no straight-line elements. They are generated only by curved lines rotating about an axis or moving so as to maintain contact with curved-line directrixes. Such a surface is, therefore, curved in every direction. Surfaces of this classification cannot be developed, but each may be approximated with a series of single-curved surfaces.

13.2. Surfaces of Revolution. Previous paragraphs have described the right-circular cylinder and cone (single-curved surfaces of revolution) and the hyperboloid of revolution of one nappe (the warped surface of revolution). All other surfaces of revolution are double-curved.

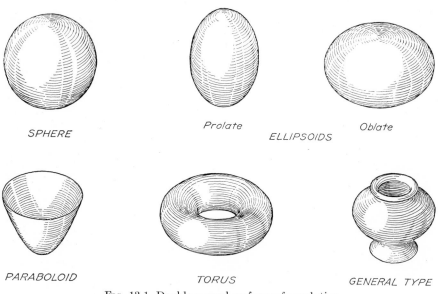

SPHERE

Prolate

ELLIPSOIDS

Oblate

PARABOLOID

TORUS

GENERAL TYPE

FIG. 13.1. Double-curved surfaces of revolution.

Surfaces of revolution are usually generated by the motion of the generatrix about an axis that lies in the plane of the generatrix. The *sphere, ellipsoids, paraboloid,* and *torus* of Fig. 13.1 will all be recognized as surfaces

212

of this type. Although without a geometric name, the general type shown is also a double-curved surface of revolution.

End and normal views of the axis are usually employed in the orthographic representations of these surfaces. The outline of the surface and the axis of

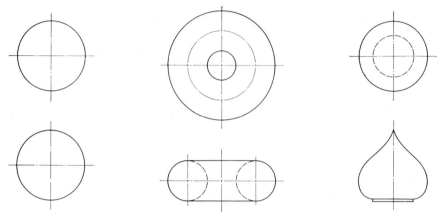

FIG. 13.2. Orthographic views of a sphere, torus, and general-type surface of revolution.

revolution is adequate in such views. An end view of the axis shows a circular outline, while a normal view of the axis shows the true shape of the generatrix as the outline elements in that view. In Fig. 13.2, the orthographic representations of several double-curved surfaces of revolution are shown.

13.3. Serpentine (Fig. 13.3). The *serpentine* is a double-curved surface that is generated by a circle moving so that its center follows a helix while its plane remains normal to that helix.

FIG. 13.3. A serpentine.

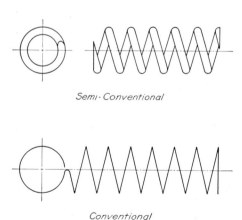

Semi-Conventional

Conventional

FIG. 13.4. Conventional representations of serpentines.

Coil springs, made from round (cylindrical) stock, have serpentine-type surfaces. The representation of the surface is usually conventionalized, as shown in Fig. 13.4.

13.4. General Type of Double-curved Surface. The surfaces named above possess such characteristics that their names alone are sufficient for the average person to visualize their forms. All double-curved surfaces are not so readily visualized—a plot of ground will serve as an example of such a surface. A glance at the land on the actual site will reveal that no outline drawing could ever describe that surface. Its representation can best be accomplished by plotting its intersections with a series of equally spaced horizontal planes. These intersections, called *contours*, are lines of the ground surface. The reader of such a drawing must interpolate for elevations between the contour lines.

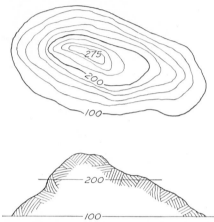

FIG. 13.5. Contour-line representation of a hill mass.

In Fig. 13.5, a hill mass is represented by a series of contours in the top view and by its outline in the front view. The front view may be omitted if the uniform spacing between the horizontal cutting planes and their elevations are known. The uniform spacing is termed the *contour interval*—in this example the interval is 20 ft.

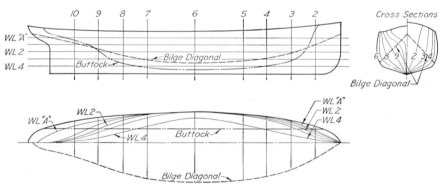

FIG. 13.6. A ship hull represented by the intersection of planes with its double-curved surface.

Three views of a ship hull are shown in Fig. 13.6. The intersections of horizontal planes with the hull may be likened to the contour lines of the previous illustration; in nautical and aircraft work such intersections are termed *water lines*. When the ship is floating with her designed load on board, the plane of the water surface intersects the hull along the *load water line*. Water lines are lettered above the load water line and numbered below it. Five water lines are shown in the front and half bottom views of the illustration.

Intersections of the hull by frontal (longitudinal) planes are termed *buttock lines* or, more simply, buttocks. One buttock is shown in both the front and half bottom views. Intersections of the hull by profile (transverse) planes are called *cross sections*. Several cross sections are shown in all three views; they are numbered from *2* through *10*, inclusive.

A check for smoothness, or *fairing*, of the surface may be achieved by intersecting the hull with a plane perpendicular to one of the principal planes of projection but inclined to the other two. The *bilge diagonal* shown is such an intersection. The half bottom view shows this bilge diagonal revolved to the horizontal plane, a practice customary in nautical work.

Any double-curved surface may be orthographically represented in a manner similar to the above. The ship hull is but one application of this procedure.

13.5. Intersection of a Plane with a Double-curved Surface. All general-type double-curved surfaces are represented by means of the intersections of planes with those surfaces, as briefly described above. Double-curved surfaces of revolution, however, are usually represented by their outlines in views that are either normal or end views of their axes. Examples of oblique-plane intersections with both types of double-curved surfaces follow.

The intersection of an oblique plane with a general type of double-curved surface is determined by finding the points where a known system of lines

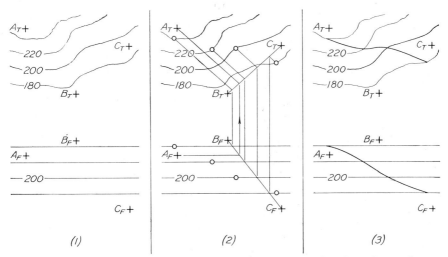

FIG. 13.7. Intersection of an oblique plane with a double-curved surface of general type.

of the surface (i.e., contours, water lines, buttocks, etc.) intersects the oblique plane.   These points are common to both the double-curved surface and the plane; hence, the required line of intersection is drawn through them.   In Fig. 13.7, a hillside is intersected by plane ABC.   The intersections of several contour lines with plane ABC are determined in (2).   The resultant intersection is drawn in (3).   If ABC represents a seam of coal, then this intersection is the *outcrop* of the seam.

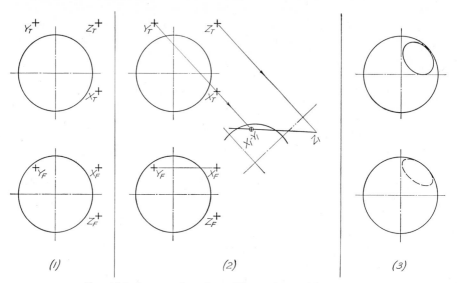

(1)   (2)   (3)

FIG. 13.8. Intersection of an oblique plane with a sphere.

The knowledge that a surface is one of revolution is often usable in determining plane intersections with that surface.   For example, the intersection of a plane with a sphere can be only a circle.   The diameter of such a circular intersection may be determined in a view that shows an edge view of the plane. The intersection of plane XYZ with the sphere is required in the problem of Fig. 13.8.   An edge view of the plane is drawn in (2).   (The fact that XY is horizontal simplifies this construction.)   The true size of the diameter of the resulting circular intersection is seen in this auxiliary view as the distance between the points of intersection of the outline circle of the sphere with plane XYZ.   The top and front views of the intersection are drawn in (3), where the procedures described in Sec. 8.6 (circle in an oblique position) are employed.

The intersection of a plane with a surface of revolution other than a sphere may be accomplished by recognizing that planes perpendicular to the axis of revolution will intersect that surface along one or more circles.   If the intersection of a surface of revolution and a plane not perpendicular to the axis is required, it may be determined by finding the points of intersection between the given plane and various circles of the curved surface.   In Fig. 13.9,

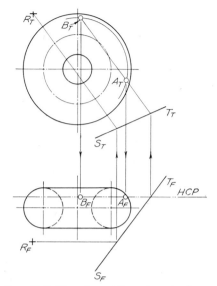

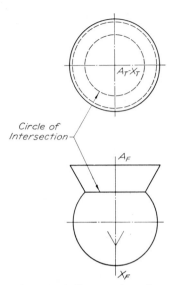

FIG. 13.9. Use of a cutting plane to determine points on the intersection of an oblique plane and a double-curved surface of revolution.

FIG. 13.10. Intersection of two surfaces of revolution having a common axis.

points A and B on the required intersection between the torus and plane RST are determined through the use of a cutting plane perpendicular to the axis of revolution. The intersections of this HCP cutting plane with the torus and plane RST intersect, in turn, at points A and B.

13.6. Intersection of Two Surfaces of Revolution Having a Common Axis. The intersection of two surfaces of revolution having a common axis is a circle whose plane is perpendicular to that axis. A normal view of the axis is an edge view of the circular intersection, and the true length of the diameter of the circle appears as the distance between the outline elements intersections in such a view. In Fig. 13.10, the circular intersection between a sphere and a right-circular cone, having AX as their common axis, is shown.

13.7. Intersection of Two Surfaces of Revolution Whose Axes Intersect. The principle expressed in the preceding paragraph is used to solve the current problem. The intersection of the two axes is used as the center for a series of concentric cutting spheres. For any one sphere, the intersections of the circles cut on the first given surface with the circles cut on the second given surface are points on the intersection of the given surfaces of revolution. This solution is particularly adapted to a presentation wherein one given view is a normal view of *both* axes and the other given view is an end view of one axis.

A right-circular cone and a right-circular cylinder are presented in Fig. 13.11(1). The intersection between these surfaces is required. In (2),

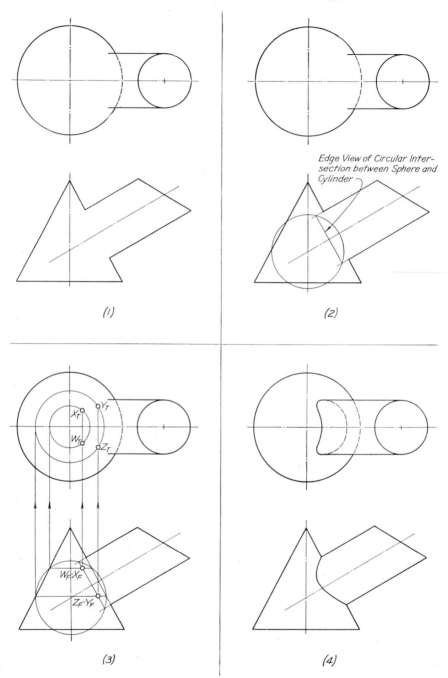

Edge View of Circular Intersection between Sphere and
Cylinder

(1)

(2)

(3)

(4)

FIG. 13.11. Intersection of two surfaces of revolution whose axes intersect—cutting-sphere method.

the front view of one cutting sphere is shown. The edge view of a circle cut by this sphere on the cylinder is drawn between the intersections of the cylinder and sphere outlines. In (3), the intersections of the cutting sphere with the cone are added. Points W, X, Y, and Z, the intersections of the resulting circles, are projected to the top view onto the corresponding circular intersections of the sphere with the cone. The completed intersection is shown in (4).

13.8. Intersection of Two Double-curved Surfaces of General Type. Intersections of this variety are usually determined through the use of a series of cutting planes. The lines of intersections of one such plane with each of the given surfaces are determined. Points common to both of the given surfaces are found at the intersection of these lines. The required intersection is drawn through a series of such points.

13.9. Plane Tangent to a Double-curved Surface. Problems of this type are usually presented with a point of the required plane being given, together with some other controlling specification. The given point may be the point of tangency. If so, that knowledge is sufficient to establish the required tangent plane.

The earlier study of planes tangent to cylinders and cones used the basic principle of tangent planes: A plane tangent to a curved surface may be determined by establishing two lines, each tangent to the curved surface at a common point.

In Fig. 13.12(1), point P is given as the point of tangency between the

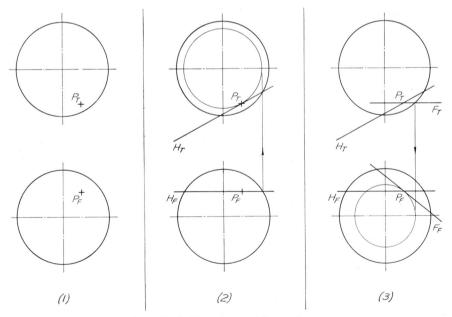

Fig. 13.12. Plane tangent to a sphere.

sphere and a plane. The horizontal plane containing P cuts a circle on the sphere. The circle is drawn in the top view of (2). Line PH is drawn tangent to this horizontal circle and is one line of the tangent plane. In (3), the line PF is established by drawing it tangent to the circle cut on the sphere by the frontal plane containing point P. The tangent plane is HPF.

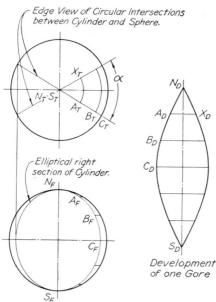

FIG. 13.13. Approximate development of a sphere—cylinder method.

13.10. Approximate Development of a Sphere.

Several procedures may be followed in approximating the development of a spherical surface. Cylinders and cones are usually employed, and they may either intersect or be tangent to the spherical surface.

Cylindrical approximations may be accomplished with a series of identical cylinders whose right sections are ellipses and whose axes contain the center of the sphere. The intersections of such a cylinder with the sphere are two circles, and these circles of intersection limit the use of that cylinder in the approximate development.

In Fig. 13.13, the top view is an edge view of the circular intersections of one such cylinder with the sphere. Note should be taken of the fact that the major diameter of the elliptical right section of the cylinder is equal in length to the diameter of the sphere. The angle α between the planes of the circular intersections decreases as the minor diameter of the elliptical right section increases in size. The accuracy of the approximation achieved is inverse to the size of this angle. The *gore*, between the semicircular intersections, is developed by the usual cylindrical procedure. The approximation of the complete sphere could be completed by repeating this gore $360/\alpha$ times.

An example of a conical approximation of the spherical surface is shown in Fig. 13.14. Secant cones, those which intersect the sphere, are used. The cones have a common axis, and the use of each is limited to the frustums that lie between the two circular intersections of each cone with the sphere. The cone shown in (1) is used to approximate the development of the sphere between the pole and horizontal plane A. In (2), the cone used for the spherical surface between horizontal planes A and B is drawn. The cone

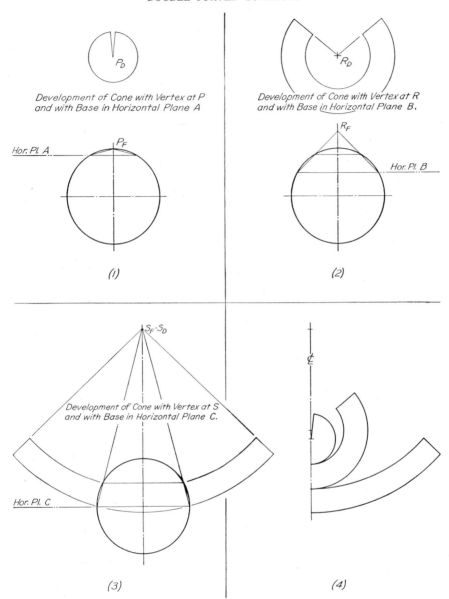

FIG. 13.14. Approximate development of a sphere—cone method.

whose apex is at point S, as shown in (3), is used for the approximation between the horizontal planes B and C. One-half of the conic frustums are developed in (4). An increase in the number of cones used will result in a more accurate approximation of the spherical surface.

PROBLEMS

Group I.   Spheres, Representations, and Intersections

13.1. The center of a 4-in.-diameter sphere is point $C(3,2\frac{1}{2},7)$.   *Scale:* full size. Which of the following points are inside this sphere: $A(4,1\frac{1}{2},6)$, $B(2,4,5\frac{1}{2})$, $Y(4,2\frac{1}{2},8)$, and $Z(1\frac{1}{2},1\frac{1}{2},8\frac{1}{2})$?

13.2. Points $A(3,1\frac{1}{2},7\frac{1}{2})$, $B(5,1\frac{1}{2},5\frac{1}{2})$, and $C(6,1\frac{1}{2},7\frac{1}{2})$ are the centers of 4-in.-diameter spheres.   A fourth sphere, whose diameter is $3\frac{1}{2}$ in. long, rests in the cup formed by the first three spheres.   *Scale:* half size.   Draw the top and front views of the four spheres.

13.3. A 2-in.-diameter sphere is centered at $D(4,1\frac{1}{2},6)$.   A 3-in.-diameter sphere has its center on line $E(1,3\frac{1}{2},7)$ $K(5,2\frac{1}{4},8\frac{1}{2})$.   *Scale:* full size.   The spheres are tangent. Draw the top and front views of the spheres, and identify their point of tangency as point T in both views.

13.4. Point $S(3,2,7)$ is the center of a 12-ft-diameter spherical tank.   Line $A(1,4,5\frac{1}{4})$ $B(4,2\frac{1}{2},7)$ is the axis of a straight length of pipe.   *Scale:* $\frac{1}{4}'' = 1'\text{-}0''$.   Preparation of the tank plate for the necessary pipe fitting requires the determination of the point of intersection of line AB with the spherical surface.   Show the top and front views of this point of intersection.

13.5. Point $C(2\frac{1}{2},2\frac{1}{2},7)$ is the center of a 3-in.-diameter sphere.   *Scale:* full size. Draw the top and front views of the intersection of this spherical surface with plane $R(3,4,5)$ $S(0\frac{1}{4},3\frac{1}{2},8)$ $T(4\frac{1}{2},2,8)$.

13.6. The center of a 3-in.-diameter sphere is point $C(2\frac{1}{2},2\frac{1}{2},7)$.   *Scale:* full size. Draw the top and front views of the intersections of this sphere with plane $M(0\frac{1}{2},3\frac{1}{2},5)$ $N(4\frac{1}{2},3\frac{1}{2},5)$ $O(4\frac{1}{2},3\frac{1}{2},9)$ $P(0\frac{1}{2},3\frac{1}{2},9)$, and with plane $NPZ(0\frac{1}{2},1,5)$.

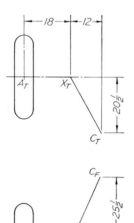

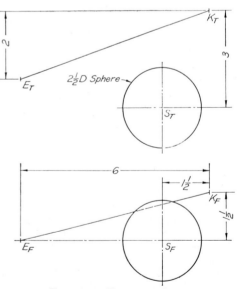

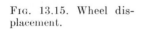
Fig. 13.15. Wheel displacement.

Fig. 13.16. Tangent spheres.

13.7. Point $C(2,2,7\frac{1}{2})$ is the center of a 2-in.-diameter sphere. *Scale:* full size. Determine the planes $M(3,3\frac{1}{2},5\frac{1}{2})$ $N(5,2,7)$ P and MNR that are tangent to this sphere. Points P and R are the tangent points of their respective planes with the sphere.

13.8. Draw the top and front views of a sphere that will fit inside the tetrahedron $A(4,4\frac{1}{4},5\frac{1}{4})$ $B(0\frac{1}{2},1,4\frac{1}{2})$ $C(3\frac{1}{2},1,7\frac{1}{2})$ $D(5\frac{1}{2},1,4\frac{1}{2})$ and be tangent to each of the four surfaces of the tetrahedron.

13.9. Point $S(2\frac{1}{2},2,7)$ is the center of a 14-in.-diameter sphere. Line $SL(6\frac{1}{2},4,7)$ is the axis of an 8-in.-diameter right-circular cylinder. *Scale:* $3'' = 1'\text{-}0''$. Draw the top and front views of the intersection between these surfaces.

13.10. Point $K(5\frac{1}{2},2\frac{1}{2},7)$ is the center of a $3\frac{1}{2}$-in.-diameter sphere. The axis of a $2\frac{1}{2}$-in.-diameter right-circular cylinder is the line $L(2,4,7\frac{1}{2})$ $M(5\frac{1}{2},2\frac{1}{2},7\frac{1}{2})$. *Scale:* full size. Draw the top and front views of the intersection between these surfaces.

13.11. In Fig. 13.15 line AX is the axis of a wheel. Line CX is the centerline of a control rod. Determine the total angular wheel displacement if the connection at point X has a 3-in. error from X along both AX and CX. (Points A and C are to remain fixed.) The location of point X, as shown, is the mean position of that point. The displacement of point X is to be confined to the nearest possible positions to the indicated position of X for both the maximum and minimum lengths of axis and control rod.

13.12. In Fig. 13.16 a 3-in.-diameter sphere has its center on the line EK to the left of point S. This sphere and the one shown (whose center is at point S) are tangent. Draw the top and front views of both spheres. Identify their point of tangency in all views drawn.

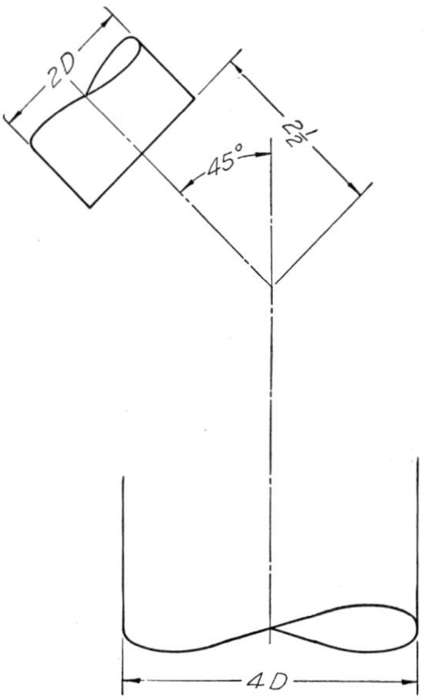

13.13. In Fig. 13.17 the view shown is a normal view of the axes of both right-circular cylindrical ducts. These axes intersect. Design a cone transition that will connect between the cylindrical ducts.

Fig. 13.17. Oblique cone transition.

Group II. Ellipsoids, Representations and Intersections

13.14. Point $S(4,0\frac{1}{2},5\frac{1}{2})$ is the center of a 12-in.-diameter circle. This circle is the lower edge of an oblate ellipsoidal cover. The frontal element of the ellipsoid has a 4-in. minor diameter, one end of which is at $P(4,1\frac{1}{2},5\frac{1}{2})$. *Scale:* half size. Draw the outline of this cover in both the top and front views. A relief valve has a vertical axis that contains point $V(5,X,4)$. Locate the point of intersection of the cover with the valve axis.

13.15. Line segment $V(1,2\frac{1}{2},6\frac{1}{2})$ $W(6,2\frac{1}{2},6\frac{1}{2})$ is the major diameter and $S(3\frac{1}{2},2\frac{1}{2},5\frac{1}{2})$ $T(3\frac{1}{2},2\frac{1}{2},7\frac{1}{2})$ is the minor diameter of an ellipse. This ellipse is the generatrix of a prolate ellipsoid. Draw the outline of this ellipsoid in both the top and front views, and locate the points of intersection between this surface and the line $K(0\frac{1}{2},1,8\frac{1}{2})$ $L(6,4,5\frac{1}{2})$.

13.16. Point $C(4,0,6)$ is the center of a 120-ft-diameter horizontal circle. This circle is the base of an ellipsoidal dome whose maximum rise above point C is 50 ft. *Scale:*

$1'' = 20'-0''$. The dome is ventilated through two symmetrically placed frontal cuts into the ellipsoidal surface. These ventilation cuts are 70 ft apart, and both have a horizontal projection length of 60 ft. Draw the top and front views of the dome and the ventilation cuts.

13.17. Line segment $A(1\frac{1}{2},2,7)$ $B(6\frac{1}{2},2,7)$ is the major diameter and $C(4,3\frac{1}{4},7)$ $D(4,0\frac{3}{4},7)$ is the minor diameter of an ellipse. This ellipse is the generatrix of a prolate ellipsoid. Draw the front view of the intersections of this ellipsoid with the frontal planes that contain points $R(X,X,6\frac{1}{2})$ and $S(X,X,6)$, respectively.

13.18. An ellipse has $M(2,2,6\frac{1}{2})$ $J(6,2,6\frac{1}{2})$ as its major diameter and $N(4,3\frac{1}{2},6\frac{1}{2})$ $R(4,0\frac{1}{2},6\frac{1}{2})$ as its minor diameter. This ellipse is the generatrix of an oblate ellipsoid. Draw the top and front views of this ellipsoid, the intersection of this surface with the frontal plane containing point $F(X,X,5\frac{1}{2})$, and the intersection of the ellipsoid with the horizontal plane containing point $H(X,3,X)$.

13.19. Line segment $O(1,0\frac{1}{2},6\frac{1}{2})$ $N(1,3\frac{1}{4},6\frac{1}{2})$ is the semiminor diameter and $OM(6,0\frac{1}{2},6\frac{1}{2})$ is the semimajor diameter of an ellipse. This ellipse is the generatrix of an ellipsoid whose axis is the major diameter of the generatrix. Line $OP(6\frac{1}{2},3\frac{1}{2},6\frac{1}{2})$ is the axis of a 3-in.-diameter right-circular cylinder. *Scale:* full size. Draw the top and front views of the intersection between these surfaces.

13.20. Points $F(2,2,7)$ and $P(5,2,7)$ are the foci of the elliptical generatrix of a prolate ellipsoid. The major diameter of this generatrix is 4 in. long. Point $C(5,3\frac{1}{4},7)$ is the center of a 3-in.-diameter sphere. *Scale:* full size. Draw the top and front views of the intersection between these surfaces.

Group III. Paraboloids, Representations and Intersections

13.21. Point $C(4,0\frac{1}{2},6\frac{1}{2})$ is the center of a 4-in.-diameter horizontal circle. This circle is the open end of a parabolic reflector. The directrix for the generatrix of the reflector surface is a horizontal line containing point $H(X,3,X)$. *Scale:* full size. Draw the outline of the reflector in both the top and front views.

13.22. Point $F(4,2\frac{3}{4},6\frac{1}{2})$ is the focal point of a paraboloid. The base of the paraboloid is a 4-in.-diameter circle that lies in the horizontal plane containing point $Z(X,0\frac{1}{2},X)$. Draw the top and front views of the intersection of this paraboloid with the frontal-receding plane that contains point $P(3,1\frac{1}{2},X)$ and dips 15° to the left.

13.23. Line $D(0,4,6\frac{1}{2})$ $R(5,4,6\frac{1}{2})$ is the directrix of a parabola whose focal point is $F(2\frac{1}{2},3,6\frac{1}{2})$. This parabola is the generatrix of a paraboloid. Line $C(2\frac{1}{2},1,6\frac{1}{2})$ $Y(6,2\frac{1}{2},6\frac{1}{2})$ is the axis of a 2-in.-diameter right-circular cylinder. *Scale:* full size. Draw the top and front views of the intersection between this paraboloid and cylinder.

Group IV. Other Surfaces of Revolution

13.24. Point $C(1\frac{1}{2},1\frac{1}{2},6\frac{1}{2})$ is the center of a 1-in.-diameter frontal circle. This circle generates a torus when revolved about axis $A(3,3,6\frac{1}{2})$ $B(3,0,6\frac{1}{2})$. *Scale:* full size. Draw

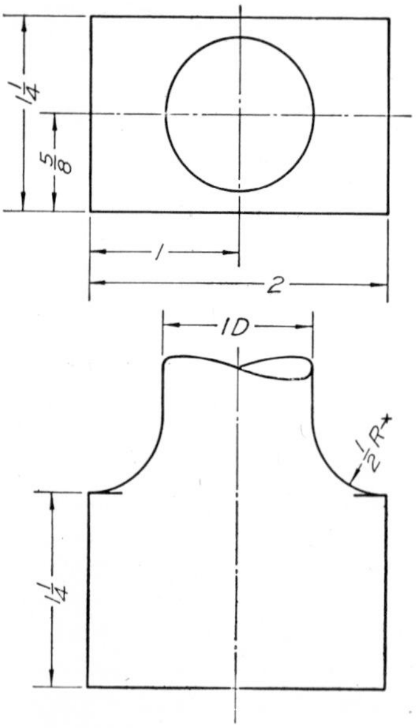

FIG. 13.18. Connecting rod.

the top and front views of the torus and its intersection with the frontal-receding plane that contains both points $P(6,3,X)$ and $Q(2\frac{1}{2},0\frac{1}{2},X)$.

13.25. One end of a wooden two-by-four (actual size: $1\frac{5}{8}$ by $3\frac{5}{8}$ in.) is turned about its axis on a lathe to a diameter of $1\frac{5}{8}$ in. This cylindrical end is joined to the rectangular section by a turned fillet of $1\frac{1}{2}$ in. radius. Draw the top, front, and right-side views of the resulting intersections.

13.26. In Fig. 13.18 a rectangular bar is turned to make the connecting rod. Draw the top and front views of the resulting rod.

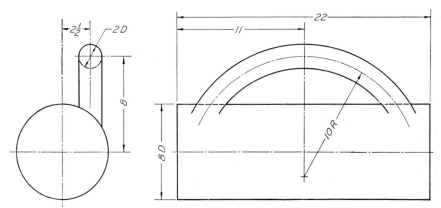

FIG. 13.19. Intersection of a pipe bend and a cylindrical casing.

13.27. In Fig. 13.19 determine the intersection between the torus pipe bend and the cylindrical casing. Develop a template for the holes that must be cut into the casing to admit the pipe bend.

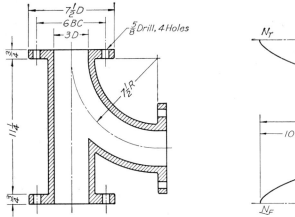

FIG. 13.20. Single-sweep flanged T.

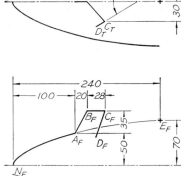

FIG. 13.21. Fuselage-windshield intersection.

13.28. A cast-iron flanged fitting is partially shown in Fig. 13.20. Complete the sectional view by drawing the curves of intersection between the torus and cylindrical voids inside the fitting.

13.29. In Fig. 13.21 the generatrix of the upper half of an aircraft nose is a conic curve. One element of this surface contains points N, A, and E. The curve is tangent to both the vertical line through point N and the horizontal-frontal line through point E. Determine the intersection of windshield plane $ABCD$ with this double-curved surface of revolution whose axis is the horizontal-frontal line through point N. Draw a normal view of the half windshield.

Group V.   General-type Double-curved Surfaces

13.30. In Fig. 13.22 the crest of an earth-fill dam is represented by the line AB. The upstream fill is made with a 1:3 slope; the downstream fill is made with a 1:2 slope. Determine the intersection of the fills with the natural ground surface. (The grid squares are 20 ft on a side.)

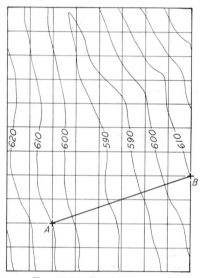

Fig. 13.22. Earth-fill dam.

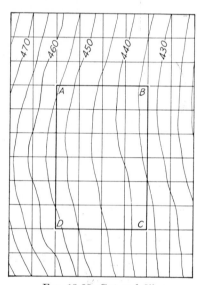

Fig. 13.23. Cut and fill.

13.31. In Fig. 13.23 rectangle $ABCD$ is the outline of an area that is to be leveled to the 445 elevation. Cuts are to be made with a 1:1 slope, and fills to a slope of $1:1\frac{1}{2}$. Show the toe of the fill and the top of the cut. (The grid squares are 20 ft on a side.)

13.32. Line $A(2,2\frac{1}{2},6\frac{3}{4})$ $B(2,0\frac{1}{2},6\frac{3}{4})$ is the axis of four cone frustums. These frustums have as their common base planes the horizontal planes containing points A and B, respectively. The inner frustum has an upper base of 4 in. diameter and a lower base of $2\frac{1}{2}$ in. diameter. The next larger frustum has an upper base of $5\frac{3}{8}$ in. diameter and a lower base of $4\frac{1}{4}$ in. diameter. The third frustum has an upper base diameter of $6\frac{5}{8}$ in. and a lower base diameter of $5\frac{3}{4}$ in. The outer frustum has an upper base diameter of $7\frac{3}{4}$ in. and a lower base diameter of 7 in. Constant-slope helical curves, wrapped on these cone frustums, are lines of the double-curved center structure of a helicoidal-type blade. The helix on the inner frustum starts at point $C(2,0\frac{1}{2},X)$ and ends at point $D(3^{15}\!\!/_{16},2\frac{1}{2},X)$. The helix on the next larger frustum starts at point $J(1^{13}\!\!/_{16},0\frac{1}{2},X)$ and ends at point $K(4\frac{1}{2},2\frac{1}{2},X)$. The third helix, on the next larger frustum, starts at point $R(1^{9}\!\!/_{16},0\frac{1}{2},X)$ and ends at point $S(4\frac{7}{8},2\frac{1}{2},X)$. The outer frustum contains the helix that starts at point $Y(1\frac{3}{16}, 0\frac{1}{2}, X)$ and ends at point $Z(5\frac{7}{16}, 2\frac{1}{2}, X)$. Plot the intersections of this blade structure with the following listed planes that contain the axis AB: (a) the profile plane, (b) the plane that makes an angle of 45° with the profile, and (c) the frontal plane. Draw normal views of these intersections.

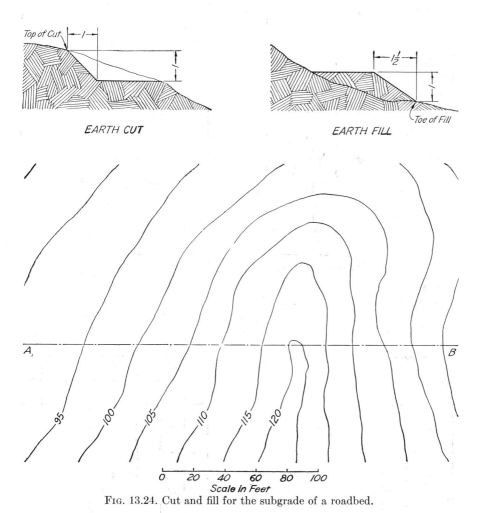

Fɪɢ. 13.24. Cut and fill for the subgrade of a roadbed.

13.33. In Fig. 13.24 the centerline of a horizontal portion of a 60-ft-wide roadbed is the line AB. The finished subgrade of this roadbed is to be at the elevation of 100. Earth cuts are to be made at a 1:1 slope; earth fills are to be made at a 1:1½ slope. Determine the intersections of the cuts and fills with the natural surface of the ground.

13.34. Loose material dumped in a pile approximates the shape of a right-circular cone. The base angle of the cone is called the *angle of repose* for the material dumped. Mine refuse is dumped from the shaft mouth S in Fig. 13.25. This refuse has a 30° angle of repose. Draw the top view of the intersection of the dump with the natural hillside.

Point S is the vertex of the conical dump.   (The contour interval is 100 ft.   The grid squares are 100 ft on a side.)

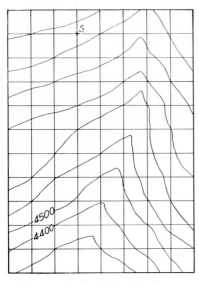

Fig. 13.25. Conical refuse dump.

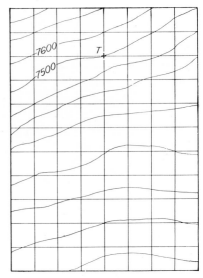

Fig. 13.26. Conical frustum refuse dump.

13.35. Dump capacity is increased by dumping refuse to form a level area around the tunnel or shaft entrance. In Fig. 13.26 point T is a tunnel entrance.   Mine refuse is to be dumped from T, and the dump capacity increased by forming a flat area at the 7500

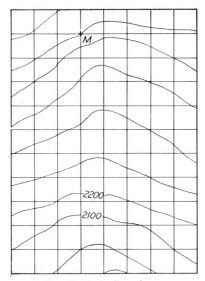

Fig. 13.27. Refuse dump.

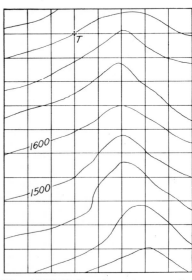

Fig. 13.28. Refuse dump to property limits.

level. This flat area is to have a radius of 100 ft and be centered at point T. The refuse has a 45° angle of repose. Draw the intersection of the completed dump with the natural hillside. (The contour interval is 100 ft. The grid squares are 100 ft on a side.)

13.36. In Fig. 13.27 the rectangle illustrated is the boundary of a mining property leased for dumping purposes. Refuse is to be dumped with a 45° angle of repose. If the dump is to be conical, what is the radius of the largest arc, centered at M, that can be used as the outline of a level area and still keep the refuse within the limits of this leased property? (The contour interval is 100 ft. The grid squares are 100 ft on a side.)

13.37. In Fig. 13.28 a mining company has leased the rectangular plot for dumping purposes. The material to be dumped has a 60° angle of repose. Draw the irregular outline of the horizontal area around the tunnel mouth T that will permit the dump to fill that portion of the leased property below the 1900 level and still not spill over the boundaries of the property. (The contour interval is 100 ft. The grid squares are 100 ft on a side.)

13.38. Design the hull of a small boat. Draw three views of the hull surface, showing several water lines, buttocks, and cross sections of the surface. Check the fairing of the design with a bilge diagonal.

CHAPTER 14

MAP PROJECTIONS

14.1. Cartography is the science and art of graphicly representing the surface of the earth. The representation may be a projection onto a plane, a single-curved surface, a combination of such developable surfaces, or a variation from actual projection procedures.

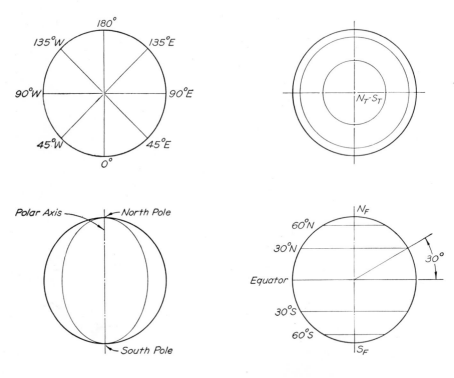

MERIDIANS OF LONGITUDE   PARALLELS OF LATITUDE

FIG. 14.1. Nomenclature of the globe.

The mapping of large areas of the surface of the earth results in something less accurate than exact representations. Distortions result from the fact that the surface of the earth (considered as a sphere) is mapped onto a plane

230

surface and only approximate developments of a sphere are possible. Sometimes it is desirable to show areas proportionally, at other times it is necessary to represent directions accurately, or the cartographer may be required to describe shapes with reasonable correctness. The selection of one of the above factors as being of primary importance will often result in corresponding distortions of the other features.

The majority of the methods used in mapping are *not* true projections. They are arrangements of intersecting lines that represent the meridians of longitude and parallels of latitude. This network of lines, the *graticule*, is selected so as to represent some feature of the surface of the earth with a minimum of distortion and to restrict the distortion of other major features in so far as possible.

14.2. Nomenclature (Fig. 14.1). The surface of the earth may be considered as a sphere that is generated by the rotation of a semicircle about its diameter. The intersections of the axis of rotation with the generatrix are the *poles*. Any one position of the generatrix is a *meridian* of longitude. Meridians are identified as being a specified number of degrees east or west of the 0° meridian (arbitrarily established through Greenwich, England).

The axis of rotation, or polar axis, is the axis of a series of circles on the surface of the earth. These circles are the *parallels* of latitude. The parallel whose plane contains the center of the earth is the *equator*. Parallels are identified, either north or south, by the subtended angle between the equator and the parallel in question. The vertex of this angle is at the center of the earth.

All circles on the surface of the earth whose planes contain its center are *great circles*. Other circles of its surface are termed *small circles*. Meridians are semigreat circles. The equator is the only great circle of the many parallels; all other parallels are small circles.

14.3. Considerations Relative to Direction, Distance, Area, and Shape. Certain relationships between meridians and parallels may be noted in Fig. 14.2. The following are listed as of major importance:

1. Meridians and parallels intersect at 90° angles in every instance.
2. Arcs of all meridians between parallels of uniform angular spacing are equal to each other.
3. Arcs of all parallels between meridians of uniform angular spacing decrease in length from the equator toward the poles.

Fig. 14.2. Relationships between meridians and parallels.

The graticule shown in Fig. 14.3 accurately shows the first and second relationships listed above. Since the meridians are represented by parallel lines, the scale of the map, in so far as distances along the several parallels are concerned, changes with each parallel. Features of the earth would not, therefore, be shown in their true shape in the resultant map.

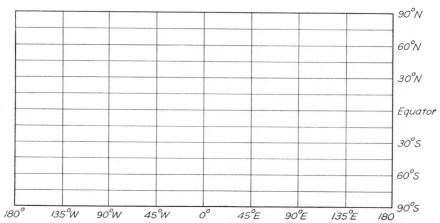

FIG. 14.3. Graticule for perpendicular relationship between meridians and parallels, and constant scale on meridians.

If it is required to keep the correct proportion between meridians and parallels, the distances between the parallels must be proportionately

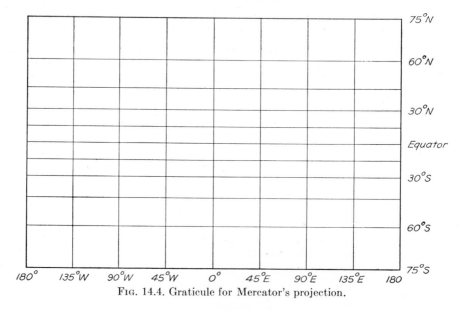

FIG. 14.4. Graticule for Mercator's projection.

increased. Mercator's projection (Fig. 14.4) shows correct proportion in the scale of meridians and parallels at any point of the map, but distances and areas are increasingly exaggerated as the mapping proceeds toward the polar regions. Such a map has two pronounced advantages: (1) It is a *conformal* map, since small features of the earth are shown in their true shape, and (2) all compass directions are accurately indicated by straight lines.

The concept of direction can be deceptive. The fact that north-south and east-west directions are on meridians and parallels may allow for an erroneous assumption that all directions are on circles of the sphere. To illustrate what actually occurs, a line whose direction is constantly northeast is shown in Fig. 14.5. Any such line is known as a *rhumb line;* its spiral approach to the North Pole is a *loxodromic curve.* Navigation by the compass, or "by the rhumb line," is readily aided by use of a Mercator's projection. Rhumb lines, however, are not the shortest routes between points on the surface of the earth.

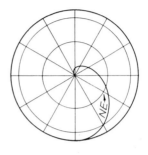

The shortest route between two points on the surface of the earth is measured on the great circle that contains the given points. A map that shows great circles projected as straight lines is obviously useful in "great-circle navigation." Since the planes of all great circles contain the center of the earth, a projection termed *gnomonic*, whose projectors all converge at the center of the earth, provides such a map (Fig. 14.6). The projection, however, exaggerates size outward from the center of the mapped area and thus denies the recording of an entire hemisphere.

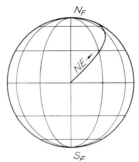

Fig. 14.5. Rhumb line, or loxodromic curve.

The preparation of maps to be used for statistical purposes will sometimes require that equal areas on the surface of the earth are represented by equal areas on the map regardless of any distortion that may occur in direction, distance, or shape. In a rectangular graticule, the distances between parallels must be reduced from the equator in order to preserve equality of area on the map (see Fig. 14.7).

14.4. Classification of Map Projections by Surface of Projection. The three principal systems of map projection, according to the surface upon which the projection is recorded, are the *zenithal, cylindrical*, and *conical.* Zenithal projections are made onto planes, while the classification of the projection surface is indicated by name in the other two systems.

14.5. Zenithal Projections. Zenithal projections are *polar, equatorial,* or *oblique,* depending upon whether the plane of projection is perpendicular, parallel, or otherwise positioned with respect to the polar axis of the earth. Examples of each projection type are shown in Fig. 14.8.

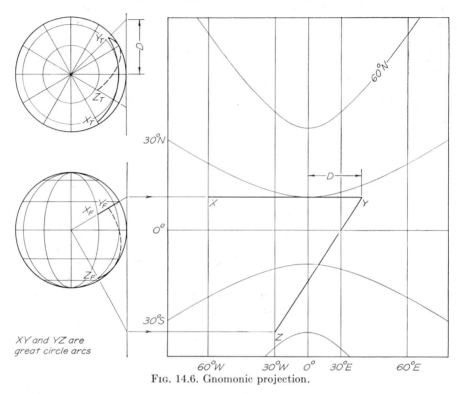

XY and YZ are
great circle arcs

Fig. 14.6. Gnomonic projection.

The projectors for zenithal maps may be either convergent or parallel. If the projectors converge at the center of the earth, the projection is

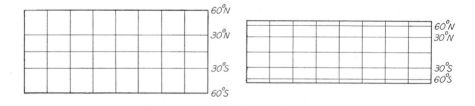

MERCATOR   EQUAL AREA

Fig. 14.7. A comparison of parallel spacings in Mercator and equal-area projections.

gnomonic; the resulting map is stereographic if the point of convergence is the antipode of the central point of the projection (see Fig. 14.9). Parallel projectors are used for orthographic projections of the earth.

All zenithal projections are azimuthal; i.e., great circles passing through the central point are represented with straight lines having correct bearings or azimuths. Gnomonic projections are of particular azimuthal importance,

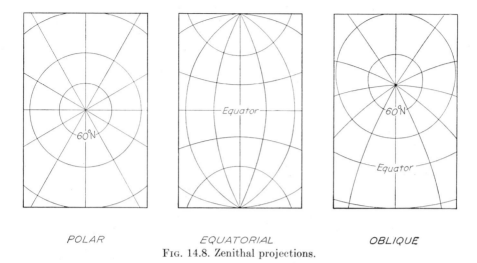

POLAR EQUATORIAL OBLIQUE

Fig. 14.8. Zenithal projections.

since *all* great circles plot as straight lines in such a projection regardless of their position with respect to the central point.

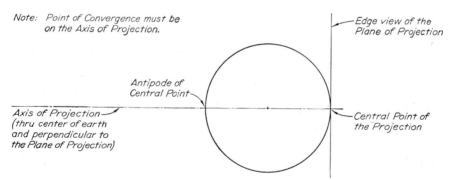

Fig. 14.9. Zenithal projection nomenclature.

True polar projections show increasing distances, outward from the pole, between the circles that represent equally spaced parallels of latitude. If these equally spaced parallels are to be shown uniformly spaced, the resulting graticule will not be a true projection. In Fig. 14.10, portions of gnomonic, stereographic, and equidistant projections are shown. For comparative purposes all three projections are of equal-size spheres. The equidistant graticule shows the parallels their true-scale distance from each other.

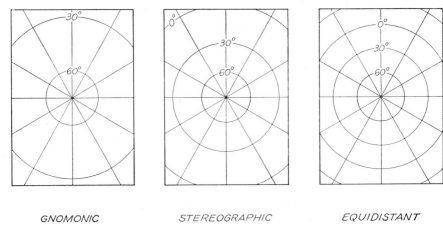

GNOMONIC   STEREOGRAPHIC   EQUIDISTANT

Fig. 14.10. Polar zenithal graticules.

14.6. Cylindrical Projections.   Cylindrical projections are usually made onto cylinders that are tangent to the surface of the earth at the equator. Such projections result in meridians being represented by a series of vertical straight lines and parallels by a series of horizontal straight lines.   Distances between meridians are true scale at the equator but nowhere else. Distances between parallels are based upon a mathematical principle selected or designed to satisfy the intended use of the resulting map.

An equal-area projection results if the projectors are all perpendicular to

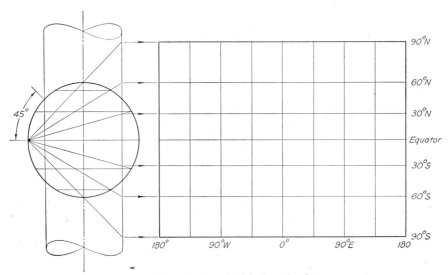

Fig. 14.11. Gall's cylindrical projection.

and intersect the polar axis of the earth. This projection has little practical value due to the distortion of shape near the poles.

Mercator's projection, previously mentioned in Sec. 14.3, results in correct proportion between meridians and parallels. This projection is actually mathematical in concept, since the map distance of any parallel of $n°$ latitude from the equator is $R \log_e \tan [45 + (n/2)]°$.

A stereographic cylindrical projection, known as Gall's projection, is made onto a cylinder that intersects the surface of the earth at parallels 45° N and 45°S (Fig. 14.11). The meridians are equally spaced vertical lines, with the equator length shortened to equal the circumference of the cylinder. The parallels are projected stereographically. This projection avoids the extreme exaggeration of areas and distances in the polar regions but does present those regions in a flattened manner.

14.7. Projections, Other Than Cylindrical, with Horizontal Parallels. The representation of parallels of latitude with horizontal lines is desirable, since climatic conditions are closely related to latitudinal locations. All projections made upon cylinders whose axes are coincident with the axis of

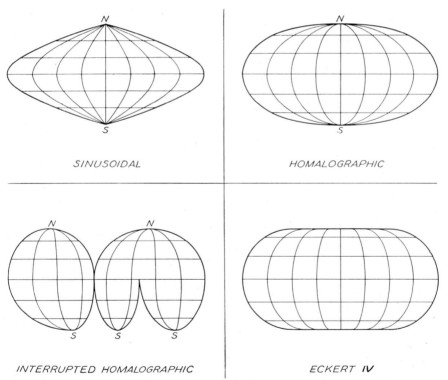

FIG. 14.12. Projections, other than cylindrical, with horizontal parallels.

the earth have this feature, but distortion in the polar regions may prevent their use.

A number of graticules have been developed in which the parallels are shown with horizontal lines, while the meridians are represented with curved lines. Such projections are used extensively in atlas and statistical works, even though they are not true projections. The *sinusoidal* (Mercator-Sanson-Flamsteed), *homalographic* (Mollweide), *interrupted homalographic* (Geode), and Eckert IV projections are among the more common systems of this series (see Fig. 14.12).

Sinusoidal projections are true scale on the central meridian and all parallels. However, distortion of shape is excessive toward the periphery of the complete graticule. The distortion usually limits the use of this projection to maps of (1) equatorial regions and (2) areas in higher latitudes if they extend in a north-south direction.

Homalographic projections are true scale on the equator. The meridians are elliptical, and a hemisphere is shown within a circle. Parallels are spaced so that the zone between any two of them has an area equal to that of the corresponding belt on the earth. Interrupted homalographic projections correct the shape distortion of the Mollweide projection by using a central meridian for each continent. The central meridians of the northern hemisphere are usually 100°W and 80°E. The central meridians used south of the equator are usually 60°W, 20°E, and 140°E. If oceanographic maps are desired, the central meridians would be selected so that the continents are cut open while the oceans are shown uninterrupted.

The Eckert IV graticule is an equal-area projection, true scale on the equator. The poles are represented as parallels having lengths equal to half the equator length. This projection shows areas in the temperate latitudes with reasonable accuracy. Polar regions are distorted in shape, but to a lesser degree than in the sinusoidal and homalographic projections.

14.8. Conical Projections. Conical projections are made onto cones that are either tangent to the surface of the earth or intersect the earth on two

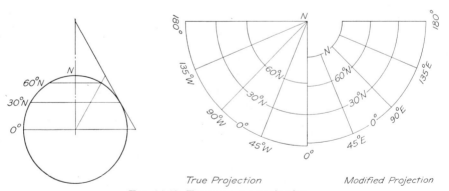

FIG. 14.13. Tangent cone projections.

coaxial circles. The circles of intersection, or tangency, are termed *stand-ard;* they are shown their true-scale length on the resulting maps.

If the cone is positioned so that its axis coincides with the axis of the earth, the standard circles will be parallels of latitude. Furthermore, all parallels will be shown by a series of concentric-circle arcs and the meridians will be represented by straight lines radiating from the developed vertex of the cone. In Fig. 14.13, a cone tangent to the sphere, along parallel 30°N, has been used to illustrate this simple conic projection. The center of the earth has been used as the point of convergence for the projectors. This true projection has little, if any, use, since parallels are unevenly spaced in the resulting map. The graticule can be modified for better use by showing the parallels their true-scale distance from the standard parallel.

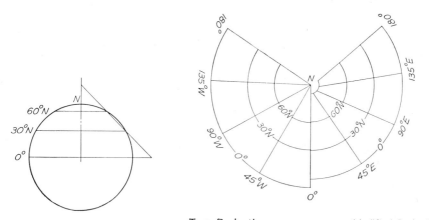

True Projection   Modified Projection

Fig. 14.14. Secant cone projections.

It should be noted, in tangent-cone projections, that distances measured on parallels are increasingly distorted, both north and south from the standard parallel. This condition cannot be eliminated, but it can be improved by use of a secant cone intersecting the surface of the earth on two standard parallels, as shown in Fig. 14.14. The modification of this projection to give true scale on meridians, as well as on the two standard parallels, introduces other variations from true projection. Meridians do not meet at a common point, nor do any of them meet at the center of the concentric arcs used to represent the parallels of latitude in the modified secant-cone projection.

Conical projections may be made either equal-area or conformal by varying the graticule spacing between parallels. Alber's equal-area projection and Lambert's conformal projection have been determined mathematically. (Both have two standard parallels, concentric parallels, and meridians which radiate from the center of the parallels. They differ only in the parallel spacing.)

The projection of narrow belts of latitude onto cones tangent to the earth is the basis for a *polyconic* projection. In Fig. 14.15, the Northern Hemisphere has been divided into belts of 30° latitude. A cone is established

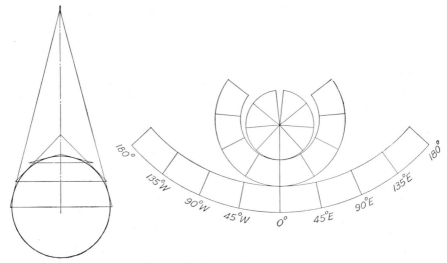

FIG. 14.15. Polyconic projection.

tangent to the earth at the center of each belt. Strips of each cone are developed to establish the graticule for the polyconic map. Parallels shown on two of the strips are represented by circle arcs that are tangent to each other on the central meridian.

The latitude belts shown in Fig. 14.15 are much wider than those customarily used in this type of projection. If the equator were used as a standard parallel, the apex of the cone would be at infinity and, for all practical purposes, the mapping surface centered on the equator would be cylindrical. Hence, in polyconic projections, the equator will usually be recorded as a straight line rather than as a circle arc. Polyconic projections are particularly useful in the preparation of topographic maps that require each sheet to be plotted independently. Sheets should be restricted to a portion of the developed strip of one cone and to not more than 1000 miles in the east-west direction.

PROBLEMS

Group I. Orthographic Projections

14.1. Point $C(4,2\frac{1}{4},6\frac{3}{4})$ is the center of a 4-in.-diameter sphere. This sphere represents the surface of the earth. Draw the top and front views of the parallels and meridians, equally spaced at 30° each.

14.2. Point $S(4,2\frac{1}{4},6\frac{3}{4})$ is the center of a 4-in.-diameter sphere. This sphere represents the surface of the earth. Point $P(3,1\frac{1}{2},X)$ is on the front half of the sphere. Draw the top and front views of the loxodromic curve from point P to the North Pole. The direction of this curve is constantly northwest.

14.3. Point $Z(4,2\frac{1}{4},6\frac{3}{4})$ is the center of a 4-in.-diameter sphere. This sphere represents the surface of the earth. Point $A(5,2,X)$ is on the front half of the spherical surface, and point $B(3\frac{1}{2},3\frac{1}{2},X)$ is on the rear half of the sphere. Draw the top and front views of the great circle between these points.

Group II. Graticules

14.4. Draw a gnomonic zenithal graticule centered at the North Pole and limited by the 30°N parallel. Parallels and meridians are to be drawn at 10° intervals.

14.5. Draw a gnomonic zenithal graticule centered on the equator at 30°W. Parallels and meridians are to be drawn at 10° intervals.

14.6. Draw a gnomonic zenithal graticule centered at 40°N 70°W. Parallels and meridians are to be drawn at 10° intervals. Draw lines representing great-circle routes from the graticule center to the following points: $C(35°N\ 85°W)$, $G(50°N\ 55°W)$, and $M(25°N\ 80°W)$.

14.7. Draw a stereographic polar zenithal graticule of the Northern Hemisphere. Parallels and meridians are to be shown at 30° intervals.

14.8. Draw a Mercator graticule for the entire earth surface; the developed length of the equator is to be represented by a line 9 in. long. Parallels and meridians are to be drawn at 30° intervals.

14.9. Draw a Gall's graticule for the entire surface of the earth; the developed length of the equator is to be represented by a line 9 in. long. Parallels and meridians are to be drawn at 30° intervals.

14.10. Draw a sinusoidal graticule for the entire surface of the earth. The developed length of the equator is to be represented by a line 9 in. long. Parallels and meridians are to be drawn at 30° intervals.

14.11. Draw the interrupted homalographic graticule for an oceanographic map of the surface of the earth. Parallels and meridians are to be drawn at 30° intervals. Central meridians are to be positioned through the approximate mid-points of the North Atlantic, North Pacific, South Atlantic, Indian, and South Pacific Oceans.

14.12. Draw a tangent cone graticule, with 40°N as its standard parallel, to cover completely an area of the surface of the earth that has a 30° range in both latitude and longitude. Parallels and meridians are to be drawn at 5° intervals.

Group III. Spherical Distances

14.13. Determine the distance between points $T(77°N\ 70°W)$ and $M(55°N\ 37°E)$, and between $H(20°N\ 158°W)$ and $O(35°N\ 135°E)$. (Distances in nautical miles are numerically equal to the number of minutes in the angle between the points in question as measured at the center of the earth.)

14.14. Determine the distance in nautical miles between $R(5°S\ 155°E)$ and $M(15°N\ 120°E)$. Determine the bearing (clockwise angle from north) for the start and end of the great-circle route from point R to point M.

CHAPTER 15

VECTORS

15.1. A quantity that may be represented by a single numerical value or graphicly by a line drawn to scale in an arbitrary direction is called a *scalar* quantity. Such quantities have magnitude only. Time, mass, temperature, area, and volume are examples. In contrast, a *vector* quantity has a particular direction of action in addition to a magnitude, and its specification must include both. Examples of vector quantities are force, displacement, velocity, acceleration, and moment.

A vector quantity, or more simply a *vector*, is represented analogously in graphics by a straight line drawn to show the direction of action and with a length proportional to the magnitude. The direction of the line segment is either identical with or parallel to the line of action of the quantity as depicted on the drawing, which ordinarily involves an arbitrary axis of reference. An arrowhead is used at one end of the line to indicate the sense of direction of the vector (see Fig. 15.1). The length of the vector is, of course, laid out to scale in representing the magnitude.

Since problems involving vector quantities occur frequently and are easily denoted through analogous representation on the drawing board, graphic solutions to such problems are widely used. Vector problems commonly require finding either the resultant effect of a system of known vectors or the magnitudes of vector components having specified lines of action that will yield the same effect as a known vector.

15.2. Classifications. Vector systems are classified as *coplanar* or *noncoplanar* depending on whether the lines of action of the vectors involved lie in a single plane or are three dimensional. An additional classification is that of *concurrent* and *nonconcurrent* vectors. With the former the lines of action all intersect in a common point, while with the latter they do not. By combining these classes, vector systems may be grouped as (1) concurrent coplanar, (2) nonconcurrent coplanar, (3) concurrent noncoplanar, and (4) nonconcurrent noncoplanar.

Graphic solutions pertaining to the first three groups are discussed in this chapter. Solutions to problems dealing with vectors of the last group involve couples and are somewhat complicated for treatment in this brief discussion.

Solutions for coplanar vector systems may be drawn on plane surfaces, since the systems are two dimensional. Noncoplanar vector systems, being three dimensional, may be represented in two or more orthographic projection views, and their solutions obtained graphicly as an application of engineering geometry.

15.3. Vector Composition and Resolution. The summation of scalar quantities is by simple arithmetic addition or by graphics as described in Sec. 1.10. Vector quantities, however, must be added geometrically because of their various directions of action.

A single vector resulting from the addition of two or more given vectors is called the *resultant*. It is the equivalent of the given vectors and can replace them by producing the same effect. The vectors added to yield a resultant are the *components*, and the addition process is known as *composition*. The reverse process, or that of finding components equivalent in their combined effect to that of a given vector, is called *resolution*.

Vectors may be added or resolved graphicly by the *parallelogram method* or by a variation, the *triangle method*. The latter is usually more convenient and, in an extended form, results in the *vector polygon*, a construction commonly used when the number of vectors involved is greater than three.

15.4. Composition—Parallelogram Method. Figure 15.1 contains given concurrent vectors V_A and V_B. As shown in the figure, the resultant V_R of these two components is obtained as the diagonal of the parallelogram having V_A and V_B as two of its adjacent sides. The resultant acts through common point P. If V_A and V_B, for example, represent forces acting on a body at P, a force through P equaling V_R in magnitude but of *opposite* direction would maintain the system in equilibrium. Such a vector is called an *equilibriant*.

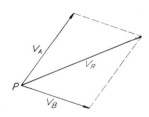

Fig. 15.1. Composition—
parallelogram method.

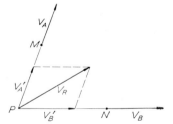

Fig. 15.2. Shifting point of
application.

In Fig. 15.2, the given coplanar vectors V_A and V_B are shown applied at points M and N, respectively. The lines of action intersect because the vectors are coplanar and are not parallel. Since *a vector may be regarded as applied at any point along its line of action*, V_A and V_B are moved along their respective lines to common point P as shown in the figure by V_A' and V_B'. The resultant V_R is now found by completing the parallelogram and obtaining the diagonal as previously explained.

The composition of three or more concurrent coplanar vectors using the parallelogram method is accomplished by proceeding in stages. First, the resultant of any two of the vectors is found. This resultant then is combined with a third vector to obtain the resultant of the first three vectors,

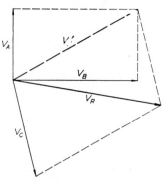

and so on. Figure 15.3, where V_A, V_B, and V_C are the given vectors, illustrates the procedure. First V_R' is obtained as the resultant of V_A and V_B. Then V_R' is combined with V_C using a second parallelogram to obtain V_R, the resultant of the entire system.

The parallelogram method, while simple when the vectors involved are few, leads to a somewhat complicated figure when the number of vectors is larger. In general, simpler constructions are had with the triangle method.

Fig. 15.3. Composition—parallelogram method.

15.5. Composition—Triangle   Method.

Observe that the parallelogram of Fig. 15.1 is divided into two triangles by the resultant V_R and that the resultant may be determined by drawing either triangle. This is illustrated in Fig. 15.4 where the vectors V_A and V_B, given in Fig. 15.1, reappear drawn parallel to their original lines of action and

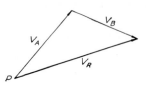

with the tail of V_B touching the head of V_A. The resultant V_R completes the triangle. Note that the given vectors proceed tail to head with a same sense of direction around the figure and that the resultant has an opposite direction sense in this respect because the effect of the resultant must equal that of the given vectors.

Fig. 15.4. Composition—triangle method.

If the direction sense of the resultant were reversed, it would represent the equilibriant of V_A and V_B and the diagram would represent a system of three vectors in equilibrium.

It should be observed from the foregoing that a vector may be moved to a different position in the drawing for purposes of finding a resultant (or components) provided its magnitude and direction are undisturbed. Also, since the resultant of Fig. 15.4 may be found by using the other triangle of Fig. 15.1, note that a resultant is determined independently of the order in which the given vectors are drawn.

15.6. Resolution.   The process of determining vector components which acting together will have an effect equivalent to that of a given vector is called resolution. The process is the reverse of composition. Although several components may be sought in connection with coplanar systems, the number is commonly two, and these are often in the horizontal and vertical directions. The discussion in this section will be limited to resolu-

tions for two concurrent components. Information must be available regarding the lines of action for the components, their magnitudes, or a combination of these data. Either the parallelogram or the triangle method may be used. If more than two components are needed, the vector polygon method described in Sec. 15.8 is desirable.

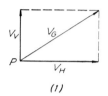 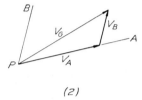 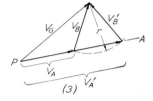

FIG. 15.5. Resolution.

In Fig. 15.5(1), the horizontal and vertical components for given vector V_G are determined using the parallelogram method.

The triangle method is used in (2) to find the magnitudes of two components for V_G that have PA and PB as their lines of action. The components are identified as V_A and V_B, respectively. Note that the diagram yields the correct magnitude and direction for V_B but not its true position.

Components for V_G meeting the following specifications are determined in (3). One component is to have the line of action PA, and the other component is to have a magnitude equal to radius r. Striking an arc of radius r, as shown, results in two pairs of components meeting the requirements. One pair is V_A and V_B, and the other is V_A' and V_B'. Both V_B and V_B' act through point P, of course.

15.7. Space and Vector Diagrams. Graphic solutions to vector problems often employ two side-by-side drawings (Fig. 15.6). One of the drawings is a *space diagram* showing the spatial positions and directions (possibly analogous representation) for the lines of action of the vector quantities. Magnitudes ordinarily are not represented to scale but may be indicated as numerical values written on the drawing, frequently along the lines expressing the directions of the quantities. The other drawing employed contains the solution to the problem and is called a *vector diagram*. The vectors are represented here both in direction and in magnitude, the latter being laid out to scale.

The vector directions as depicted in the two diagrams ordinarily agree. The relative positions of their lines of action in the diagrams often do not agree, however, because the vectors are usually drawn at new positions in the vector diagram in solving the problem. The answer found in the vector diagram may be transferred and represented in the space diagram if required there or applied elsewhere as needed.

15.8. The Vector Polygon. This is an extension of the triangle method that may be employed in both composition and resolution and with all classes of vectors. It is especially useful when more than three vectors occur in the problem.

In composition, the vector polygon is started by drawing the given vectors consecutively, tail to head, all having the same sense of direction around the figure. Each vector is drawn parallel to its line of action, as shown in the space diagram. The closing side of the polygon represents the resultant. The resultant has a direction sense around the polygon that is opposite to that of the given vectors which it may replace. Application of the vector polygon to nonconcurrent vectors ordinarily requires additional work to find the position in the space diagram for the line of action of the result and is discussed for coplanar systems in Sec. 15.9.

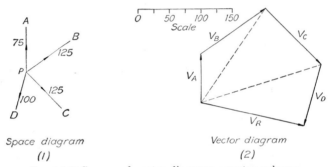

Space diagram   Vector diagram
(1)   (2)

Fig. 15.6. Space and vector diagrams—vector polygon.

The lines of action and magnitudes of four concurrent, coplanar vector quantities are indicated in the space diagram [Fig. 15.6(1)]. A vector polygon for determining their resultant V_R is shown in the vector diagram at (2). Since the sequence of drawing the vectors in the polygon is inconsequential, polygons of other appearances are possible; all, however, will yield identical resultants. Because the given vector quantities are concurrent acting through point P of the space diagram, the line of action of the resultant also will pass through this point and will be parallel to the direction of the resultant in the vector diagram. Note that the vector polygon is actually composed of a number of vector triangles and that the diagonals (dotted) each represent resultants of two other vectors.

In using a vector polygon for resolution, the given vector is drawn first and the components then established. The magnitudes of the components, their lines of action, or a combination of these are sufficient data when two components in a coplanar system are needed. If a given vector is to be resolved into more than two coplanar components, both the line of action and the magnitude of each additional component are required to lay out the polygon. Even so, alternate solutions are possible and a knowledge of the desired result is necessary to fix the polygon.   Two or more given vectors may be resolved into common components by drawing the given vectors first and consecutively in the polygon.

A vector diagram in which the polygon is a closed figure and the vectors all have the same sense of direction around the figure indicates that the system is in equilibrium.   Any one vector in such a polygon may be considered the equilibriant of all the other vectors.   Also, if the direction sense of any one vector were reversed with respect to that of the other vectors, it would represent the resultant of the other vectors as in Fig. 15.6(2).

15.9. The Funicular Polygon.   When a vector polygon is used to find the resultant of nonconcurrent, coplanar vectors, the position in the space diagram for the line of action of the resultant must be determined by additional work.   One method for accomplishing this utilizes an addition to the space diagram called a *funicular* or *string polygon*.

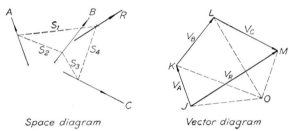

Space diagram   Vector diagram

FIG. 15.7. Funicular polygon.

The lines of action for three nonconcurrent, coplanar vector quantities A, B, and C are given in the space diagram of Fig. 15.7.   The quantities have known magnitudes and are represented by their respective vectors in the vector diagram where their resultant V_R is determined also.   The direction for the line of action of the resultant in the space diagram is parallel with its direction in the vector diagram.   The position, which is not known for this line of action, may be found through a funicular polygon as follows.

An arbitrary point O, called a *pole*, is selected in the vector diagram and connected with the vertexes of the vector polygon by lines OJ, OK, OL, and OM.   These lines, or *rays*, may be regarded as vectors just as are the original vectors of the diagram.   Consequently, each original vector (including the resultant) together with two of the rays may be considered as forming a vector triangle in which the rays are the components for and hence may replace the original vector.   The "ray components" for each triangle have, of course, a direction sense around the triangle opposite to that of the original vector.   Ray OK as a component of vector V_A is thus equal in magnitude but opposite in direction to ray KO as a component of vector V_B.   Similarly, component OL of V_B is equal but opposite to component LO of V_C.

The funicular polygon is constructed on the space diagram by first selecting a convenient point on line of action A and through it drawing lines (termed strings) S_1 and S_2 parallel, respectively, with rays JO and OK of the vector diagram. String S_3 is now drawn parallel with ray OL and through the point where S_2 intersects line of action B. Finally, string S_4 is drawn parallel with ray OM and through the point where S_3 cuts line of action C. The four strings comprise a string or funicular polygon for the original vectors. Observe that the two strings intersecting on each line of action represent the ray components which may replace the original vector having that line of action. Hence, by regarding the strings as components, each original vector in the space diagram may be considered as being replaced by the two strings that intersect on its line of action.

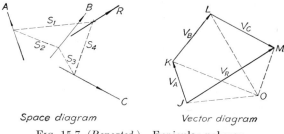

Space diagram   Vector diagram

FIG. 15.7. (*Repeated.*)   Funicular polygon.

Since component OK of V_A and component KO of V_B are collinear, equal in magnitude, but of opposite directions, their sum is zero and they neutralize each other. Inasmuch as these components are both represented in the funicular polygon by string S_2, this string is canceled in effect. Similarly, string S_3 is canceled, since the components OL and LO represented by this string are components that also neutralize each other. Strings S_1 and S_4, which remain uncanceled, represent, respectively, components JO and OM, and these are the components of the resultant V_R. Therefore, the point of intersection of the uncanceled strings S_1 and S_4 is a point on the line of action of the resultant which is drawn through this point and parallel with its direction as determined in the vector polygon.

The funicular polygon will change in shape depending on the position of point O, which was arbitrarily selected for the pole. Regardless of the position of O, the strings representing the components of the resultant will intersect on the same line of action.

The discussion in Sec. 15.8 on using a vector polygon for resolution with coplanar vectors is applicable to the nonconcurrent as well as the concurrent type. With the nonconcurrent, however, it will be possible to locate the components in innumerable, related positions in the space diagram unless sufficient information is available to fix their positions. On occasion, the funicular polygon may be useful in locating the unknown position for the line of action of a component belonging to a nonconcurrent system.

15.10. Concurrent Noncoplanar Vectors. Vector systems of this class are three dimensional, and representation in two or more orthographic views is necessary for graphic solutions. In general, the principles used with coplanar vector problems apply with these solutions. Both the parallelogram and the vector polygon methods are applicable.

A vector system comprised of two components and their resultant (or a given vector and two components into which it is resolved) constitutes a two-

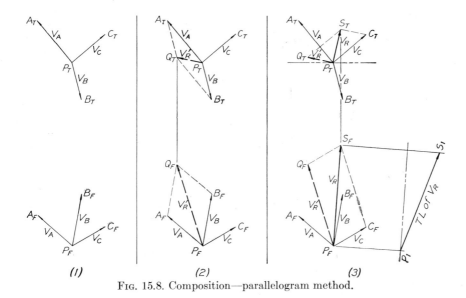

Fig. 15.8. Composition—parallelogram method.

dimensional system, hence is restricted to the coplanar sense. For a system to be noncoplanar, at least three components for a resultant must occur (in resolution, a given vector must be resolved into at least three components to qualify). The resultant of any number of concurrent, noncoplanar vectors may be found without difficulty. In resolution, however, the solution is usually limited to three components and is discussed in Sec. 15.13.

When a vector polygon is used in connection with noncoplanar vectors, each vector in the polygon is represented parallel in space with the line of action of the corresponding vector quantity of the space diagram. The vector polygon thus is three dimensional and will appear as a polygon in each orthographic view of the vector diagram.

Many noncoplanar vectors are oblique lines and do not appear in true length or show true magnitude in the given views. Consequently, auxiliary views or rotations must be used to lay out such vectors and to find their magnitudes for results.

15.11. Composition of Concurrent Noncoplanar Vectors—Parallelogram Method. The resultant of three or more concurrent, noncoplanar vectors may be found by first treating any two of the vectors as a plane and determining their resultant by the parallelogram method; the resultant, of course, lies in the plane of the two vectors. This resultant, regarded as replacing the first two vectors, is combined in a similar manner with a third vector to find the resultant of the first three vectors. The procedure is continued as necessary until the resultant of the entire system is determined.

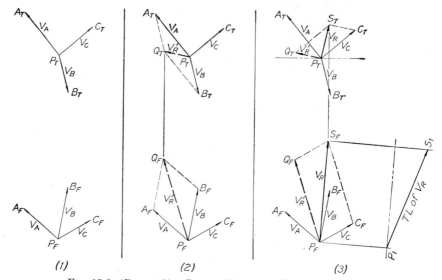

Fig. 15.8. (*Repeated.*)   Composition—parallelogram method.

Figure 15.8(1) shows three concurrent noncoplanar vectors V_A, V_B, and V_C represented by means of orthographic top and front views. The resultant of the vectors is required. In (2), the parallelogram method is used to find the resultant V_R' of the two vectors V_A and V_B. In (3), V_R' is combined with the third vector V_C using a second parallelogram to determine V_R, the resultant of the entire system. An auxiliary view in (3) gives the true length of the resultant V_R for determining its magnitude.

15.12. Composition of Concurrent Noncoplanar Vectors—Vector Polygon Method. The space diagram of Fig. 15.9 contains front and top views of the lines of action PA, PB, and PC for three concurrent noncoplanar vector quantities whose magnitudes also are indicated. The resultant is required. In the vector diagram, the given quantities are represented as V_A, V_B, and V_C, respectively.

The vector diagram is started by establishing front and top views of vector V_A, drawn from a conveniently selected point O. The vector is established by first locating a line that has the direction and position required for the vector. This line, OX, is drawn in each view parallel with PA in the corresponding view of the space diagram. A normal view of the line is now obtained (rotation is used in the figure) to permit layout of the vector magnitude. The vector is then projected to the front and top views of line OX.

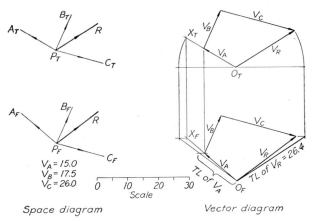

Space diagram   Vector diagram

Fig. 15.9. Composition—vector polygon method.

After establishing V_A, vector V_B is established in both views following a like procedure and is connected tail to head with V_A as shown. Vector V_C is then similarly established and connected to V_B. The closing side V_R, drawn in both views of the vector polygon, is the resultant. The true length of the resultant, shown obtained by rotation, is scaled for the magnitude. Since the system is concurrent, the line of action of the resultant passes through point P in the space diagram and is drawn in each view there parallel with the direction of the resultant in the corresponding view of the vector diagram.

15.13. Resolution of Concurrent Noncoplanar Vectors. The resolution of a vector into component vectors may be regarded as the inverse of finding the resultant of given vectors. For vector systems of the above class, the idea may be pictured in connection with Fig. 15.9. Assume the resultant R (determined in the figure) to be the given vector. Then, the magnitudes of components for the given vector that have given lines of action PA, PB, and PC are to be found. Accomplishing this ordinarily requires the establishment of a special view condition to permit layout of the vector polygon.

It will be remembered that a given vector must be resolved into at least three components in order that the system be noncoplanar. When three such components are sought, their lines of action are sufficient information for a solution. If a given vector is to be resolved into more than three components, the magnitudes as well as the lines of action of the additional components will be required. Two or more given vectors may be resolved into common components through adding the effect of each vector to each component.

A number of procedures are available for graphicly resolving a vector into concurrent noncoplanar components. Several are described in the following paragraphs.

15.14. Resolution Using Edge View of Plane. A method frequently used for resolving a vector into concurrent noncoplanar components requires a view in which the lines of action for two of the components appear coincident. The coincident condition is important in establishing the vector polygon. If the required condition is nonexistent in a given view, an auxiliary view which provides it is drawn, as in the following example.

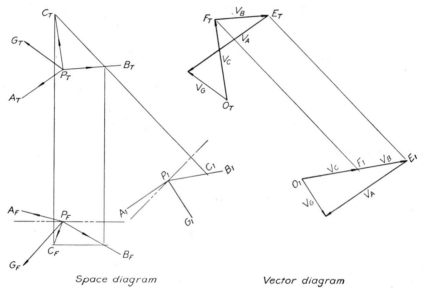

Space diagram   Vector diagram

Fig. 15.10. Resolution using edge view of plane.

The space diagram of Fig. 15.10 shows top and front views of the line of action PG for a given vector quantity. The magnitudes of three component vectors having lines of action PA, PB, and PC are required. The given vector and the components are designated in the vector diagram as V_G, V_A, V_B, and V_C, respectively. To obtain a view showing the lines of action for two of the components coincident, the auxiliary elevation in which plane PBC (plane of lines PB and PC) appears as a line is drawn.

The vector diagram is started by establishing known vector V_G in the top and auxiliary views. The vector is parallel in each view with its line of action in the corresponding view of the space diagram. The magnitude of V_G must be laid out in a normal view of the line as described in Sec. 15.12.

To establish the component vectors in the vector diagram, the two components whose lines of action coincide in the auxiliary view (V_B and V_C) *must* be drawn consecutively and preferably last. To proceed, the line of V_A is located in each view of the diagram, parallel with its line of action in the corresponding view of the space diagram and through the head end of V_G. (The direction senses around the polygon for the components are reversed to that of V_G because the combined effect of the components must equal that of V_G.) Point E, the tail end of vector V_A, will be determined through the remaining components V_B and V_C. Since components V_B and V_C are consecutive, and because their lines of action appear to coincide in the auxiliary view of the space diagram, they also will appear to coincide in the corresponding view of the vector diagram. This common line is therefore located in the auxiliary view of the vector diagram, passing through point O, the tail end of V_G, and closes the polygon in this view. The auxiliary view of point E is thereby determined and is projected to the top view. The top view of the vector diagram is completed now by establishing vector V_B through point E and vector V_C through point O, the directions for the vectors, of course, being parallel with their respective lines of action in the top view of the space diagram. Point F, determined in the top view by the intersection of V_B and V_C, is projected to the auxiliary view to complete the view. The magnitudes of the components would be determined by finding and scaling their true lengths in the vector diagram.

This method for resolving a vector into components is simplified somewhat when the plane of the lines of action for two of the components appears as an edge in one of the given views of the space diagram, thus obviating the need for an auxiliary view. When two or more given vectors are to be resolved into common components, the procedure follows that described in the example with the given vectors being drawn consecutively and first in the vector diagram.

15.15. Resolution Using Point View of Line. In resolving a vector into concurrent noncoplanar components, the line of action specified for one of the components may happen to appear as a point, or normal, in one of the given views of the space diagram. When this occurs, the vector polygon may be constructed by utilizing the special condition.

The space diagram of Fig. 15.11 shows top and front views of the line of action PG for a given vector quantity. The magnitudes of three component vectors having lines of action PA, PB, and PC are required. The given vector and the components are designated in the vector diagram as V_G, V_A, V_B, and V_C, respectively. This example is a special case because component line of action PA appears as a point in the front view.

The vector diagram is started by establishing known vector V_G in the front and top views. The line of vector V_A is then located in these views and, of course, appears as a point in the front view. The remaining vectors now can be established in the front view, V_B passing through the point representing vector V_A and V_C through point O to complete the polygon in this view. The intersection of V_B and V_C in the front view determines point F there.

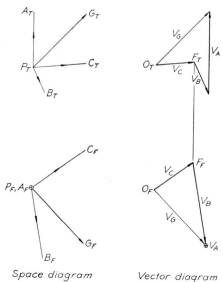

In the top view, the line of vector V_C is drawn passing through O, and point F located on it by projection from the front view. Vector V_B is now established through point F in the top view and completes the vector polygon. With the exception of vector V_A, which is normal in the top view, the true lengths of the vectors must be found in order to scale their true magnitudes.

The above procedure may be followed when the line of action for one of the components is normal in one of the given views of the space diagram. With this condition, an auxiliary view is first made in which the line under consideration appears as a point. The vector diagram is then prepared, working from the auxiliary view and the view with which the auxiliary is in projection.

Space diagram   Vector diagram

Fig. 15.11. Resolution using point view of line.

PROBLEMS

Solve the following vector problems graphicly. Choose appropriate scales.

Group I. Concurrent Coplanar

15.1. The voltage E_P required at the powerhouse end of a single-phase electrical transmission line may be found as the vector sum of the voltage vectors indicated in Fig. 15.12, where E_L is the voltage across the load, and E_{RI} and E_{XI} are the voltage drops

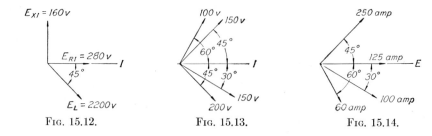

Fig. 15.12.   Fig. 15.13.   Fig. 15.14.

due to the line resistance and reactance, respectively. Determine E_P and the (phase) angle by which it leads or lags the current I.

15.2. Figure 15.13 indicates voltage vectors determined from measurements across each of the four components of a single-phase series circuit. The terminal-voltage vector for the circuit may be found as the vector sum of the component vectors. Determine the terminal voltage and the (phase) angle by which it leads or lags the current I.

15.3. Figure 15.14 indicates current vectors determined from measurements of each of the four parallel branches of an a-c circuit. The vector representing the total current in the circuit may be found as the vector sum of the branch-circuit vectors. Determine the total current and the angle by which it leads or lags the voltage E.

15.4. A vehicle weighing 3500 lb is traveling on a banked curve having a slope of 1.5-ft rise per 10-ft horizontal distance. The speed of the vehicle and radius of the curve are such that equilibrium exists for the vertical and centrifugal forces. Determine the centrifugal force.

15.5. An airplane is flying on course bearing 90°[1] at 300 mph air speed with wind 35 mph from 150°. Determine the heading and the ground speed of the airplane.

15.6. A ship is proceeding on a course parallel to and at a distance of 6 miles from a coastline when a lighthouse on the coast is perceived bearing 10° to the starboard of the ship. A coastal current of 4 knots is flowing parallel with the coast and in a direction opposite to that of the ship. The speed of the ship (with respect to the water) is 15 knots. If the ship must pass the lighthouse at a distance of exactly 15 miles, determine the new course and heading for the ship and the time to the point closest to the lighthouse.

15.7. A ferryboat is to cross a ¾-mile-wide south-flowing river from the east bank to a point directly opposite on the west bank. The river has an average velocity of 3.8 mph, and the forward speed of the boat is 8 mph. A wind blowing toward the northeast imparts a velocity of 1.5 mph to the boat in that direction. Determine the heading for the boat and the time for the trip.

15.8. The wind strikes a roof having 30° slope with a horizontal force of 2000 lb. Determine the components of the force perpendicular and parallel to the roof.

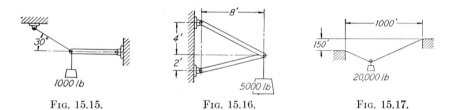

FIG. 15.15.   FIG. 15.16.   FIG. 15.17.

15.9. In Fig. 15.15, determine the forces due to the 1000-lb load acting in the bar and cable, and state whether each is compression or tension

15.10. In Fig. 15.16, determine the forces due to the 5000-lb load acting in the two frame members, and state whether each is compression or tension.

15.11. In Fig. 15.17, a cable 1100 ft long is suspended across a gorge between points spaced as shown in the figure. A trolley, loaded as shown, is at its natural resting place on the cable. Assuming that the two segments of the cable are straight (cable is weightless), determine the angle between the cable and the horizontal, the lengths of the cable segments, and the tension in the cable.

15.12. A machine weighing 1500 lb is being moved on rollers up a smooth plane inclined 30° with the horizontal. The machine is held momentarily at rest by a hori-

[1] Bearings are true azimuth (angle in degrees measured from true north in a clockwise direction).

zontal push of 150 lb and a pull P parallel with the plane. Neglecting friction, determine the force P and the normal reaction of the plane.

Group II. Relative Motion

15.13. At the time the airplane A of Prob. 15.5 passes over a point O on its course, a second airplane B leaves its base P, 425 miles due southeast of point O, to intercept plane A. The airspeed of plane B is 450 mph and wind conditions are the same as for plane A. Determine the heading, the course, and the time from take-off to interception for plane B.

15.14. An airplane with fuel for 4 hr flight at an air speed of 110 knots leaves its carrier to scout a maximum distance on course 200°[1] and return to the carrier. The wind is 30 knots from 250°, and the carrier is on course 270° at 28 knots. Determine the heading out, the heading back, the course back, the time of turn, and the distance out for the airplane. *Note:*

$$\text{Time out} = \frac{\text{ground speed back} \times \text{hours of fuel}}{\text{ground speed out} + \text{ground speed back}}$$

and $\qquad\qquad$ Distance out = time out × ground speed out

Group III. Noncurrent Coplanar

15.15. In Fig. 15.18, given the forces acting on the bridge supports. Determine the magnitude, line of action, and sense of direction of the resultant.

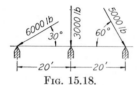

FIG. 15.18.

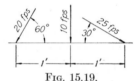

FIG. 15.19.

15.16. Given the nonconcurrent velocity vectors shown in Fig. 15.19. Determine the magnitude, line of action, and sense of direction of the resultant.

15.17. A horizontal beam 18 ft long weighs 60 lb and has its center of mass at the middle. In addition, vertical forces as follow act upon the beam: 30 lb 2 ft from the left end, 50 lb 8 ft from the left end, and 100 lb 3 ft from the right end. Determine the point at which a single rope will support the beam, and the tension in the rope.

15.18. For the beam and load of Prob. 15.17, determine the reactions when the beam is supported at the ends.

15.19. For the beam and load of Prob. 15.17, determine the reactions when the beam is supported at the left end and 2 ft from the right end.

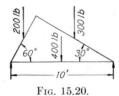

FIG. 15.20.

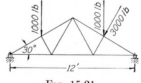

FIG. 15.21.

15.20. Determine the reactions of the truss in Fig. 15.20.

15.21. Determine the reactions of the truss in Fig. 15.21.

[1] See footnote, page 255.

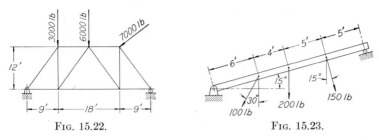

FIG. 15.22.   FIG. 15.23.

15.22. Determine the reactions of the truss in Fig. 15.22.

15.23. Determine the reactions of the beam in Fig. 15.23.

Group IV. Concurrent Noncoplanar

15.24. Given three concurrent velocity vectors with magnitudes $V_A = 26$, $V_B = 40$, and $V_C = 31$, all in feet per second and having respective lines of action $P(4,1\frac{1}{2},7)$ $A(3,2\frac{3}{4},5\frac{1}{2})$, $PB(3\frac{1}{2},3\frac{1}{2},8\frac{3}{4})$, and $PC(5\frac{3}{4},3,7)$. The vectors act upward from point P. Determine the magnitude, line of action, and sense of direction of the resultant by the parallelogram method.

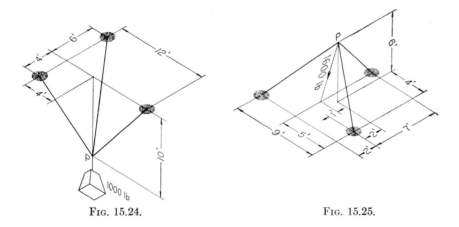

FIG. 15.24.   FIG. 15.25.

15.25. In Fig. 15.24, determine the forces acting in the members of the hanging frame due to the 1000-lb load.

15.26. In Fig. 15.24, disregarding the 1000-lb load shown, determine the magnitude, sense of direction, and line of action of the force acting through point P that would produce a tension of 500 lb in each member of the hanging frame.

15.27. In Fig. 15.25, determine the forces acting in the members of the tripod due to the 1600-lb force.

15.28. In Fig. 15.25, determine the forces acting in the members of the tripod due to the load if the 1600-lb force shown were directed vertically downward through point P rather than as shown.

15.29. Given three concurrent forces with magnitudes $F_A = 23.5$ lb, $F_B = 32.0$ lb, and $F_C = 27.5$ lb, and having respective lines of action $A(1\frac{1}{4},1,6)$ $P(2,2\frac{1}{2},7)$, $B(1\frac{1}{2},4,8\frac{1}{4})$ P, and $C(3\frac{1}{4},2,7\frac{1}{2})$ P. Force F_B acts downward and the others upward through point P. Determine the magnitude, line of action, and sense of direction of the equilibriant.

15.30. Given four concurrent acceleration vectors with magnitudes $A_A = 100$, $A_B = 80$, $A_C = 75$, and $A_D = 60$, all in feet per second per second and having respective lines of action $A(1,3,7\frac{3}{4})$ $P(2\frac{1}{4},2\frac{1}{4},7)$, $B(2\frac{1}{2},4,5\frac{3}{4})$ P, $C(3\frac{1}{2},2\frac{3}{4},8)$ P, and $D(2\frac{3}{4},1,8\frac{1}{4})$ P. Vector DP acts upward and the others downward through point P. Determine the magnitude, line of action, and sense of direction of the resultant.

15.31. A velocity vector is directed vertically downward through point $P(2,3,7)$ and has a magnitude of 125 fps. Determine the magnitudes and senses of direction of the components to replace the vector that have lines of action $PA(1,1\frac{3}{4},6\frac{1}{2})$, $PB(1,1\frac{3}{4},8\frac{1}{4})$, and $PC(2\frac{3}{4},1\frac{3}{4},7)$.

15.32. An acceleration vector has a horizontal frontal direction toward the right through point $P(1,3,7)$ and a magnitude of 200 fpsps. Determine the magnitudes and senses of direction of the components to replace the vector that have lines of action $PA(1,1\frac{1}{2},7)$, $PB(1\frac{3}{4},1\frac{1}{2},6)$, and $PC(2\frac{1}{2},4,8\frac{1}{4})$.

15.33. A force of 800 lb directed to the left has the line of action $G(2\frac{3}{4},1\frac{1}{2},7\frac{1}{4})$ $P(2,1\frac{1}{2},6\frac{3}{4})$. Determine the magnitudes and senses of direction for the components to replace the vector that have lines of action $PA(0\frac{1}{2},0\frac{1}{2},7)$, $PB(0\frac{1}{2},3,5\frac{1}{4})$, and $PC(0\frac{1}{2},1\frac{1}{2},9)$.

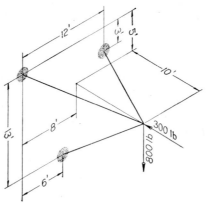

FIG. 15.26.

15.34. In Fig. 15.26 the frame hangs from a vertical wall. Determine the forces acting in the members of the frame due to the horizontal and vertical loads.

15.35. A vector having a magnitude of 200 units and acting from $G(0\frac{3}{4},3\frac{1}{2},5\frac{3}{4})$ through $P(1\frac{1}{4},2,5\frac{1}{2})$ is to be resolved into four components all acting in the same general direction. One component is to have a magnitude of 25 units and the line of action $PD(2\frac{1}{2},0\frac{1}{2},5\frac{3}{4})$. Determine the magnitudes of the remaining components whose lines of action are $PA(0\frac{1}{2},0\frac{1}{2},4\frac{3}{4})$, $PB(2,0\frac{1}{2},3\frac{1}{2})$, and $PC(1,0\frac{1}{2},6\frac{3}{4})$.

CHAPTER 16

GRAPHIC SCALES

16.1. Graphic scales are commonly occurring devices. The yardstick, the thermometer, the dials of radios and clocks, and the instruments on an automobile dashboard all are examples.

One or more graphic scales must be employed in the graphic solution of a numerical problem. Ordinary draftsman's scales suffice for many problems, while other problems require the use of specially designed scales. In solving problems of the latter type, an understanding of the principles used in scale design is essential.

16.2. General Definitions. A graphic scale is a curved or straight line to which are attached a series of short marks called *graduations* (Fig. 16.1).

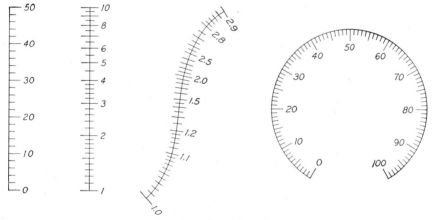

Fig. 16.1. Graphic scales.

The graduations represent numerical values which, in general, are arranged in an increasing or decreasing order of magnitude. Certain of the values appear adjacent to their graduations and are known as *calibrations*. Sufficient calibrations must appear so that the values of intervening subdivisions are clearly understood.

Scales may be classified as uniform or nonuniform. In general, the graduations on uniform scales are equally spaced and on nonuniform scales are unequally spaced. Ordinary draftsman's scales are examples of the uniform class, and most of the scales occurring on general-purpose slide rules are examples of the nonuniform class. Uniform scales are actually special cases of the more general, nonuniform class.

16.3. Scale Variable and Scale Function. The numerical values represented by the graduations along a scale are successive values of a variable quantity called the *scale variable*. The spacings of the graduations, however, are proportional to values of some particular function of the scale variable. Thus each scale is prepared to represent a certain special function known as the *scale function*.

Every scale can be represented by an equation that gives the distance from the scale origin to any graduation. The scale variable may be denoted in the equation by letters such as u, v, or w, in which case the resulting scale is called a u scale, a v scale, or a w scale.

Scales can be prepared to represent practically a limitless number of functions and, consequently, are of great value in graphic solutions. Since preparing scales requires an understanding of the function concept, the following is offered in explanation.

16.4. Functions. If two variable quantities x and y are so related that a change in the value of x introduces a corresponding change in the value of y, then y is said to be a *function of* x. This may be written as $y = f(x)$.

For example, in $A = s^2$, the relationship between the area A and the side s of a square, any change in the numerical value of s introduces a corresponding change in the numerical value of A. Therefore, the values of A depend upon the values assigned s; hence, A is a function of s, or $A = f(s)$. Since (in this particular example) A is equal to s^2, s^2 can replace A in $A = f(s)$, which then is $s^2 = f(s)$. The latter expression simply relates that the particular function of s under consideration is s^2.

Similarly, the relationship between the volume V and the side s of a cube may be expressed as $V = f(s)$. Since $V = s^3$, the function of the variable s involved in this instance is s^3, or $f(s) = s^3$.

16.5. Representing a Function by a Scale. In the equation $d = f(u)$, u is the variable, $f(u)$ is the function of the variable to be represented, and d is numerically equal to various values of the function. A graphic scale can be prepared to represent an equation of the type $d = f(u)$ if, for each value of the variable u, a single value of the function of the variable $f(u)$ results.

EXAMPLE. Consider the equation

$$d = u^2$$

where the function of the variable u is u^2, or $f(u) = u^2$.

The following table can be prepared showing values of d for several values of u.

u	0	1	2	3	4	5
$d = u^2$	0	1	4	9	16	25

The scale of Fig. 16.2, representing the function u^2, is plotted (as space will permit) from the tabular data by laying off the various values of d as distances measured from the scale origin and by marking each point located

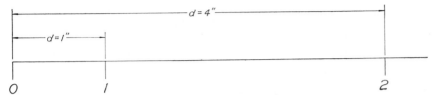

FIG. 16.2. Scale for $d = u^2$.

with a graduation. The graduations are identified with the numerical values of the variable u they represent. Observe, in the example, that while a given graduation is identified by a value of the variable u, *the distance from the scale origin to that graduation is proportional to the corresponding value of the function of the variable* u^2.

Although distances on the scale of Fig. 16.2 have been measured in inches, as will be the general practice in this text, any unit of measurement might have been used. Also, while the zero graduation serves as the origin for the scale, this is not always the case, as will be seen with future examples.

16.6. Function Modulus and the Scale Equation. The scale of Fig. 16.2, for which $d = u^2$, would be 25 in. long if drawn with a range of from 0 to 5 of the variable u and the inch used as the unit of measurement. If a scale length other than 25 in. is desired for this range of the variable, it becomes necessary to use a different unit of measurement or, more conveniently, to introduce a factor or multiplier M called the *function modulus* into the equation $d = u^2$ so that values of d may be measured directly in inches.

The equation $d = u^2$ thus becomes $d = Mu^2$ and is called the *scale equation*. The modulus for the scale of Fig. 16.2 is 1. The general form of the scale equation is

$$d = Mf(u) \tag{1}$$

EXAMPLE. Prepare the scale for the equation $d = Mu^2$ where the scale length is to be 4 in., the variable u is to range from 0 to 5, and $f(u) = u^2$. Since

$$d = Mu^2$$

$$M = \frac{d}{u^2}$$

also, when $d = 4$ in. (the scale length), u will be 5 and u^2 will be 25. Therefore,

$$M = \frac{4}{25} = 0.16$$

and the scale equation becomes

$$d = 0.16u^2$$

The following table can be prepared, and the scale (Fig. 16.3) drawn.

u	0	1	2	3	4	5
u^2	0	1	4	9	16	25
$d = 0.16u^2$	0	0.16	0.64	1.44	2.56	4.00

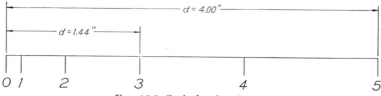

Fig. 16.3. Scale for $d = 0.16u^2$.

16.7. The Range of the Function. This is the difference between the numerical values of the function for the extreme values of the scale variable. The scale of Fig. 16.3, for example, has 0 and 5 as the extreme values of the variable. The values of the function for these values of the variable are 0 and 25; hence, the range of the function is $25 - 0 = 25$. Care should be exercised to distinguish between range of the variable and range of the function of the variable.

Recalling that distances on a scale are proportional to the values of the function of the variable, the actual distance between any two graduations is equal to the product of the function modulus and the difference between the values of the function for the two graduations. For example, in the scale of Fig. 16.3, the distance in inches between graduations 3 and 4 is

$$d = M[f(u_4) - f(u_3)]$$
$$d = 0.16(16 - 9)$$
$$d = 1.12 \text{ in.}$$

If the values of the function for the extreme *right* and *left* values of the scale variable are substituted in the above equation, we have

$$d = M[f(u_r) - f(u_l)]$$

where the expression $f(u_r) - f(u_l)$ is the range of the function and d is numerically equal to the scale length L. Therefore, the equation may be written as

$$L = M[f(u_r) - f(u_l)] \tag{2}$$

16.8. Calculation of Function Modulus. Equation (2) may be written as

$$M = \frac{L}{f(u_r) - f(u_l)} \tag{3}$$

and used to calculate the function modulus for scales to be of a specified length, function, and range of the variable.

EXAMPLE 1. Calculate M for the scale of Fig. 16.3 where $L = 4$ in., u ranges from 0 to 5, and $f(u) = u^2$. Substituting in Eq. (3),

$$M = \frac{L}{f(u_r) - f(u_l)}$$

$$M = \frac{4}{5^2 - 0^2}$$

$$M = 0.16$$

EXAMPLE 2. Prepare the scale where $f(u) = u^2$, u is to range from 2 to 5, and $L = 3.75$ in. The scale equation is $d = Mu^2$. Solving for M by substituting in Eq. (3),

$$M = \frac{3.75}{5^2 - 2^2}$$

$$M = \frac{3.75}{25 - 4}$$

$$M = 0.1786$$

Substituting for M, the scale equation becomes

$$d = 0.1786u^2$$

The following table may be prepared, and the scale (Fig. 16.4) drawn. Observe that the origin for plotting the scale is *not* the initial graduation.

u	2	3	4	5
u^2	4	9	16	25
$d = 0.1786u^2$	0.715	1.608	2.858	4.465

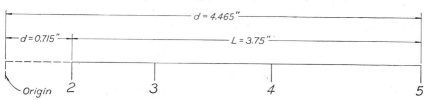

FIG. 16.4. Scale for $d = 0.1786u^2$.

16.9. Predetermined Function Modulus. The given information for the scales used as examples thus far has been (1) the function of the variable (scale function), (2) the range of the variable, and (3) the scale length. With this information, the function modulus may be calculated, substituted in the scale equation, and the table of values calculated from which the scale may be drawn.

Frequently, in the practical application of graphic scales, a predetermined value for the function modulus must be used. In this event, the scale length may be calculated by knowing, in addition, the scale function and the range of the variable and by using Eq. (2).

16.10. Adjusting Scales to the Initial Graduation. Observe with the scale of Fig. 16.4 that the distance $d = 0.715$, from the origin to the initial graduation 2, might have been subtracted from the value of d for each graduation. The resulting values then could be used to plot the scale using the initial graduation, i.e., graduation for $u = 2$, as the origin.

The procedure can be accomplished most simply by writing the general scale equation (1) as

$$d = M[f(u) - f(u_l)] \qquad (4)$$

in which $f(u)$ represents the value of the function for any value of the variable u and $f(u_l)$ represents the value of the function for the extreme left-hand variable of the scale.

EXAMPLE. Substituting data for the scale of Fig. 16.4 in Eq. (4) gives as the adjusted equation for that scale

$$d = 0.1786(u^2 - 2^2)$$

The table prepared from this equation is

u	2	3	4	5
u^2	4	9	16	25
$u^2 - 2^2$	0	5	12	21
$d = 0.1786(u^2 - 2^2)$	0	0.893	2.143	3.750

By employing values of d from the table, the scale can be plotted using the initial graduation as the origin.

It is essential with some scales to follow the procedure described above because the zero point for making measurements is inaccessible.

16.11. Mating Scale Concept. A concept may be had with the general scale equation $d = Mf(u)$ in which two adjacent, mating scales exist. One, the d scale, is a uniform scale representing the unit of measurement, while the other scale represents the function and may be uniform or nonuniform.

EXAMPLE. Consider the scale equation $d = 0.5(u + 1)$ where $M = 0.5$, $f(u) = u + 1$, and u is to range from 0 to 7. The table prepared from this scale equation is

u	0	1	2	3	4	5	6	7
$u + 1$	1	2	3	4	5	6	7	8
$d = 0.5(u + 1)$	0.5	1	1.5	2	2.5	3	3.5	4

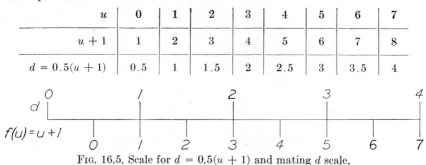

FIG. 16.5. Scale for $d = 0.5(u + 1)$ and mating d scale.

Figure 16.5 illustrates both the d scale and the scale representing the function $u + 1$.

Observe in this example that the effect of the constant term $+1$ of the scale function is to shift the zero graduation of the scale with reference to the mating d scale. Other than for this shift, the scale is the same as one for which $f(u) = u$.

16.12. Scale Direction. In general, scales will have the values of the variable arranged from left to right in either an increasing or decreasing order of magnitude; hence, a scale may be said to have a direction. With the concept in mind of mating d and $f(u)$ scales (discussed in Sec. 16.11), it should be observed that when values of d increase algebraically as values of $f(u)$ so increase, the d and $f(u)$ scales will both have the same direction. If one set of values increases as the other set of values decreases, the scales will have opposite directions.

In this text, measurements of d will be laid off from *left to right* as values of d *increase* algebraically. Therefore, in general, the scale for a function preceded by a minus sign, e.g., $f(u) = -u^2$, will have values of the variable *decreasing* algebraically from left to right and the d and $f(u)$ scales will have opposite directions. Another condition resulting in scales of opposite directions occurs with reciprocal functions, e.g., $f(u) = 1/u$.

EXAMPLE. Prepare the scale where $f(u) = 1/u$, u to range from 2 to 5, and $L = 4.5$ in. Calculating the function modulus with Eq. (3)

$$M = \frac{4.5}{\frac{1}{2} - \frac{1}{5}}$$
$$M = 15$$

Substituting in general scale equation (4), the scale equation becomes $d = 15(1/u - \frac{1}{5})$. The table below shows data calculated using this equation, and the scale appears in Fig. 16.6.

u	2	3	4	5
$1/u$	$\frac{1}{2}$	$\frac{1}{3}$	$\frac{1}{4}$	$\frac{1}{5}$
$1/u - \frac{1}{5}$	$\frac{3}{10}$	$\frac{2}{15}$	$\frac{1}{20}$	0
$d = 15(1/u - \frac{1}{5})$	4.50	2.00	0.75	0

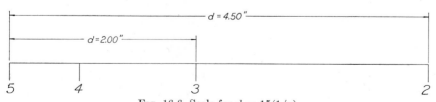

FIG. 16.6. Scale for $d = 15(1/u)$.

From the foregoing, it may be observed that the negative reciprocal function $-1/u$ will result in mating d and $f(u)$ scales having the same direction.   Complex functions may be encountered, for example, for which values of d will increase to a certain value as values of u increase and then diminish as values of u continue to increase, etc.

16.13. Algebraic Sign of Function Modulus.   The function modulus should be a positive value if undesirable complications are to be avoided; its numerical value may be of practically any magnitude other than zero.

The value of the range of the function used in the calculation of function modulus is determined from the expression $f(u_r) - f(u_l)$.   The terms $f(u_r)$ and $f(u_l)$ represent, respectively, the values of the function for the extreme right- and left-hand variables of the scale.   If the calculation of the modulus for the scale of Fig. 16.6 is reviewed, it will be observed that the range of the function and hence the modulus are positive when the values of the function are treated in the order used.   A negative modulus will result if the reverse order is taken.

Mating d and $f(u)$ scales of the same direction will have the algebraically highest value of u to the right, while d and $f(u)$ scales of opposite directions will have the algebraically lowest value of u to the right.   Inspection of the function will usually indicate the relative directions of the d and $f(u)$ scales. With complex functions, simple calculations may be necessary to indicate the treatment of the values of the functions in order to obtain a positive function modulus and knowledge of the relative directions of the scales.

16.14. Scale Types.   As has been stated, scales are commonly classed as uniform and nonuniform.   A uniform scale has equal spaces between regular graduations; a nonuniform scale has varying spaces between graduations.   Figure 16.5 illustrates a uniform scale, and Fig. 16.6 a nonuniform scale.

In general, nonuniform scales must be plotted by calculating the value of d for each value of the variable u.   As will be described in Sec. 16.21, the plotting of uniform scales can be simplified by calculating the positions of the terminal graduations and locating the intervening graduations mechanically.   Since the procedure is saving in time and labor, it becomes expedient to distinguish uniform from nonuniform scales by their functions.   A linear scale equation will result in a uniform scale, since values of d will be proportional to values of u; correspondingly, a nonlinear scale equation will result in a nonuniform scale.

The number of functions which scales can represent is practically endless. The following examples are fairly typical:

$$d = Mu^3 \qquad \text{(variable to a constant power)}$$
$$d = Me^u \qquad \text{(constant to a variable power)}$$
$$d = M\,\frac{1}{u^2} \qquad \text{(reciprocal of the power of the variable)}$$
$$d = M \log u \qquad \text{(logarithm of the variable)}$$
$$d = M \sin u \qquad \text{(trigonometric function)}$$
$$d = M\left(\frac{u^2}{1+u}\right) \qquad \text{(complex function)}$$

Scales for the above equations all will be nonuniform. Uniform scales may be thought of as special cases where the function is the variable to a constant power with unity as the exponent. The general equation for uniform scales may be written as

$$d = M(au + b)$$

in which a and b are constants; however, a will not be equal to zero except in certain very special instances where the scale consists of but a single graduation.

16.15. Logarithmic Scales.[1] The scales most commonly used in elementary graphic solutions are the uniform and logarithmic. Distances on logarithmic scales are proportional to the logarithm of the variable.

EXAMPLE. Prepare the scale for $f(u) = \log u$, u to range from 1 to 100, and $M = 2$. The scale equation is $d = 2 \log u$. A table showing calculations for some of the points follows, and the scale appears in Fig. 16.7.

u	1	5	10	50	100
$\log u$	0	0.699	1.000	1.699	2.000
$d = 2 \log u$	0	1.398	2.000	3.398	4.000

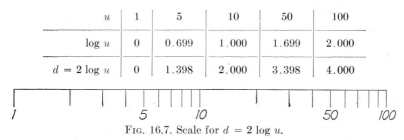

FIG. 16.7. Scale for $d = 2 \log u$.

Note that the scale consists of two logarithmic cycles, i.e., from 1 to 10 and from 10 to 100. Observe that zero as a value of the variable can never be shown on a logarithmic scale. If the next cycle to the left were added to the scale in Fig. 16.7, the terminal values of the variable for the added cycle would be 0.1 at the left and 1 at the right. The cycle to the left of this would have the terminal values 0.01 and 0.1, etc.; hence, each succeeding cycle to the left would approach closer to zero, but zero itself could not be plotted. This feature may at times constitute a disadvantage with logarithmic scales.

Frequently, an advantage of logarithmic scales is that the number of significant digits which may be read for a number remains the same regardless of the magnitude of the number. For example, 0.36, 3.6, 3600, and 3,600,000 are all read from a logarithmic scale to the same number of significant digits. A uniform scale, however, provides readings to a uniform decimal accuracy. For example, readings could be made as 0.36, 10.36, 10,000.36, etc.

16.16. The Significance of Function Modulus. The function modulus may be defined as the distance in inches on the scale necessary to represent a change of 1 (unit change) in the numerical value of the scale function.

---

[1] The logarithmic scales described in this chapter represent common logarithms exclusively.

For example, consider the scale of Fig. 16.5 where each unit change in the value of the function is represented on the scale by 0.5 in.; the value 0.5 is equivalent to the function modulus. Also, consider the scale of Fig. 16.4 where a change of $25 - 4 = 21$ in the value of the function is represented by the distance 3.75 in. on the scale. The distance required to represent a unit change in the value of the function is 3.75 in./21 = 0.1786 in., which is equal to the function modulus.

The above concept of modulus can be helpful when plotting certain uniform and logarithmic scales. For example, the uniform scale of Fig. 16.5 could have been prepared without calculating the tabular values by recognizing that unit increases in the values of the variable are represented by a distance equal to the modulus 0.5 in.

16.17. Scale Modulus. If the scale function contains a constant coefficient, the function modulus will be supplanted, when the scale equation is simplified, by what is termed the *scale modulus*. The scale modulus is the product of the coefficient of the scale function and the function modulus.

EXAMPLE. Prepare the scale for $f(u) = 0.5u$, u to range from -1 to 2, and $M = 3$. Substituting in the general scale equation

$$d = M[f(u) - f(u_l)]$$
we have
$$d = 3[0.5u - 0.5(-1)]$$
simplifying
$$d = 1.5(u + 1)$$

which is the scale equation. Note that 3 is the function modulus and 1.5 is the scale modulus. A table prepared from the scale equation follows. The scale appears in Fig. 16.8.

u	-1	0	1	2
$f(u) = 0.5u$	-0.5	0	0.5	1
$u + 1$	0	1	2	3
$d = 1.5(u + 1)$	0	1.5	3	4.5

-1   0   1   2

Fig. 16.8. Scale for $d = 1.5u$.

Observe from the table that a unit change in the value of the function $0.5u$ is represented by a distance equal to the function modulus 3 in. Also, observe that *a distance equal to the scale modulus 1.5 in. represents a unit change in the value of the variable u*. If this had been known, the scale could have been plotted by spacing the graduations for successive values of the variable 1.5 in. apart, hence obviating the need for tabular calculations.

With uniform scales, the scale modulus, and hence the function modulus if no constant coefficient occurs in the scale function, is the distance in inches on the scale necessary to represent a unit change in the value of the variable. This, however, is not the case for nonuniform scales. Consider the nonuniform scale equation $d = 0.1(5u^3)$, where $f(u) = 5u^3$ and $M = 0.1$. The equation simplifies to $d = 0.5u^3$ in which 0.5 is the scale modulus. A distance on the scale equal to the function modulus 0.1 in. will represent a unit change in the value of the function $5u^3$; a distance equal to the scale modulus 0.5 in. will represent a unit change in the value of u^3. Therefore, neither the function nor scale modulus is of *direct* value in laying out the scale.

16.18. Modulus and Logarithmic Scales. Modulus can be of considerable value when plotting common logarithmic scales. The function modulus for the scale of Fig. 16.7 is 2 in., a distance which represents a unit change in the value of the function $\log u$ (e.g., increase from $\log 1 = 0$ to $\log 10 = 1.000$). A unit change in the value of the function corresponds to a change of one decimal place in the value of the variable u, and such a change in the value of the variable corresponds to one logarithmic cycle on the scale. Hence, the modulus of a logarithmic scale such as illustrated in Fig. 16.7 represents the length in inches of one logarithmic cycle. Advantage may be taken of this fact when plotting logarithmic scales by using a preexisting logarithmic scale but of different length, or a modulus chart, to position the graduations within each logarithmic cycle. Explanation of the procedures occurs in Secs. 16.21 and 16.22.

If the scale function for a logarithmic scale contains a constant coefficient, the scale modulus will represent the length in inches of the logarithmic cycle.

EXAMPLE. Prepare the scale where $f(u) = 2 \log u$, u to vary from 7 to 100, and the scale length to be *about* 4.5 in. Calculating M for a scale length of 4.5 in.

$$M = \frac{4.5}{2 \log 100 - 2 \log 7}$$

$$M = \frac{4.5}{4.000 - 1.690}$$

$$M = 1.95$$

For convenience, let $M = 2$, which will lengthen the scale slightly, and the scale equation becomes

$$d = 2(2 \log u - 2 \log 7)$$

or $\qquad d = 4(\log u - \log 7)$

The following table contains the calculations for a few points on the scale, and the scale is shown in Fig. 16.9.

u	7	10	20	50	100
$\log u$	0.845	1.000	1.301	1.699	2.000
$\log u - \log 7$	0	0.155	0.456	0.854	1.155
$d = 4(\log u - \log 7)$	0	0.620	1.824	3.416	4.620

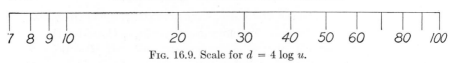

Fig. 16.9. Scale for $d = 4 \log u$.

Observe that a distance equal to the function modulus 2 in. represents a unit increase in the value of the function 2 log u. For example, the values of the functions for $u = 10$ and $u = 100$ are 2.000 and 4.000, respectively. The increase in the value of the function over this range is 2, and the distance on the scale representing the increase is 4 in. Therefore, a unit increase of the function is represented by 2 in. on the scale. Of more practical value is the fact that a distance on the scale equal to the scale modulus 4 in. represents a unit change in the value of log u. Since such a change in log u corresponds to one logarithmic cycle, the scale modulus is thus equal to the length of one logarithmic cycle. Advantage may be taken of this fact to plot the scale without calculating a table of values.

16.19. Summary on Function and Scale Moduli. In summarizing what has been said with regard to function and scale moduli, it may again be pointed out that the scale modulus is merely the product of the function modulus and any constant coefficient occurring in the scale function. If no such constant occurs, the two moduli have the same value. If a constant does occur, the use of the scale modulus in plotting the scale accommodates for the constant by changing the scale length in proportion to the constant.

The scale modulus is useful in the practical plotting of uniform and logarithmic scales, since its value is indicative of the spacing for certain graduations. Knowledge of the function modulus is required for calculations correlating the several scales occurring in certain applications of graphic scales.

16.20. General-purpose Slide Rules. These make extensive use of logarithmic scales and constitute a graphic application of logarithms. It may be of interest to write the scale equation for the D scale of a 10-in. slide rule. The unit of measurement for plotting slide-rule scales is the centimeter, and the D scale on a so-called 10-in. slide rule is actually 25 cm long. Since the range of the variable is from 1 to 10 and covers one logarithmic cycle, the scale equation is $d = 25 \log u$. The equation for the A scale on the same slide rule is $d = 12.5 \log u$ with a range of the variable of from 1 to 100. All measurements, of course, are made in centimeters.

16.21. Subdividing Scales with Existing Scales. The scales used in the various examples thus far in this chapter have been plotted through the use of calculated tabular values. In general, this procedure must be followed with nonuniform scales. Uniform scales, however, having equal spaces between the principal graduations, can always be laid out following a simpler procedure which eliminates most if not all calculations.

EXAMPLE. Prepare the scale for $f(u) = 2u$, u to range from 0 to 15, and $L = 4.062$ in. Figure 16.10 illustrates the procedure where the scale stem, 4.062 in. long, is uniformly graduated into the 15 equal spaces by the

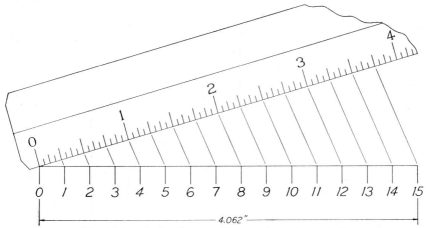

FIG. 16.10. Graduating a uniform scale, scale method.

"draftsman's scale method" for dividing a line into a predetermined number of equal parts. Subdivisions can be had with equal ease where required. On uniform scales with but few graduations, the subdividing may be accomplished with draftsman's dividers.

The draftsman's scale method may be employed to subdivide nonuniform scales when a scale representing the required function, but of different modulus, is at hand. This is frequently so with logarithmic scales, in which case the terminal graduations of each logarithmic cycle are first located by measurement using the value of the scale modulus. An existing logarithmic scale, such as a slide-rule C scale, then is used to subdivide the cycles following the method of Fig. 16.10.

With scales where a specific length is unimportant, it will be expedient to select a value for the scale modulus corresponding to that of an existing scale of the same function and of approximately the desired length. The existing scale then can be used directly to lay out the required scale. As an example, suppose that the scale of Fig. 16.10 had to be merely *about* 4.062 in. long. The function modulus calculated for the scale of this length is 0.1354 in., and the scale modulus is 0.271 in. If the value 0.250 is substituted as the scale modulus, the even $\frac{1}{4}$-in. graduations on a draftsman's scale can be employed directly to space the graduations for the new scale. The new scale will be 3.75 in. long.

16.22. Modulus Charts. When many scales for the same function but with varying moduli occur, it is desirable to make use of a proportionality or modulus chart. Such charts are readily available for uniform and logarithmic scales but must be prepared specially for most nonuniform scales.   Figure 16.11 shows a logarithmic modulus chart reduced in size and simplified for illustrative purposes.   A description of its application in graduating logarithmic scales will indicate the method for using similar

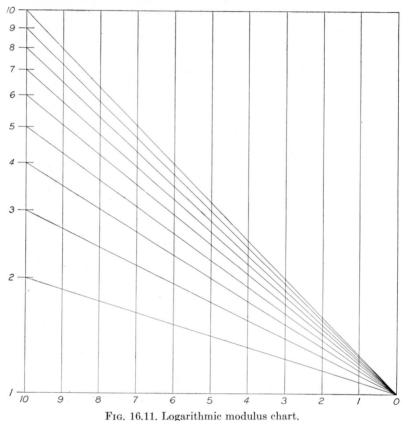

FIG. 16.11. Logarithmic modulus chart.

charts in graduating scales of other types.   The vertical scale $d = 10 \log u$, ranging through one logarithmic cycle, is drawn at the left.   The modulus 10, used for convenience, results in a scale length of 10 in.   Slanting lines are drawn from each graduation of the scale to the lower right-hand corner of the chart.   A uniform scale ranging from 0 to 10 occurs along the bottom, and vertical lines are drawn across the chart from each graduation.   The slanting lines cut each vertical line, producing new logarithmic scales with moduli respectively proportional to the distances between each new scale and the right side of the chart.   The modulus of each scale will be equal to the corresponding calibration of the uniform scale at the bottom.

To use the chart, suppose that a logarithmic scale with a scale modulus of 6 is to be drawn.   The chart may be folded along the vertical line corresponding to graduation 6 at the bottom. The folded edge is then placed in the proper position on the paper, and the graduations of the new scale marked. Instead of folding, it may be preferred to align the chart with respect to the position of the required scale and project the graduations across with the T square.

Modulus charts may be prepared for any scale function by drawing a scale representing the function and proceeding as described in the foregoing.

16.23. Drawing the Scale. Most scales are inked for permanence. The weight of line used should be relatively fine to ensure a high degree of precision in using the scale. The line weight should be the same for all graduations and the scale stem. Prior to the inking, it is necessary to plan the scale completely and to draw it lightly in pencil. All work should be performed as accurately as possible.

Graduations of several lengths should be used to facilitate reading the scale. Examination of any good draftsman's scale or slide rule will illustrate this point. It usually is not desirable to use more than three different lengths for the graduations, and the sizes to use depend somewhat on the use to which the scale is to be put. Good judgment is desirable. For most scales, graduations made $\frac{1}{8}$, $\frac{3}{16}$, and $\frac{1}{4}$ in., respectively, for the three sizes are satisfactory. Scales for alignment charts preferably have the graduations cross the scale stem, i.e., project on both sides of the stem, and be somewhat greater in total length (see Fig. 16.1). Guide lines drawn parallel with the stem should always be used to assist in keeping like graduations the same in length.

Scales should be sufficiently long so that values can be read to the required degree of precision without having the graduations undesirably close. In general, with handmade scales, graduations should not be spaced closer than $\frac{1}{16}$ in. for accuracy in results and ease in reading.

Most scales for engineering work will be divided and subdivided on the decimal basis. Occasionally numerical data will occur as common fractions, degrees and minutes, etc., in which case the scale should be graduated and calibrated accordingly.

Sufficient graduations should carry calibrations, i.e., be identified with values of the variable, so that the values of intervening graduations are clear. With most scales, the primary graduations will be calibrated and perhaps others. Again good judgment is desirable. An examination of the log-log and trigonometric scales of a slide rule should prove helpful. A lettering size of $\frac{1}{8}$ in. should be satisfactory for the calibrations of most scales. Guide lines should be provided for this lettering, and about $\frac{1}{16}$-in. clearance should be maintained between the calibrations and the ends of the graduations.

Each scale should have a descriptive caption lettered adjacent and in a position where it will least interfere with the use of the scale.

PROBLEMS

Data for the work specified in the groups below are to be obtained from the following table:

Problem no.	Scale function $f(u)$	Range of variable u	Function modulus M, in.	Scale length L, in.
16.1	$3u$	0 to 30	....	9
16.2	$2u + 3$	4 to 14	....	10
16.3	$\frac{9}{5}u + 32$	−10 to 100	0.05	
16.4	u^3	−3 to 3	0.15	
16.5	$0.5\sqrt{u} + 5$	0.1 to 100	....	9
16.6	$\dfrac{4.5}{u}$	1 to ∞	....	9
16.7	$\dfrac{2}{u^2}$	¼ to ∞	....	8
16.8	$\log u$	1 to 15	7	
16.9	$3 \log u$	1 to 10,000	0.7	
16.10	$\log u^2$	1 to 10	....	8
16.11	$\log \dfrac{10}{u}$	1 to 10	....	8
16.12	$\sin u$	0 to 90°	....	8
16.13	$2 \cos u$	0 to 90°	4	
16.14	$\log (10 \tan u)$	5.71 to 45°	....	8
16.15	$\dfrac{4u}{1 + u}$	2 to 10	....	9
16.16	$\dfrac{u^2}{2u + 1}$	−4 to 5	2	

Group I. Uniform or Nonuniform

Determine by inspection of the function for each problem which will result in a uniform and which will result in a nonuniform scale.

Group II. Function Modulus and Length

Calculate either the function modulus M or the scale length L for each problem.

Group III. Scale Modulus

Determine the scale modulus for each problem.

Group IV. Scale Equation

Write the scale equation for each problem.

Group V. Drawing Scales

Draw the scales for the problems, providing suitable primary- and subgraduations and calibrations. The scales will fit on 8½- by 11-in. paper, and should be drawn in ink unless otherwise specified. In each case, indicate the function represented as the scale caption.

CHAPTER 17

STATIONARY ADJACENT AND SLIDING SCALES

17.1. Stationary adjacent scales and sliding scales constitute important applications of graphic scales. Both types are particularly useful in solving equations encountered in engineering and scientific practice. Ordinarily, the scales are specially designed to provide solutions for a specific recurring equation, although the common, general-purpose slide rule is an important example of sliding scales. Stationary adjacent scales are often called *conversion scales* because of their frequent use for the conversion of units from one system to another.

The scales used in these applications are graduated and arranged so that some function of a number on one scale appears opposite the number on another scale. The application is closely allied with alignment charts, being a branch of nomography. Stationary adjacent scales are limited to the solution of certain forms of equations in two variables. Sliding scales are more flexible. The number of variables which may be handled is theoretically without limit; however, practical considerations ordinarily reduce this to from four to six.

17.2. Stationary Adjacent Scales. An equation relating two variables u and v may be represented graphicly by two stationary adjacent scales if the equation can be expressed in the form

$$f_1(u) = f_2(v)$$

that is, the variables are separable. This being the case, scales representing each function are constructed, one on each side of a common stem, in a manner so that any two values occurring opposite each other on the scales are ones which satisfy the given equation.

The scale equations for the u and v scales are, respectively,

$$d_u = M_u f_1(u)$$

and
$$d_v = M_v f_2(v)$$

In order that graduations for values of u and v which satisfy the equation $f_1(u) = f_2(v)$ occur opposite each other, measurements d_u and d_v for these values of the variables must be equal; consequently, M_u and M_v must be equal. As a result, the two scales are constructed *using the same origin and the same function modulus.*

17.3. General Example of a Conversion Scale. Construct adjacent scales to convert diameters D of circles to areas A, or vice versa, for a range of A of from 10 to 100. The scale length is to be 4.5 in.

The equation relating the variables is

$$A = \frac{\pi D^2}{4}$$

or
$$A = 0.785D^2 \tag{1}$$

The left and right sides of Eq. (1) become the respective functions for the A and D scales.

The function modulus is calculated for the A scale:

$$M_A = \frac{L}{f(A_r) - f(A_l)}$$
$$M_A = \frac{4.5}{100 - 10}$$
$$M_A = 0.050$$

The A scale equation is

$$d_A = M_A[f(A) - f(A_l)]$$
$$d_A = 0.050(A - 10)$$
$$d_A = 0.050A - 0.500 \tag{2}$$

By substituting, in turn, the extreme values (10 and 100) of the variable for the A scale in Eq. (1), the corresponding values (3.57 and 11.30, respectively) for the range of the variable for the D scale are obtained. The function modulus of the D scale must be the same as that for the A scale, i.e., 0.050. The D scale equation is

$$d_D = M_D[f(D) - f(D_l)]$$
$$d_D = 0.050[(0.785D^2) - (0.785 \times 3.57^2)]$$
$$d_D = 0.0392D^2 - 0.500 \tag{3}$$

Note that the scale modulus for the D scale differs from the function modulus owing to the constant coefficient of the scale function.

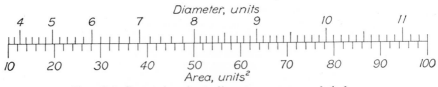

Fig. 17.1. Conversion chart, diameters vs. areas of circles.

The conversion scale prepared from Eqs. (2) and (3) is shown in Fig. 17.1.

17.4. Observations and Simplified Procedures. It should be noted with the preceding example that the scale length employed in connection with the specified range of the A variable yielded an even value for the function modulus. Foresight in this direction makes it possible to lay out the A scale directly using a draftsman's scale, since the A function indicates that that scale will be uniform. Thus, there is no need to make calculations for the A scale or even to write its equation. The 4.5-in. scale length need simply be subdivided into the required number of equal parts ranging from 10 to 100.

Furthermore, had an existing scale for the function u^2 been at hand, the D scale could have been subdivided by the proportional method described in Sec. 16.21. Modulus charts for this function are rather uncommon but could likewise be used. In either case, the subdividing would be for those values between the range (3.57 to 11.30) of the D variable, and all calculations except for finding these values would be unnecessary.

The general procedure described in Sec. 17.3 is that which must be followed with nonuniform scales when existing scales representing the function involved are not available. In the case of the example described there, one might prepare the chart utilizing logarithmic scales. Doing so would permit layout of the D scale, without calculating the positions of the graduations, through the use of an existing logarithmic scale. The method is described in Sec. 17.6.

When functions for the scales of a conversion chart indicate that both scales are uniform, the procedure can be very simple. The following example illustrates.

17.5. Conversion Scale, Uniform Scales. Construct a conversion scale to convert degrees Fahrenheit to degrees centigrade and vice versa. The equation relating the variables is

$$F = \tfrac{9}{5}C + 32 \qquad (4)$$

F is to range from 32 to 212°, and the scale length is to be 4.5 in.

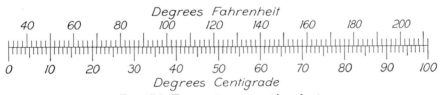

Fig. 17.2. Temperature conversion chart.

By substituting, in turn, the extreme values (32 and 212°) of the variable for the F scale in Eq. (4), the corresponding values (0 and 100°, respectively) for the range of the variable for the C scale are obtained.

The left and right sides of Eq. (4) are the respective functions of the F and C scales. Since both functions are linear, their scales will be uniform, and the chart (Fig. 17.2) can be drawn without further calculation.

The F scale is prepared by equally dividing the 4.5-in. scale length into the required number of subdivisions, e.g., 90 parts if graduations for the even-value degrees are to be provided as in Fig. 17.2. The C scale is prepared by subdividing the 4.5-in. scale length into 100 equal parts. Note that the scale length and range of the F function have been correlated so the modulus (0.025 in.) of the F scale is one which permits direct layout of that scale using an existing draftsman's scale. The determination of this modulus and the scale equations, although not needed to prepare the chart, are given in the following as a matter of interest.

Function modulus for the F scale:

$$M_F = \frac{L}{f(F_r) - f(F_l)}$$
$$M_F = \frac{4.5}{212 - 32}$$
$$M_F = 0.025$$

F scale equation:

$$d_F = M_F[f(F) - f(F_l)]$$
$$d_F = 0.025(F - 32)$$
$$d_F = 0.025F - 0.800$$

C scale equation:

$$d_C = M_C[f(C) - f(C_l)]$$
$$d_C = 0.025[(\tfrac{9}{5}C + 32) - (\tfrac{9}{5} \times 0 + 32)]$$
$$d_C = 0.045C$$

Note that the scale modulus of the C scale differs from the function modulus owing to the constant coefficient of the scale function.

17.6. Logarithmic Scales. These may be useful in connection with conversion scales even when the functions themselves are not logarithmic. For example, the relationship $u = v^{\frac{2}{3}}$ when written in logarithmic form is $\log u = \frac{2}{3} \log v$. The two scale equations become

$$d_u = M \log u$$
and
$$d_v = M\tfrac{2}{3} \log v$$

The scales now can be drafted with the assistance of a logarithmic modulus chart using a scale modulus of M (the cycle length) for the u scale and a scale modulus of $\frac{2}{3}M$ for the v scale. By using logarithmic scales here, the necessity for tabular calculations is eliminated.

Similarly, the equation $A = 0.785D^2$ for the chart described in Sec. 17.3 could be rewritten as $\log A = \log 0.785 + 2 \log D$, $\log 0.785$ being a constant and equal to -0.105. Disregarding adjustments for scale origins, the scale equations become

$$d_A = M \log A$$
and
$$d_D = M(2 \log D - 0.105)$$

Hence, the scale modulus for the A scale will be M and that of the D scale $2M$. The actual effect of the constant term -0.105 in the D scale equation is to shift that scale with respect to the A scale, thus accomplishing multiplication by the constant 0.785 of the original equation.

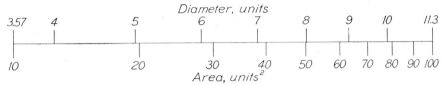

FIG. 17.3. Conversion chart, diameters vs. areas of circles using logarithmic scales.

The chart, without secondary subdivisions, is shown in Fig. 17.3. A scale modulus of 4.5 in. was used for the A scale which requires one logarithmic cycle. The D scale was then plotted using a logarithmic scale oriented so that its graduations 3.57 and 11.30 aligned with graduations 10 and 100, respectively, of the A scale. By this manipulation, the constant term -0.105 is automatically provided for.

17.7. General-purpose Slide Rules. These employ several combinations of scales operating as conversion scales. For example, the D and L scales convert a number to the value of its logarithmic mantissa and vice versa; the D and A scales convert a number to the square of the number or to the square root of the number; etc. In the case of the D and A scales, as with others, the scales are prepared with logarithmic functions because the scales must be logarithmic to meet other requirements. A conversion scale for obtaining the squares and square roots of numbers represents the equation $u^2 = v$. In logarithmic form, the equation is $2 \log u = \log v$; consequently, the scale modulus of the slide-rule D scale is double that of the A scale.

17.8. Sliding Scales. The general-purpose slide rule has scales based largely on logarithmic functions which enable users to perform calculations of a general nature such as multiplications, divisions, extraction of roots, etc. Special-purpose slide rules operate on the same principles but ordinarily employ scales representing functions of a specific equation calling for repeated solutions. Ranges provided for the variables on such rules are limited to values encountered in actual practice.

17.9. Principles of Sliding Scales. The operation of sliding scales is based on two principles: (1) A distance on one scale can be added to, subtracted from, or equated to a distance on another scale graphicly, and (2) distances on the scales are proportional to values of the scale functions. The first principle is illustrated in Fig. 17.4, where the u scale has been moved a distance a with respect to the stationary v scale. With respect to distances,

$$c = a + b \tag{5}$$

and
$$a = c - b \tag{6}$$

From the scale equations,

$$a = M_v f_1(v_a)$$
$$b = M_u f_2(u_b)$$
and $$c = M_v f_1(v_c)$$

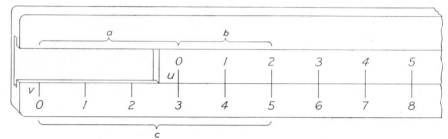

Fig. 17.4. Adding or subtracting distances with sliding scales.

Hence, Eqs. (5) and (6) may be written, respectively, as

$$M_v f_1(v_c) = M_v f_1(v_a) + M_u f_2(u_b) \tag{7}$$
and $$M_v f_1(v_a) = M_v f_1(v_c) - M_u f_2(u_b) \tag{8}$$

If the function moduli M_u and M_v for the scales *are made equal*, Eqs. (7) and (8) simplify to

$$f_1(v_c) = f_1(v_a) + f_2(u_b) \tag{9}$$
and $$f_1(v_a) = f_1(v_c) - f_2(u_b) \tag{10}$$

Consequently, by merely setting and reading values of the variables on the scales, *the sum or difference of the corresponding values of the functions of the variables is obtained.* Equations of type (9) and (10) can be solved with two sliding scales. It is essential that the relationship be one involving either the sum or difference of values of the scale functions.

The functions of the scales of Fig. 17.4 are $f_1(v) = v$ and $f_2(u) = u$; hence, the scales are uniform, and distances on the scales are directly proportional to the variables. Since both scales have been prepared using the same value for the function moduli, they are identical and can be used to add or subtract numbers.

17.10. Equations Represented by Two Sliding Scales. Figure 17.5 shows scales prepared to solve the equation

$$v + 2u = x$$
or $$x - 2u = v$$

Since the v and x functions are the same, a single scale may be used for both, thereby permitting solution with two scales. The equations of the v and x scale are

$$d_v = 0.25v$$
and $$d_x = 0.25x$$

where 0.25 was selected as the value for the function modulus. This is also the value of the scale modulus. The equation of the u scale is

$$d_u = 0.25(2u)$$

or

$$d_u = 0.50u$$

where 0.25 is the function modulus and 0.50 the scale modulus.

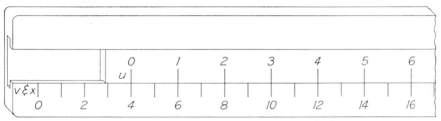

FIG. 17.5. Sliding scales representing $v + 2u = x$ and $x - 2u = v$.

In many applications of two sliding scales, the functions of both scales, hence the scales, are the same. This is not necessarily always the case, as illustrated by the preceding example. It is necessary, however, in order to solve an equation of three variables with two scales, that the functions of two of the variables be identical so that one scale may serve two variables.

17.11. Sliding, Nonuniform Scales. These will be required when the functions so dictate. For example, prepare sliding scales to solve the Pythagorean theorem. The equation relating the variables is $x^2 = u^2 + v^2$. Since the functions are the same for all three variables, the equation can be solved with two sliding scales. Scales representing the functions u^2 and v^2 are prepared. The v scale is to serve also as the x scale. The same

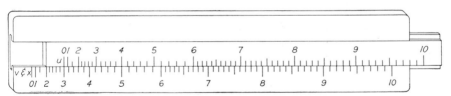

FIG. 17.6. Sliding scales for solving right triangles.

function modulus must be used for both scales, of course. The scales are shown in Fig. 17.6, where the u scale has been slid to position its origin opposite 3 on the v scale. A right triangle with sides of 3 and 4, respectively, will have a hypotenuse of 5; hence, 5 appears on the x scale opposite 4 on the u scale. Within their range, these "squared" scales may be used to find the unknown side of any right triangle for which two sides are known.

17.12. Sliding Logarithmic Scales. Where the variables are related through the sum or difference of their respective functions, the scales may be prepared directly from the functions as described in the preceding examples. If the relationship is one involving multiplication or division, the functions are expressed in logarithmic form, thereby converting a multiplication to addition or a division to subtraction, and Eq. (9) or (10) then applies.

A common example is that of the C and D scales on the general-purpose slide rule. To perform the multiplication $u \times v = x$, the equation is expressed in logarithmic form,

$$\log u + \log v = \log x$$

All functions are the same. The D scale represents the functions $\log u$ and $\log x$, while the C scale represents the function $\log v$. To multiply $u \times v$, u is set on the D scale, v on the C scale, and the answer x read on the D scale. By adding distances proportional to the logarithms of the variables, a multiplication of the variables is effected. Of course, as always, the variables are set and read directly.

As described in connection with conversion scales in Sec. 17.6, logarithmic scales may also be useful with sliding scales when a scale function involves a root or power. For example, the scale function $u^{3/2}$ becomes $3/2 \log u$ in logarithmic form, which will simplify scale calculations and layout.

17.13. Three Sliding Scales. Together with an arrow or pointer these can be used to solve equations of the form

$$f_1(u) + f_2(v) + f_3(x) + c = 0$$

where c is a constant. Several arrangements of scales and pointer may be made. Usually, two scales are fixed or stationary on the body or stock of the slide rule while the other scale and the pointer are on the slide.

A slide rule to solve the equation

$$\frac{u}{v^2} \times 3 = x \tag{11}$$

will be prepared as an example. Since multiplication and division are called for, the equation is written in logarithmic form

$$\log u - 2 \log v + \log 3 = \log x$$

Scales are prepared with the respective functions of $\log u$, $-2 \log v$, and $\log x$, using the same function modulus for all scales (Fig. 17.7). The u and x scales have been made stationary, and the v scale sliding. In the illustration, the slide has been set to solve the equation for $u = 8$, $v = 2$ by locating these values opposite each other on the u and v scales. The corresponding value for x is read on the x scale opposite the arrow on the slide.

FIG. 17.7. Sliding scales representing $(u/v^2) \times 3 = x$.

The v scale whose function is preceded by a minus sign would normally have values increasing in a direction opposite to that shown in Fig. 17.7. The scale has been deliberately inverted so that a subtraction of distances, hence a division, is accomplished by setting u and v values opposite each other. The arrow is located on the slide to the right of the $v = 1$ graduation by a distance equivalent to $M \log 3$; hence, the multiplication by 3 is accomplished through the addition of this distance to a distance on the u scale. The distance on the u scale is the result of subtracting $M\ 2 \log v$ from $M \log u$. The answer is recorded on the x scale opposite the arrow. The arrow is an instance of a scale employing but a single graduation.

Since, in this example, the u and x functions are identical, the x scale of Fig. 17.7 could be eliminated and the answer read on the u scale. In this event, the arrow would be located on the v scale. Separate u and x scales have been employed with the above description in the interest of a more general explanation, that is, applicable in cases where the u and x functions, hence their scales, are different. A careful study of Fig. 17.7 should clarify the operation of this rule, which is a fairly typical application of special-purpose slide rules.

Equation (11) might have been written differently, for example, as

$$\frac{3u}{v^2} = x$$

which in logarithmic form is

$$\log 3u - 2 \log v = \log x$$

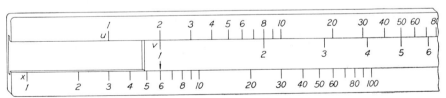

FIG. 17.8. Sliding scales representing $3u/v^2 = x$.

The slide rule prepared from this equation (Fig. 17.8) has scales identical with those of Fig. 17.7. However, the u scale is shifted to the right with respect to the x scale by a distance equal to M log 3. The pointer is opposite the $v = 1$ graduation. A disadvantage is the lengthening of the rule due to the scale shift. This rule, as with the preceding one, may be simplified by eliminating the x scale and reading the answer on the u scale. To do so, the pointer is located on the v scale a distance equal to M log 3 to the right of the $v = 1$ graduation, thus producing a rule identical with the simplified version explained for Fig. 17.7.

17.14. Four or More Sliding Scales. An equation of four variables of the type

$$f_1(u) + f_2(v) + f_3(x) + f_4(w) = 0$$

can be solved with four scales, two stationary and two on the slide. The planning is similar to that described in Sec. 17.13 but with the scale representing the additional function replacing the arrow.

Equations with more than four variables can be solved with special-purpose slide rules by employing two or more slides as called for.

17.15. Constructing Special-purpose Slide Rules. In constructing a special slide rule, pieces of cardboard may be glued together to form the blank, or inexpensive, general-purpose slide rules utilized for this purpose. Wooden blanks are sometimes obtainable from slide-rule manufacturers. It is usually best to prepare the scales on a good grade of paper and to cement them to the blank. Thinned shellac or clear lacquer can be applied to protect the scales.

On occasion, it may be expedient to make the slide rule circular in form. The scales are prepared with the stems as circle arcs and mounted on disks of cardboard, metal, or plastic, using a rivet at the center as a pivot. The slide rule of Fig. 17.7, for example, could be prepared in this form by placing the u scale near the periphery of one disk and the v scale along the edge of a slightly smaller, superimposed disk. The x scale would be on the larger disk and nearer the center. A window with an adjacent arrow would be provided in the smaller disk so the answer on the x scale can be read.

Special-purpose slide rules often are used as an advertising media by industrial organizations, the rules being designed to solve an equation encountered frequently in connection with the company's product. Such rules commonly are made of celluloid or other plastic with the scales printed. Among other fields where special slide rules are widely used is the military. Applications include graphic firing and bombing calculators, navigation devices, etc.

PROBLEMS

In the following problems suggested ranges for the variables appear in parentheses. In general, solutions should be planned to fit on $8\frac{1}{2}$- by 11-in. paper and should be inked unless otherwise specified. Scales are to have appropriate primary- and subgraduations and calibration values; each is to have a descriptive caption including units of measurement. Completed charts or slide rules are to have a title that includes the equation represented. Slide rules should carry a key describing their operation.

In designing special slide rules, it will be helpful in many instances to lay out the scales of the rule roughly on commercial coordinate paper having scales of the proper type. A narrow strip of the paper can serve as the slide. The scales may then be drawn with altered moduli, if necessary, and in finished form on plain paper, with the slide a separate strip. This arrangement will be found satisfactory for projects in which it is not desired to utilize slide-rule blanks.

Specification of scale subdivisions and scale length is given with a few of the two-variable problems; hence the solutions to these are relatively fixed. With the remaining problems, decisions as to scale lengths or moduli and the degree of subdividing must be made by the student. A few problems require selection of the ranges for the variables, and, in addition, some of these require arriving at the equation to be represented.

The special slide-rule problems of Group II contain three to four variables and result in slide rules bearing from two to four scales. In some instances, scales will represent arbitrary constants, and hence will bear only a few graduations (arrows or indexes).

Group I. Stationary Adjacent (Conversion) Scales

Prepare adjacent scales for the following equations:

17.1. $K = 1.069M$, where K (0 to 5, scale length 5 in.) = kilometers, and M = miles. Graduate the K scale for each $\frac{1}{10}$-km value, and the M scale for each $\frac{1}{10}$-mile value.

17.2. $I = 0.03937M$, where I (0 to 4, scale length 8 in.) = inches, and M = millimeters. Graduate the M scale for each millimeter value, and the I scale for every five $\frac{1}{100}$-in. value. (Alternate—graduate the I scale for each $\frac{1}{32}$-in. value, or supply a third scale so reading.)

17.3. $W_{grain} = 15.43W_g$, where W_{grain} (100 to 500, scale length 8 in.) = grains, and W_g = grams. Graduate the W_{grain} scale for each 5-grain value, and the W_g scale for each $\frac{1}{2}$-g value.

17.4. $P = 14.22K$, where P (10,000 to 70,000, scale length 6 in.) = pounds per square inch, and K = kilograms per square centimeter. Use uniform scales (see Prob. 17.5.)

17.5. Use the same equation as that in Prob. 17.4 but with P ranging from 10 to 100,000 psi and having a scale 8 in. long. Use logarithmic scales. What is the advantage of logarithmic scales in this instance?

17.6. $K = 0.7457H$, where K (0 to 100, scale length 6 in.) = kilowatts, and H = horsepower.

17.7. $P = (62.4/144)H$, where P = pressure in pounds per square inch, and H (10 to 130, scale length 6 in.) = height (head) of a column of water in feet.

17.8. $T = 25 - 2R$, where T (8 to 14) = stair-tread width in inches, and R = rise in inches.

17.9. $V = 1,053 + 1.10T$, where V = approximate velocity of sound in air in feet per second, and T (−20 to 100) = temperature in degrees Fahrenheit.

17.10. Prepare three adjacent scales relating liters, gallons (40 to 100), and cubic feet (1 gal = 3.785 liters = 0.1337 cu ft).

17.11. Prepare a chart of adjacent scales that gives the common logarithms of numbers from 1 to 10.

17.12. $A = 0.215R^2$, where A = area, in square inches, of a spandrel (cross section of a fillet), and R (0.125 to 2) = radius in inches. The chart will thus yield volumes of fillets per unit length and should be so captioned. The chart is for use in determining weights of machine parts through volume calculations.

17.13. $H = V^2/2g$, where H (1 to 15) = velocity head of flowing water in feet, V = velocity in feet per second, and g = 32.2.

17.14. Prepare a chart of adjacent scales that gives the weight in pounds per lineal foot for round steel bars ranging from 0.25 to 2 in. in diameter. Use a weight for steel of 0.283 lb per cu in.

17.15. $P = 0.0032V^2$, where P = approximate pressure, in pounds per square foot, of the wind on a normal surface, and V (5 to 100) = wind velocity in miles per hour.

17.16. $Q = 2.50H^{5/2}$, where Q = rate of discharge of water, in cubic feet per second, through a 90° V-notch weir, and H (0.1 to 2) = head in feet.

17.17. $W = P^{0.941}/330$, where W = weight of 1 cu ft of saturated steam in pounds, and P (1 to 100) = pressure in pounds per square inch.

17.18. $L = 11,800/F$, where L = wavelength of short waves in inches, and F (2000 to 12,000) = frequency in megacycles per second.

17.19. $B = 7300/(130 - R_B)$, an approximate relationship between Brinell B and Rockwell (B scale) R_B hardness numbers for values of R_B ranging from 40 to 100.

17.20. $S = 145/(145 - B)$, where S = specific gravity, and B (0 to 65) = degrees Baumé (heavy). The latter is a scale used to express densities of liquids heavier than water.

17.21. Prepare a chart of adjacent scales that gives tangents of angles ranging from 1 to 45°.

17.22. $P = 29.9 \times 10^{-0.0869H}$, where P = atmospheric pressure in inches of mercury, and H = altitude in miles.

17.23. $D = 0.045V^2 + 1.1V$, where D = approximate minimum distance traveled, in feet, by an automobile in stopping after the driver realizes an accident is impending, and V (0 to 80) = speed in miles per hour. The equation is for average drivers and best conditions.

17.24. $H = D^2 + 517D$, where H (0 to 15,000) = elevation in feet above sea level, and D = decrease in temperature, in degrees Fahrenheit, below 212°, at which water boils. Calibrate the D scale in actual temperature values rather than temperature drop below 212°F.

17.25. $E = A - 0.6A^{1/2}$, where E (1 to 100) = "effective area" of a chimney in square feet, and A = actual area in square feet.

17.26. $B = (1,520,000 - 4500R_C)/(100 - R_C)^2$, an approximate relationship between Brinell B and Rockwell (C scale) R_C hardness numbers for values of R_C ranging from 10 to 40.

Group II. Sliding scale

Design special slide rules for the following equations. The problems for Chap. 18 (alignment charts) can provide an additional source of equations.

17.27. $T = T_0 - 0.0035A$, where T (−120 to 120) = approximate temperature at an altitude in degrees Fahrenheit, T_0 (−40 to 120) = temperature at sea level, and A (0 to 50,000) = altitude in feet above sea level.

17.28. $C = kF + L$, where C = estimated cost for a new building and the lot, F = cubic footage of the building, and L = cost of the lot. The constant k represents the cost of the building per cubic foot, and varies with the type of building and the locality. Use a value for k representative of your locality and type of building desired.

17.29. $C = Pk$, where C (10 to 1000) = weight of an iron casting, and P (1 to 100) = pattern weight, both in pounds. The arbitrary constant $k = 8.5$ for mahogany patterns and 14.7 for white pine patterns.

17.30. Design a special slide rule that gives the weight in pounds per lineal foot for various sizes and materials of either (a) round, (b) square, or (c) hexagon bar stock. Materials to be represented are steel (0.283 lb per cu in.), brass (0.309 lb per cu in.), aluminum (0.095 lb per cu in.), and copper (0.322 lb per cu in.). Graduate the size scale with common-fraction values corresponding to available stock sizes.

17.31. $M = T/G$, where M (5 to 50) = gasoline mileage in miles per gallon, T (100 to 10,000) = miles traveled, and G (5 to 200) = gallons of gasoline consumed.

17.32. $S = 0.2618DR$, where S (100 to 10,000) = surface speed of a rotating wheel in feet per minute, D (1 to 10) = wheel diameter in inches, and R (100 to 10,000) = revolutions per minute.

17.33. $T = 5{,}252H/S$, where T (10 to 1000) = torque in foot-pounds, H (1 to 45) = horsepower, and S (100 to 5000) = revolutions per minute.

17.34. $A = 1.273WT$, where A (100 to 1,000,000) = cross-sectional area of a rectangular electrical conductor in circular mils, and W (10 to 5000) and T (10 to 1000) = cross-sectional dimensions in mils. A mil is $\frac{1}{1000}$ in.

17.35. $D = 0.01299P/T$, where D (0.016 to 0.324) = amount, in inches, to deduct from the major diameter of an American National form screw thread to obtain a required thread depth, P (50 to 100) = per cent of full thread depth required, and T (4 to 40) = threads per inch. Graduate the T scale for the commonly used numbers of threads per inch (see American Standards Association thread table).

17.36. $P = I^2R$, where P = electric power in watts, I = current in amperes, and R = resistance in ohms.

17.37. $I = BH^3/12$, where I (0.1 to 1000) = moment of inertia, in in.^{4}, of a rectangle about the axis parallel to B, B (1 to 10 in.) = breadth, and H (1 to 12 in.) = height of the rectangle.

17.38. $H = 0.38V^{1.86}/D^{1.25}$, where H (0.1 to 100) = head lost, in feet, due to friction per 1000 ft of pipe by flowing water, V (1 to 20) = velocity of water in feet per second, and D (1 to 3) = pipe diameter in feet.

17.39. $B = (D - 4)^2L/16$ (Doyle log rule), where B (1 to 1000) = board feet of lumber that can be sawed from a log, D (6 to 40) = diameter of log at small end, in inches, and L (6 to 18) = length of log in feet. The Doyle rule gives values that are much too low for small-diameter logs but, nevertheless, it is widely used; it is the legal standard in some states.

17.40. $W = (D^2 - d^2)/0.352$, where W = weight in pounds per lineal foot for brass pipe or tubing, D = outside diameter, and d = inside diameter, both in inches. Use a weight for brass of 0.309 lb per cu in.

17.41. $1/R = 1/R_1 + 1/R_2$, where R = total resistance of two separate resistances, R_1 and R_2, connected in parallel.

17.42. Design a special slide rule that gives the weights of castings of various metals when the pattern weights are known. Arrows or indexes for both mahogany and white pine patterns are to be incorporated, and the metals to be represented include cast iron, cast steel, brass, aluminum, copper, and zinc. Refer to a handbook for relative weights of the materials. Pattern weights are to range from 10 to 100 lb.

17.43. Design a special slide rule that gives the weight in pounds per lineal foot for various sizes and materials of rectangular bar stock. Materials to be represented are steel, brass, aluminum, and copper (see Prob. 17.30 for weights per cubic inch). Graduate the size scales with common-fraction values corresponding with available stock sizes.

17.44. $T = L/RF$, where T (1 to 100) = time, in minutes, required for one pass (cut) over the work for a lathe or milling machine, L (5 to 150) = length of cut in inches, R (10 to 500) = revolutions per minute, and F (0.05 to 0.5) = feed in inches per revolution.

17.45. $P = 0.0251GH/E$, where P (0.5 to 500) = horsepower required (neglecting pipe friction) to pump G (100 to 5000) gal of water per minute a height of H (10 to 200) ft, and E (10 to 100) = per cent of pump efficiency.

17.46. $R_2 = R_1(234 + T_2)/(234 + T_1)$, where R_2 (10 to 40) = resistance of an annealed-copper conductor at temperature T_2 (1 to 200), and R_1 (1 to 20) is the resistance at temperature T_1 (1 to 100). Resistances are in ohms and temperatures in degrees centigrade.

17.47. $Y = 0.125WS^2/H$, where Y (1 to 100) = sag, in feet, at mid-span of a cable suspended between points at the same level, W (0.5 to 5) = weight of cable in pounds per foot, S (100 to 1000) = span in feet, and H (1000 to 20,000) = horizontal tension in pounds. The equation assumes the cable to hang in a parabolic arc, an assumption sometimes made with electric power transmission lines and suspension bridges.

17.48. $T = 1.5708SWD^2$, where T (10 to 5000) = torque, in inch-pounds, on a thin-walled tube, S (3000 to 15,000) = shearing stress in pounds per square inch, W (0.01 to 0.1) = thickness of tube wall in inches, and D (0.3 to 1.5) = mean diameter of tube in inches.

17.49. $Q = 19.6CD^2H^{\frac{1}{2}}$, where Q (0.4 to 300) = rate of discharge of water through an orifice in gallons per minute, C (0.5 to 1.5) = orifice coefficient, D (0.2 to 1) = diameter of orifice in inches, and H (1 to 100) = head in feet.

17.50. $V = 1.486R^{\frac{2}{3}}S^{\frac{1}{2}}/N$ (Manning formula), where V (0.1 to 100) = velocity of flow for a liquid in feet per second, R (0.1 to 10) = mean hydraulic radius in feet, S (0.0001 to 0.1) = mean slope of hydraulic gradient, and N (0.01 to 0.1) = coefficient of roughness.

17.51. $L_S = 12.85L_B(r/R)^{0.83}$, where L_S = length of straight pipe offering a resistance to air flow equivalent to that of a bend, L_B = length along center line of bend, r = inside radius of pipe, and R = mean radius of the bend; all are in feet.

17.52. $P = EI \cos \theta/1000$, where P (0.1 to 100) = power, in kilowatts, for a single-phase electrical circuit, E (100 to 1000) = effective voltage across circuit, I (10 to 100) = effective current through circuit in amperes, and θ (0 to 84.26) = phase angle in degrees. $\cos \theta$ is the power factor.

CHAPTER 18

ALIGNMENT CHARTS OR NOMOGRAPHY

18.1. An alignment chart, frequently called a nomogram, provides a convenient way to obtain solutions for a recurring equation relating three or more variables. In general, the charts employ separate scales for each variable in the equation represented; the scales may be straight or curved. The simplest alignment chart is composed of three parallel scales each representing the function of a variable. The scales are graduated and arranged so that any straight line, called the *index line*, crossing the chart cuts the scales at values of the three variables which will satisfy the equation relating the variables. By using an index line determined by known values of two variables, the corresponding unknown value of the third variable can be read from the chart.

Being of an introductory nature, this chapter will deal only with alignment charts of the three-parallel-scale type. For a more advanced treatment, see the bibliography for texts dealing exclusively with nomography.

18.2. General Procedure for Equation of Form $f_1(u) + f_2(v) = f_3(w)$. An alignment chart of three parallel scales may be prepared for an equation of three variables which can be put in the form

$$f_1(u) + f_2(v) = f_3(w) \tag{1}$$

Scales are prepared for each variable, u, v, and w, using as each scale function the function of the variable appearing in the equation relating the variables. The scales are arranged as indicated in Fig. 18.1 with the u and v scales to the outside and the w scale between. The ranges of the variables for two of the scales, usually the u and v scales, must be decided upon as must be their lengths. It may prove expedient to use a predetermined scale modulus for either or both of these scales rather than a predetermined length, in which event the lengths are calculated. The lengths of the scales need not be the same. From the foregoing information, the scale equations for the u and v scales can be written and the scales drawn. The space $a + b$ (Fig. 18.1) separating the u and v scales is arbitrarily decided upon.

To complete the chart, all of the following ordinarily must be calculated for the w scale: (1) position of the scale both horizontally and vertically, (2) scale modulus, and (3) range of the variable. The horizontal position of the w scale and the function modulus of the scale are obtained through formulas which relate the three scales of the chart.[1]

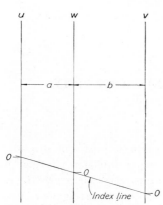

FIG. 18.1. Diagram of three-parallel-scale alignment chart.

The expression relating the horizontal spacing of the scales is

$$\frac{a}{b} = \frac{M_u}{M_v} \qquad (2)$$

where a and b are distances as indicated in Fig. 18.1 and M_u and M_v are the function moduli, respectively, of the u and v scales.

The formula yielding the w function modulus is

$$M_w = \frac{M_u \times M_v}{M_u + M_v} \qquad (3)$$

or the function modulus of the w scale equals the product of the function moduli of the u and v scales divided by the sum of these moduli.

Knowing the function modulus of the w scale, the scale equation can be written. The range of the w variable is obtained by substituting, in turn, the high and the low values of u and v in the equation relating the variables. The vertical position of the w scale may be had by locating the low value of the w variable on the index line connecting the corresponding low values of u and v (Fig. 18.1).

18.3. Example of Alignment Chart for Equation of Form $f_1(u) + f_2(v) = f_3(w)$. Given the equation $u + 2v = w$ relating the variables u, v, and w. The range of u is from 3 to 7, and the range of v is from 4 to 9. The length of both the u and the v scales is to be 2 in. This short scale length is employed here mainly as suitable for illustrative purposes. The calculations are as follows:

u function modulus:

$$M_u = \frac{L_u}{f_1(u_r) - f_1(u_l)}$$
$$M_u = \frac{2}{7 - 3}$$
$$M_u = 0.5 \text{ in.}$$

v function modulus:

$$M_v = \frac{L_v}{f_2(v_r) - f_2(v_l)}$$

[1] The formulas are given here without proof; their derivation may be had in any text dealing extensively with alignment charts.

$$M_v = \frac{2}{(2 \times 9) - (2 \times 4)}$$
$$M_v = 0.2 \text{ in.}$$

SPACING OF SCALES: The spacing of the scales is obtained with Eq. (2)

$$\frac{a}{b} = \frac{M_u}{M_v}$$

or

$$\frac{a}{b} = \frac{0.5}{0.2}$$

consequently, in this example, if space a is made 1.00 in. and space b made 0.40 in., the conditions are fulfilled.

RANGE OF THE w SCALE: Substitute, in turn, in the equation $u + 2v = w$, the low and the high values of u and v to determine the low and high values of w.

$$w_{\text{low}} = 3 + (2 \times 4) = 11$$
$$w_{\text{high}} = 7 + (2 \times 9) = 25$$

Since all scales in this example will be uniform, the chart (Fig. 18.2) can be drawn without further calculations. To do so, the u and v scales are prepared with 2-in. lengths and with a space of $a + b = 1.40$ in. separating them. The w scale is drawn in between, spaced 1.00 in. from the u and 0.40 in. from the v scales. The w scale must have its graduation 11 on the index line connecting $u = 3$ and $v = 4$ and its graduation 25 on the index line connecting $u = 7$ and $v = 9$. The scale is then subdivided into 14 equal parts covering its range of from 11 to 25. Further subdividing of all scales can be accomplished if needed.

To complete the chart, each scale should be captioned and a descriptive title added. Figure 18.2 is a miniature chart; ordinarily alignment charts are larger with the scales carrying subdivisions (see Fig. 18.4).

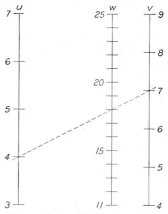

FIG. 18.2. Alignment chart representing $u + 2v = w$.

18.4. Additional observations are in order relative to the preceding example (Fig. 18.2).

Had any of the functions been such as to preclude using an existent scale to aid in the scale layout, it would be necessary to write the equations for such scales in order to calculate the positions of their graduations. To this end, the calculations for the chart of Fig. 18.2 are continued below to show the procedure.

w FUNCTION MODULUS: Substituting in Eq. (3)

$$M_w = \frac{0.5 \times 0.2}{0.5 + 0.2}$$
$$M_w = 0.143$$

SCALE EQUATIONS: Substituting in the general scale equation (4), Chap. 16, $d = M[f(u) - f(u_l)]$, the scale equations for the u, v, and w scales are, respectively,

$$d_u = 0.5(u - 3)$$
$$d_u = 0.5u - 1.5$$
$$d_v = 0.2[2v - (2 \times 4)]$$
$$d_v = 0.4v - 1.6$$
$$d_w = 0.143(w - 11)$$
$$d_w = 0.143w - 1.573$$

LENGTH OF w SCALE:

$$L_w = M_w[f(w_r) - f(w_l)]$$
$$L_w = 0.143(25 - 11)$$
$$L_w = 2 \text{ in.}$$

The lengths of the u and v scales of Fig. 18.2 need not have been the same as was established for the example. If the length of either or both scales were altered, the function moduli would be altered accordingly. Such change, through Eq. (3), would produce a corresponding change in the modulus for the w scale and, hence, affect its length.

18.5. Alignment Chart for Equation of Form $f_1(u) - f_2(v) = f_3(w)$. The steps in preparing an alignment chart to represent an equation of this form are the same as described in the foregoing paragraphs. The negative sign preceding the v function will result in the v scale being inverted. Except for this difference, the alignment chart will be the same as one for which all functions are positive.

18.6. Alignment Chart for Equation of Form $f_1(u) \times f_2(v) = f_3(w)$. By writing this type of equation in logarithmic form, the indicated multiplication becomes addition and the chart may be constructed following the procedures described in Secs. 18.2, 18.3, and 18.4. The scales will have logarithmic functions and may be drawn with the assistance of a logarithmic modulus chart.

As an example, prepare the alignment chart (Fig. 18.4) for determining forces on hydraulic pistons having diameters varying from 1 to 10 in. and subject to pressures varying from 10 to 800 psi. The equation relating the variables is

$$F = \frac{\pi D^2}{4} \times P$$

where F is the force on the piston in pounds, D is the piston diameter in inches, and P is the pressure in pounds per square inch. The equation reduces to

$$F = 0.785D^2P$$

and when written in logarithmic form becomes

$$\log F = \log 0.785 + 2 \log D + \log P$$

or $\qquad \log P + 2 \log D = \log F - \log 0.785$

The P, D, and F scales are prepared in accordance with their respective functions, $\log P$, $2 \log D$, and $\log F - \log 0.785$. The effect of the term $-\log 0.785$ in the F function will be to alter the vertical position of the F scale. It is convenient to assume suitable values for the scale moduli of the P and D scales to facilitate drafting. The scale modulus assumed for the P scale will represent the logarithmic cycle size of that scale. The logarithmic cycle size (scale modulus) of the D scale will be double the D scale function modulus because of the constant 2 occurring in the D scale function.

P SCALE: Let $M_P = 3$ in.   Then

$$L_P = M_P[f(P_r) - f(P_l)]$$
$$L_P = 3(\log 800 - \log 10)$$
$$L_P = 5.709 \text{ in.}$$

The P scale may be drawn as shown in Fig. 18.4 using a logarithmic cycle size of 3 in. and a scale length of 5.709 in.

D SCALE: Let $M_D = 2$ in. (function modulus).   Then

$$L_D = M_D[f(D_r) - f(D_l)]$$
$$L_D = 2(2 \log 10 - 2 \log 1)$$
$$L_D = 4 \text{ in.}$$

Thus, the D scale is drawn with a length of 4 in. The scale modulus which is equivalent to the length of one logarithmic cycle in the scale is equal to 2 times the function modulus or 4 in. Since the scale ranges through one logarithmic cycle exactly, the scale modulus and the scale length are equal.

In Fig. 18.4, the distance separating the P and D scales has been made 4 in. arbitrarily. Vertically, the D scale may be drawn in any practical position with reference to the P scale, and in Fig. 18.4, the scales are centered vertically with respect to each other.

F SCALE: The horizontal position of the F scale is determined through Eq. (2)

$$\frac{a}{b} = \frac{M_P}{M_D} = \frac{3}{2}$$

or $\qquad 2a = 3b$

Also, since $\qquad a + b = 4$ in.

then $\qquad 2a = 12 - 3a$

and $\qquad a = 2.4$ in.

Therefore, the F scale is located 2.4 in. from the P scale.

Finding the F function modulus, using Eq. (3),

$$M_F = \frac{M_P \times M_D}{M_P + M_D}$$

$$M_F = \frac{3 \times 2}{3 + 2} = 1.2 \text{ in.}$$

The F function modulus 1.2 in. is equivalent to the scale modulus for the F scale inasmuch as no constant coefficient occurs in the function. Therefore, the length of each logarithmic cycle in the F scale is 1.2 in. long.

The lowest and highest values which must appear on the F scale are determined by substituting, in turn, the low values and the high values of D and P in the equation $F = 0.785D^2P$. Substituting,

$$F_{\text{low}} = 0.785 \times 1^2 \times 10 = 7.85 \tag{4}$$
$$F_{\text{high}} = 0.785 \times 10^2 \times 800 = 62,800$$

The necessary range of the F scale is therefore contained in the five consecutive logarithmic cycles ranging from 1 to 100,000. The F scale prepared to cover the range of five complete logarithmic cycles will be

$$5 \times 1.2 \text{ in.} = 6 \text{ in. long}$$

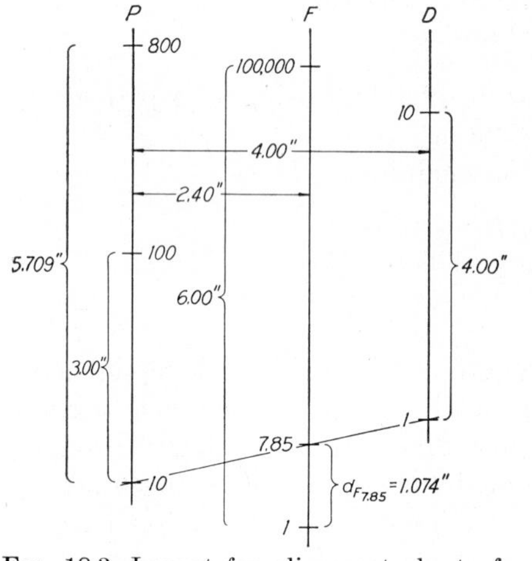

To locate the F scale vertically, an index line is first drawn connecting a given value on the P scale with a given value on the D scale; the F scale is located so that the corresponding F value also lies on this index line. Using the index line connecting $P = 10$ and $D = 1$, the value of F which will lie on this index line is 7.85 [see Eq. (4)].

To facilitate layout of the F scale, the location for graduation 1 is obtained by calculating the distance $d_{F_{7.85}}$ between graduations 1 and 7.85 (Fig. 18.3). This distance can be found by substituting in the F scale equation.

FIG. 18.3. Layout for alignment chart of Fig. 18.4.

$$d_{F_{7.85}} = 1.2(\log 7.85 - \log 1)$$
$$d_{F_{7.85}} = 1.074 \text{ in.}$$

Hence, graduation 1 on the F scale is located 1.074 in. below the index line connecting $P = 10$ and $D = 1$. The graduation for 100,000 will lie 6 in. above graduation 1. By dividing the 6-in. scale length into five equal spaces, each space of 1.2 in. will represent one logarithmic cycle in the scale. The cycles may be subdivided with the assistance of a logarithmic modulus

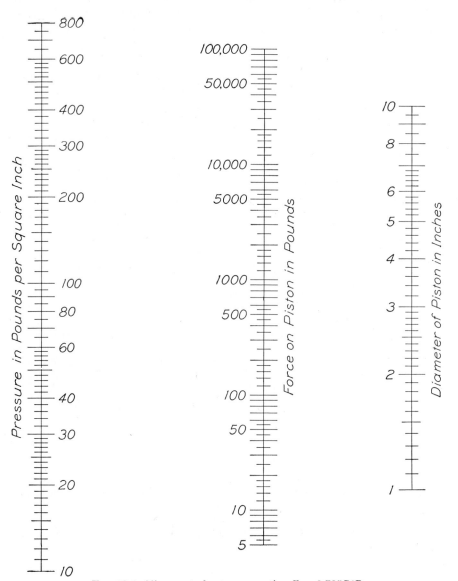

FIG. 18.4. Alignment chart representing $F = 0.785D^2P$.

chart. Although the F scale might have been prepared following slightly different procedures, the method described will probably produce a more accurate scale.

18.7. Alignment Chart for Equation of Form $f_1(u)/f_2(v) = f_3(w)$. This type of equation when written in logarithmic form becomes the type $\log u - \log v = \log w$. The preparation of the alignment chart to represent the equation expressed in logarithmic form is similar to that described in Sec. 18.6 except that the negative sign preceding the v function will cause inversion of the v scale.

PROBLEMS

Prepare alignment charts for the following equations. Suggested ranges for the variables appear in parentheses. Solutions should be planned to fit on 8½- by 11-in. paper and should be inked unless otherwise specified. Scales are to have appropriate primary- and subgraduations and calibration values; each is to have a descriptive caption including units of measurement. Completed charts are to have a title that includes the equation represented.

The problems are limited to equations of three variables, and, in most cases, have ranges specified for but two of the variables. In these instances, it will be necessary to substitute in the equation and solve for the range of the third variable. Decisions as to scale lengths or moduli are to be made by the student. A few problems require selection of the ranges for the variables, and, in addition, some of these require arriving at the equation to be represented.

The problems of Chap. 17, Group II (sliding scales), can provide an additional source of equations.

18.1. $A = G + 0.4912B$, where A = absolute pressure in pounds per square inch, G (5 to 25) = gauge pressure in pounds per square inch, and B (28 to 32) = atmospheric pressure in inches of mercury.

18.2. $A = 0.524T + 1.571R$, where A = "allowance" for a 90° bend in sheet metal, T (0 to 0.5) = metal thickness, and R (0 to 1) = inside radius of the bend, all in inches. The allowance determined is the length of material to be provided in the development or pattern to go around the bend. The equation assumes the neutral line to be a distance $T/3$ from the inner side of the bend.

18.3. $A = 0.785ab$, where A = area of an ellipse, and a and b are the major and minor diameters.

18.4. $S = 0.262DR$, where S (10 to 300) = cutting speed for a lathe in feet per minute, D (0.5 to 10) = diameter of work in inches, and R (10 to 1500) = revolutions per minute.

18.5. $V = W/16.4S$, where V = volume of a body in cubic inches, W (1 to 100) = weight of the body in grams, and S (1 to 2.2) = specific gravity of the material.

18.6. $H = 0.000583PG$, where H = theoretical horsepower equivalent of a hydraulic pump, P (100 to 5000) = oil pressure in pounds per square inch, and G (10 to 500) = rate of delivery in gallons per minute.

18.7. $A = R/T$, where A = axial advance of a nut in inches, R (0.01 to 1) = number of revolutions, and T (4 to 80) = threads per inch. Graduate the T scale for the commonly used numbers of threads per inch (see American Standards Association thread table).

18.8. $n = \sin I/\sin R$, where n (1 to 3) = index of refraction for a material, I (40 to 90°) = angle of incidence, and R (20 to 50°) = angle of refraction.

18.9. Prepare an alignment chart that gives the weight in pounds per lineal foot for various sizes of rectangular steel bar stock. Use a weight for steel of 0.283 pounds per cubic inch. Graduate the size scales with common-fraction values corresponding with available stock sizes.

18.10. Prepare an alignment chart that gives the weight in pounds per lineal foot for various sizes and materials of round bar stock. Materials to include are steel (0.283 lb per cu in.), brass (0.309 lb per cu in.), copper (0.322 lb per cu in.), aluminum (0.095 lb per cu in.), and zinc (0.258 lb per cu in.). Graduate the size scale with common-fraction values. *Hint:* Provide a "material scale" having a graduation for, and identified by the name of, each type material.

18.11. $C = 5.875D^2L$, where C = capacity of a cylindrical tank in gallons, D (1 to 6) = diameter of tank in feet, and L (1 to 10) = length of tank in feet.

18.12. $R = 0.003V^2A$, where R = approximate air resistance, in pounds, for vehicles moving in still air, V (10 to 100) = speed in miles per hour, and A (15 to 150) = frontal projecting area in square feet.

18.13. $S = 1.273P/D^2$, where S = stress, in pounds per square inch, for a round rod in tension, P (500 to 100,000) = load in pounds, and D (0.2 to 2) = rod diameter in inches.

18.14. Tan $\theta = V^2/gR$, where tan θ = slope of a highway surface (θ being the angle between the highway surface and the horizontal as seen in cross section), V (10 to 150) = vehicle speed in feet per second, R (500 to 10,000) = radius of curve in feet, and $g = 32.2$. The equation gives the amount of slope (bank) required on highways to counteract the effect of the centrifugal force. Double-graduate the slope scale so that it reads slope values both in tangents and in angles in degrees. Also, double-graduate the speed scale so that it reads in feet per second and in miles per hour.

18.15. $Q = 3.33BH^{3/2}$ (Francis formula), where Q = rate of discharge of water, in cubic feet per second, through a sharp-crested rectangular weir, B (1 to 10) = breadth of weir in feet, and H (0.2 to 2) = head in feet.

18.16. $H = 0.38V^{1.86}/D^{1.25}$, where H = head lost, in feet, due to friction per 1000 ft of pipe by flowing water, V (1 to 20) = velocity in feet per second, and D (1 to 2.5) = pipe diameter in feet.

18.17. $V_2^2 = 50,000$ $(H_1 - H_2)$, where V_2 = maximum velocity of vapor flow in a nozzle in feet per second, and H_1 (800 to 1600) and H_2 (800 to 1600) are heat rates in Btu per pound.

18.18. $G = 314H^{1/2}(D^2 - 0.678D)$ (based on Kent's chimney formula), where G = chimney capacity in pounds of flue gas per hour, H (30 to 300) = height of chimney in feet, and D (2 to 10) = inside diameter, in feet, at top of chimney.

CHAPTER 19

EMPIRICAL CURVES AND EQUATIONS

19.1. Many scientific laws are derived by empirical methods, i.e., through experimentation. Usually, in conducting the experiment, a number of simultaneous readings are made for the numerical values of two or more presumably related variables. The readings are recorded in tabular form and subjected to study. The study may be facilitated by preparing a graph of the data. If the points plotted on the graph lie on or close to a smooth curve, the variables are apparently associated by some functional relationship which may be expressed approximately by the mathematical equation of the curve. *The relationship should not be assumed to hold true beyond the range of the experimentally obtained values.* A curve so obtained is called an *empirical curve,* and its equation an *empirical equation.*

19.2. General Procedure for Determining an Empirical Equation. The data are first plotted on rectangular coordinate paper to discover if a functional relationship exists. Paper with uniform scales is used. If a smooth curve can be made to fit the data, the curve is studied to determine, if possible, its type, e.g., parabolic, hyperbolic, exponential, etc. Next, the data are replotted on a rectangular coordinate system employing scales whose functions are such that the data will plot as a straight line provided the assumed curve type is correct. If the curve *rectifies,* i.e., plots as a straight line, its form of equation is known. It remains then to determine the values of the constants of the equation.

Frequently, the values of the constants can be determined by graphic methods. Mathematical methods can be used which usually will yield more accurate results but will require a greater expenditure of time and labor. In most instances where graphic methods can be employed, the constants can be determined by this means to a degree of precision consistent with the accuracy of the empirically obtained data.

19.3. The Graph. The first plot of the experimental data is made on rectangular coordinate paper of uniform graduation. The scale moduli of the scales employed for the two axes should be such that the curve will fit nicely into the space available. The curve should be neither too steep nor too flat. The scale moduli of the two scales will usually be different. The independent variable is ordinarily plotted as the abscissa or X axis, and the dependent variable is ordinarily plotted as the ordinate or Y axis.

Plotted points are represented best by short, fine crosslines drawn parallel with the X and Y axes. If the graph is to be inked for display or reproduction purposes, the points should be represented by small circles of $\frac{1}{16}$ to $\frac{1}{10}$ in. diameter.

Since slight inaccuracies are ordinarily inherent in the measurements made for the values from which the points are plotted, it will usually be impossible to draw a smooth, or "fair," curve containing all points. The curve should be drawn smooth and fair as the average, or *best representative*, line. The position of the curve should be such that points not lying on it are distributed to either side with the deviations of the points on one side equaling the deviations on the other side. It is well to sketch the curve freehand before drawing it with instruments.

To complete the drawing of the graph, the scales should be calibrated, captioned and a descriptive title added.

19.4. The Straight Line. If the first plot of the data made on plain coordinate paper yields a straight line as the best representative line, the relationship between the variables is apparently linear and can be expressed approximately by the equation of the straight line. The slope-intercept form of the equation for a straight line on plain rectangular coordinates is most convenient to use. It may be written as

$$y = a + mx \qquad (1)$$

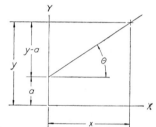

FIG. 19.1. The straight line.

where x and y are the variables, a is the y intercept, and m is the slope of the line expressed as the tangent of the angle θ (Fig. 19.1).

To write the equation representing a specific straight line, the constants a and m are obtained and substituted in Eq. (1). Constant a may be either positive or negative and is the value of y when $x = 0$. The slope m also may be either positive or negative, positive if the line slopes upward to the right, negative if the slope is downward to the right. The line of Fig. 19.1 has positive slope. If the X and Y scales employ the same scale modulus, the angle of slope will appear true; hence, the angle can be measured and its tangent sought as the value of m. A simpler procedure is to construct a right triangle with the hypotenuse on the best representative line and with sides respectively parallel to the X and Y axes. By making the side of the triangle parallel to the X axis 1 in. long, the length of the other side (parallel with Y axis) will be equal to the tangent of the angle θ and, consequently, equal to the slope m.

If the scales used for the X and Y axes are different, i.e., have different scale moduli, the slope of the line does not appear true and must be calculated. This may be accomplished by reading x and y values for two widely separated points 1 and 2 on the line. Then

$$m = \frac{y_2 - y_1}{x_2 - x_1} \qquad (2)$$

which solves a right triangle for the tangent of the true angle θ. If the y intercept is used as point 1, $y_1 = a$ and $x_1 = 0$; hence, Eq. (2) becomes

$$m = \frac{y - a}{x} \qquad (3)$$

where x and y are the coordinates of any point on the line other than the y intercept.

19.5. Example with Empirical Data Yielding a Linear Equation. The following table gives heating values H in Btu per pound for dry Pennsylvania anthracite silts of various percentage dry ash A contents.

H	5950	6700	7600	9400	10,750	12,200
A	56.5	49.0	44.5	34.0	26.0	17.5

Figure 19.2 shows the data plotted on a rectangular coordinate system composed of appropriate uniform scales. The data can be represented

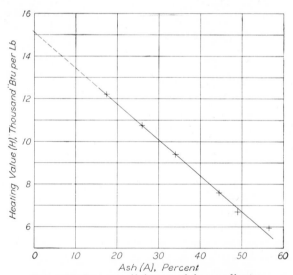

Fig. 19.2. Data rectifying on plain coordinates.

approximately by a straight line, and the equation of the straight line may be used to represent the data approximately. The general equation may be written as $H = a + mA$, where a and m are the constants to be determined. The value of $a = 15,100$ is found by extending the best representative line to obtain the H intercept (value of H for $A = 0$). The slope m

may be determined by substituting in Eq. (3), $m = (H - a)/A$. To accomplish this, a point is selected on the line, say for $A = 50$, and the corresponding value for H read from the graph. This value is $H = 6700$. From Eq. (3)

$$m = \frac{6700 - 15,100}{50} = -168$$

The negative value for m indicates that the line has negative slope; i.e., it slopes downward to the right rather than upward to the right. The equation for the line is

$$H = 15,100 - 168A$$

19.6. Method of Selected Points. The constants of the equation also can be determined by calculation. Several methods are available. In general, slightly greater accuracy may be expected and special treatment is unnecessary if the ordinate for $x = 0$ is not available on the graph. The simplest of the methods, known as the method of selected points, is as follows. The x and y coordinates for two widely separated points on the line are read from the graph. By substituting the coordinates of each point in the general equation $y = a + mx$, two equations result which can be solved simultaneously for a and m.

For example, in Fig. 19.2, two points are selected which have, respectively, the coordinates $A = 24.5$, $H = 11,000$, and $A = 50$, $H = 6700$. These values result in the equations

$$11,000 = a + 24.5m$$
and
$$6700 = a + 50m$$

Solving the equations simultaneously yields

$$a = 15,130 \quad \text{and} \quad m = -168.6$$

which gives as the equation relating the variables

$$H = 15,130 - 168.6A$$

19.7. The Power Curves. Many natural phenomena are related by the power law which has the form

$$y = ax^m \tag{4}$$

where x and y are variables and a and m are constants. When plotted on plain coordinate paper, variables connected by the power law will approximate parabolic or hyperbolic curves. The plotted curves will resemble parabolas for positive values of m and hyperbolas for negative values of m.

Equation (4) written in logarithmic form becomes

$$\log y = \log a + m \log x \tag{5}$$

It will be noted that Eq. (5) has the form of the general linear equation

$y = a + mx$ and that log y is linear with respect to log x.   Consequently, by plotting the logarithms of the x values against the logarithms of the y values on plain coordinate paper, empirical data will approximate a straight line if the relationship between the variables can be expressed by the power law.   Observe from Eq. (5) that log a = log y when log x = 0; hence, constant a can be determined from the graph.   The slope m can be measured directly from the graph as described in Sec. 19.4 if the scales employ the same scale moduli.   Otherwise, coordinates for two points on the rectified line are read from the graph and substituted in the equation

$$m = \frac{\log y_2 - \log y_1}{\log x_2 - \log x_1} \qquad (6)$$

Equation (6) solves a right triangle for the tangent m of the true angle of slope.

19.8. Example with Data Yielding a Power Equation.   The following table contains related values of the variables x and y and, in addition, the common logarithms of these values.

x	2	4	6	8	10
y	2.5	4.5	6.0	7.6	9.0
log x	0.301	0.602	0.778	0.903	1.000
log y	0.398	0.653	0.778	0.881	0.954

The data have been plotted as x vs. y on plain coordinates in Fig. 19.3. Since the resulting curve suggested a parabola, the data were replotted on

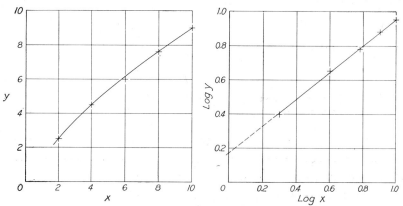

FIG. 19.3. Plain coordinates, x vs. y.   FIG. 19.4. Plain coordinates, log x vs. log y.

plain coordinates as log x vs. log y, whereby it rectified (Fig. 19.4).   The intercept, log y = 0.176, is equal to log a; hence, a = 1.5.   Since the scale moduli of the two scales are the same, the slope can be measured directly or it can be calculated, as would be necessary if the scale moduli were different. Selecting two points on the curve with the respective coordinates $\log x_1 = 0.000$, $\log y_1 = 0.176$ and $\log x_2 = 1.000$, $\log y_2 = 0.954$ and then substituting in Eq. (6) gives

$$m = \frac{0.954 - 0.176}{1.000 - 0.000} = 0.778$$

The equation of the line expressed in logarithmic form is

$$\log y = \log 1.5 + 0.778 \log x$$

and in power form is

$$y = 1.5x^{0.778}$$

19.9. Logarithmic Coordinate Paper. When data are suspected of being related by a power equation, it is more convenient to test for rectification by plotting the variables x and y directly on logarithmic coordinate paper than to plot $\log x$ vs. $\log y$ on plain coordinates. Logarithmic paper has scales with logarithmic functions; that is, $f_1(x) = \log x$, and $f_2(y) = \log y$. This results in the distances between graduations being proportional to the logarithms[1] of the values of the variables calibrating the scales. Consequently, when the variables x and y are plotted directly on logarithmic paper, the distances laid off will be proportional to the logarithms of the variables and rectification will occur if the data are related through a power equation.

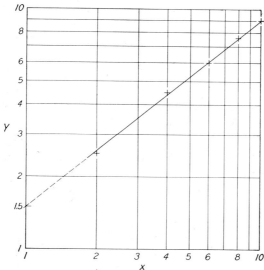

FIG. 19.5. Logarithmic coordinates, x vs. y.

[1] Logarithms to base 10 are ordinarily used.

The data encountered in Sec. 19.8 have been plotted on logarithmic paper in Fig. 19.5. Observe in the equation $y = ax^m$ that $y = a$ when $x = 1$; hence, a, read from the graph, equals 1.5. The slope m can be measured directly because the scale moduli are the same. This is usually true for most commercial logarithmic paper. If the scale moduli are not the same, the slope may be calculated with Eq. (6).

In using Eq. (6), it is convenient to select points whose x values differ exactly by one decimal place; on the graph, such points will lie exactly one logarithmic cycle apart in the abscissa direction. Points so selected will have unity as the difference between the logarithms of their respective x coordinate values. Accordingly, the denominator of Eq. (6) will be unity, which simplifies the calculation of m.

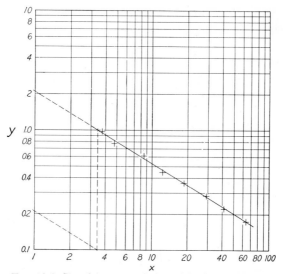

FIG. 19.6. Two-by-two cycle logarithmic coordinates.

Logarithmic coordinate paper is available commercially with various sizes and numbers of cycles. Figure 19.6 shows data plotted on 2-by-2 cycle logarithmic paper. The line has been extended into the upper cycle to obtain the value of $a = 2.1$. If the upper cycle had not been available, the value of a could have been obtained from the lower cycle as shown by the dotted lines of Fig. 19.6. The decimal point will require adjustment if a is read on the scale of the lower cycle. The slope m of the curve, obtained by measurement, is -0.60; it is negative because the slope is downward to the right. The equation for the curve is $y = 2.1x^{-0.60}$.

A power curve rectified on logarithmic coordinates will have a value greater than 1 for the slope m if the true angle of slope is greater than 45°. Likewise, m will be less than 1 if the true angle of slope is less than 45°.

If the true angle of the slope is exactly 45°, the slope m will be 1 and the equation will be linear, i.e., the equation for a straight line. A linear equation is a special case of a power equation where the slope m is unity.

19.10. The Exponential Curves. Many empirical facts are related by the exponential equation

$$y = a(b)^x$$

where a and b are constants. The equation relates variables where x changes in arithmetic ratio while y changes in geometric ratio.

In working with the equation, it is convenient to let b equal either e^m or 10^m, in which event m will be either the natural or the common logarithm of b. Making the substitutions gives

$$y = a(e)^{mx}$$

and
$$y = a(10)^{mx} \qquad (7)$$

The equation will be used in the latter form in this discussion. Rewriting Eq. (7) in logarithmic form results in

$$\log y = \log a + mx \qquad (8)$$

Equation (8) will be recognized to have the form of the general linear equation with $\log y$ being linear with respect to x; a and m are constants. By plotting x values against the logarithms of the y values on plain coordinate paper, data will rectify if related by an exponential equation.

Figure 19.7 shows data plotted on plain coordinates. The curve suggests an exponential relationship; accordingly, the data are replotted on plain

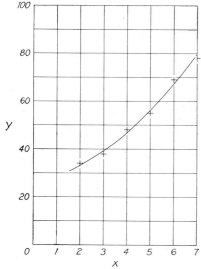

FIG. 19.7. Plain coordinates, x vs. y.

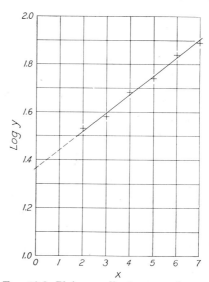

FIG. 19.8. Plain coordinates, x vs. $\log y$.

coordinates as x vs. log y, and rectification occurs (Fig. 19.8). If the data do not rectify with the independent variable as x, the dependent variable should be tried as x.

From Eq. (8), log a = log y when x = 0; therefore, log a is read from the graph (Fig. 19.8) as 1.365; hence, a = 23. The slope m must be calculated, since the scales employ different scale moduli. Two points on the curve are selected, and their coordinates substituted in the equation

$$m = \frac{\log y_2 - \log y_1}{x_2 - x_1} \tag{9}$$

Equation (9) solves for the tangent of the true angle of slope. Using the points where x = 7 and x = 0, we have

$$m = \frac{1.905 - 1.365}{7 - 0} = 0.077$$

The equation for the line in logarithmic form is

$$\log y = \log 23 + 0.077x$$

and in exponential form is

$$y = 23(10)^{0.077x}$$

19.11. Semilogarithmic coordinate paper is graduated with a uniform scale in one direction and a logarithmic scale in the other. Data suspected

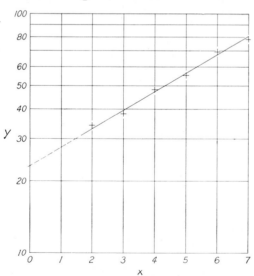

FIG. 19.9. Semilogarithmic coordinates, x vs. y.

of being related by an exponential equation may be tested for rectification by direct plotting of the variables on this type paper. The variable plotted on the logarithmic scale will have the distances between points proportional to the logarithms of the variable.

The data plotted in Figs. 19.7 and 19.8 are shown plotted on semi-logarithmic coordinates in Fig. 19.9. From Eq. (7), $y = a$ when $x = 0$; hence, a is read directly from the semilogarithmic plot as 23. Since the scales are dissimilar, the slope m is found by reading the coordinates of two points on the curve from the graph and substituting in Eq. (9).

Semilogarithmic paper is available in combinations of various uniform and logarithmic scales; the logarithmic scales may be of one or more cycles. Figure 19.10 shows data plotted on semilogarithmic paper of two logarithmic

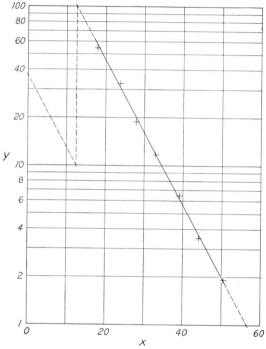

Fig. 19.10. Two-cycle semilogarithmic coordinates.

cycles. Since the y intercept is inaccessible, the constant $a = 370$ is read with adjusted decimal point as indicated in the illustration. The slope m is found by substituting coordinates for two points on the curve in Eq. (9). Calculations are simplified if the points selected have ordinate positions separated by exactly one logarithmic cycle. For example, if the points selected are such that $y_2 = 10$ and $y_1 = 1$, Eq. (9) becomes

$$m = \frac{\log 10 - \log 1}{34.5 - 56.5} = \frac{1}{-22}$$

or
$$m = -0.0454$$

The equation for the line is $y = 370(10)^{-0.0454x}$.

19.12. Curve Fitting—General. Determining an equation that will represent experimental data is often termed *curve fitting*. The idea is to find a curve of known equation which for a portion of its length will closely "fit" the data. Since portions of curves of different types, e.g., power and exponential, may be nearly the same, experimental data can sometimes be represented by equations of more than one type for the limited range of the data. Therefore the relationship used should not be assumed to apply beyond the range of the data fitted, nor should it be thought that the type of equation employed of necessity indicates the type of law actually governing the data, especially when the range of the data is small.

The following observations will be helpful in determining from the direct plot of the data whether the simple-type equations and methods described in this chapter may possibly provide an equation fitting the data.

1. Power curves with equations of form $y = ax^m$ will pass through the origin for positive values of m and will be asymptotic to both axes for negative values of m.

2. Exponential curves with equations of form $y = a(10)^{mx}$ will cross the Y axis at $y = a$ and will be asymptotic to the X axis. (*Note:* For equations of form $x = a(10)^{my}$ the curve will cross the X axis at $x = a$ and will be asymptotic to the Y axis.)

For a small range of the data, natural phenomena governed by complex laws may often be fitted by a simple equation through the methods described in this chapter. Hence, for more extensive ranges of data, complex relationships may sometimes be represented by a combination of several simple-type equations through dividing the curve of the direct plot into segments. However, such data are generally handled through a more advanced treatment, like attaching a constant to a simple-type equation, using an equation of other form, etc., as applicable. Discussion of such methods will be found in textbooks dealing extensively with the subject (see Bibliography).

PROBLEMS

With the problems of Groups II–V, plot the data, using an appropriate coordinate system to obtain rectification, and determine an empirical equation that will represent the data. The problems of Group V should first be plotted on plain coordinates to determine the system best suited for rectification. Graphs are to be complete with scale captions and calibrations, a title, and the equation.

Group I.   Curve Shapes and Effect of Constants

19.1. Calculate a few values for the equation $y = a + mx$ in each case: (1) with $a = 2$, $m = 2$, (2) with $a = 2$, $m = 1$, (3) with $a = 2$, $m = 0$, and (4) with $a = 2$, $m = -1$. Plot the values on a sheet of plain coordinate paper using common scales for the four curves. Compare the positions of the curves and the effect of the constants a and m.

19.2. Calculate a few values for the equation $y = ax^m$ in each case: (1) with $a = 2$, $m = 2$, (2) with $a = 2$, $m = 1$, (3) with $a = 2$, $m = \frac{1}{2}$, (4) with $a = 2$, $m = 0$, and (5) with $a = 2$, $m = -1$. Plot the values (*a*) on a sheet of plain coordinate paper and (*b*) on a sheet of log log coordinate paper, using common scales for the five curves in each instance. Compare the positions and shapes of the curves and the effect of the constants a and m in each type of plot.

19.3. Calculate a few values for the equation $y = a(10)^{mx}$ in each case: (1) with $a = 2$, $m = 2$, (2) with $a = 2$, $m = 1$, (3) with $a = 2$, $m = \frac{1}{2}$, (4) with $a = 2$, $m = 0$, and (5) with $a = 2$, $m = -1$. Plot the values, (a) on a sheet of plain coordinate paper, and (b) on a sheet of semilogarithmic paper, using common scales for the five curves in each instance. Compare the positions and shapes of the curves and the effect of the constants a and m in each type of plot.

Group II. Linear Relationships

19.4. The tensile strength S, in pounds per square inch, of an alloy steel, and the Brinell hardness number B.

S, psi	91,000	112,000	135,000	156,000	180,000	197,000	222,000
B	191	210	271	322	353	403	436

19.5. The nominal diameter D, in inches, of American Standard regular bolts, and the width across flats W, in inches, of the bolt heads.

D, in.	$\frac{1}{2}$	1	$1\frac{1}{2}$	2	$2\frac{1}{2}$	3	$3\frac{1}{2}$	4
W, in.	$\frac{3}{4}$	$1\frac{1}{2}$	$2\frac{1}{4}$	3	$3\frac{3}{4}$	$4\frac{1}{2}$	$5\frac{1}{4}$	6

19.6. The rate of expansion E, in inches per foot, of a chrome-nickel alloy for various temperatures T in degrees Fahrenheit.

E, in. per ft	800	1000	1200	1400	1600	1800	2000
T, °F	0.101	0.125	0.152	0.177	0.199	0.227	0.251

Group III. Power Relationships

19.7. The rate of discharge Q, in cubic feet per second, of water through a sharp-crested, 90° V-notch weir for various heads H in feet.

H, ft	0.40	0.60	0.80	1.00	1.20	1.40	1.60
Q, cu ft per sec	0.27	0.69	1.45	2.57	3.85	5.87	7.78

19.8. The cutting life L, in minutes, for a single-point machine-tool cutting bit of high-speed steel, and the cutting speed S in feet per minute.

S, fpm	28	30	32	35	38	42
L, min	44.0	27.5	16.3	8.5	4.8	2.2

19.9. The terminal voltage E for a tungsten-filament lamp, and the current I in amperes.

E, volts	8	10	20	40	60	80	100
I, amp	0.054	0.061	0.104	0.167	0.230	0.275	0.331

Group IV. Exponential Relationships

19.10. The difference D, in degrees Fahrenheit, between the temperature of heated water cooling in air and the air temperature, and the time T, in minutes, after the start of cooling.

T, min	10	20	30	40	50
D, °F	50	41	33	27	22

19.11. The penetration P, in inches, of cast steel by X rays (2000 kv, 1.5 ma), and the time of exposure T in minutes.

T, min	2	5	10	20	40	60	80
P, in.	6.3	7.5	8.3	9.0	9.9	10.2	10.6

19.12. The rate of speed S, in revolutions per minute, of a flywheel being retarded by fluid friction, and the time T, in seconds, after friction is applied.

T, sec	10	15	20	25	30	35	40	45	50
S, rpm	340	270	195	155	125	93	70	56	45

Group V. Linear, Power, or Exponential Relationships

19.13. The rate of creep C, in per cent per 1000 hr, for a low-carbon steel at 1200°F, and the stress S in pounds per square inch.

S, psi	300	400	500	600	700	800	1000	1200
C, % per 1000 hr	0.011	0.029	0.051	0.094	0.155	0.205	0.455	0.710

19.14. The water-cement ratio W/C, in gallons of water per sack of cement, for a concrete mixture, and the compressive strength S, in pounds per square inch, of the concrete after a 28-day curing period.

W/C, gal per sack	3	4	5	6	7
S, psi	6650	4900	4050	2950	2200

19.15. The axial deflection D, in inches, of a ball bearing for various axial loads P in tons.

P, tons	1	2	3	4	5	6	7	8
D, in.	0.0025	0.0034	0.0043	0.0048	0.0053	0.0059	0.0062	0.0067

19.16. The electric resistivity R, in microhm-centimeters, of annealed carbon steel for various percentages C of carbon.

C, per cent	0.2	0.4	0.6	0.8	1.0	1.2
R, microhm-cm	14.3	16.2	17.1	18.7	20.4	21.3

19.17. The quantity of charge Q, in coulombs times a constant, on a 0.25 microfarad condenser in an RC circuit, and the time T of flow, in seconds, of the charging current. The resistor is 24 megohms.

T, sec	2	4	6	8	10	14	20	26	38	56
Q, coulombs × k	3.80	8.35	10.50	12.60	13.60	15.90	18.00	19.45	21.80	24.35

19.18. The resistance R, in ohms, in a ground connection, and the depth D, in feet, of the ground rod in the soil.

D, ft	2	3	4	6	8	10	12
R, ohms	89	66	51	37	28	24	21

19.19. The velocity V, in feet per second, of a small-arms projectile, and the weight of charge C, in grains, of a type of propellent powder.

V, fps	1905	2210	2500	2670	2790
C, grains	27.0	32.0	37.0	39.5	42.0

19.20. The drawdown D, in feet, of the water in a well as correlated with the length of time T, in minutes, of pumping a nearby well.

T, min	1	2	4	6	10	20	40	80
D, ft	0.14	0.18	0.23	0.25	0.29	0.33	0.37	0.42

19.21. The input horsepower P for various depths of cut C, in inches, in milling a mild steel.

P, hp	4.1	6.4	8.8	11.3	12.3	15.6	17.7
C, in.	0.030	0.050	0.085	0.110	0.125	0.165	0.185

19.22. The carburizing time T, in hours, for a steel and the case depth C, in inches.

T, hr	2	3	4	6	8	10	15	20
C, in.	0.013	0.016	0.019	0.023	0.027	0.031	0.038	0.044

19.23. The life L, in hours, of a ball-bearing grease for various temperatures T, in degrees Fahrenheit, of the outer race.

T, °F	65	92	117	153	180	205	242
L, hr	50,500	33,800	21,200	12,500	7400	5200	2700

19.24. The nominal diameter D, in inches, of American Standard heavy bolts and the width across flats, W, in inches, of the bolt heads.

D, in.	½	1	1½	2	2½	3
W, in.	⅞	1⅝	2⅜	3⅛	3⅞	4⅝

CHAPTER 20

GRAPHIC CALCULUS

20.1. Problems in engineering and science commonly deal with rates and changes of related quantities that vary. Determining rates and changes frequently involves a study of the magnitudes while in a state of change and falls naturally into the realm of the calculus. The subject is important in engineering and science, often being essential in determining displacements, velocities, accelerations, lengths, areas, volumes, moments, and the like.

Formal or algebraic calculus is limited in application to situations where the algebraic equation relating the variable quantities is known. Many practical problems have only empirical data consisting of a series of measurements or readings; the equations, if available at all, may be too complex to utilize. In such cases, solutions meeting practical requirements ordinarily may be had through simple graphic application of the basic principles of calculus. Stated briefly, graphic calculus determines rates or changes through curves drawn from data obtained from the graph representing the given data. Knowledge of formal calculus is unnecessary in working with the graphic approach.

Graphic calculus is a valuable tool, especially in experimental work where often no equation relating the variables is known. Even in instances when the equation is available, its use through formal calculus may be so consuming of time that the graphic solution, being faster, is preferred. In cases where formal calculus provides the most advantageous approach, the graphic procedure may be useful as a check. In addition the latter is to be valued for the clear understanding of the problem it provides through its graphic presentation of the physical factors.

20.2. Derived Curves. Curves representing functions have geometric relationships through which are formed groups of associated or related curves. The relationships are such that all member curves of a group can be derived from any one given curve belonging to the group; hence, the subject is sometimes called *derived curves*.

In graphic solutions, the related curves of a group are commonly drawn in a vertical bank as shown in Fig. 20.6. They are usually arranged in a descending order so that each curve, with respect to the curve above, is the next lower curve both in the degree of its algebraic equation and in its position on the drawing. This arrangement is followed in this discussion with the exception of Fig. 20.12, where the curves are superimposed.

The factors relating the curves involve curve slopes, curve ordinates, and areas under a curve. There are two basic relationships, actually complementary. Briefly, one, the *slope relationship*, relates the slopes of a curve to the ordinates of the next lower curve, while the other, the *area relationship*, relates the area under a curve to the ordinates of the next higher curve.

20.3. Slope Relationship. The slope of a curve at any point is the slope of the straight line tangent to the curve at that point. The numerical value of the slope is equivalent to the trigonometric tangent of the true angle made by the X axis and the line tangent to the curve, hence is determined through the ordinate and abscissa scale units.

The slope relationship may be stated: *The slope at any point in a curve equals the ordinate of the corresponding point in the next lower curve.*

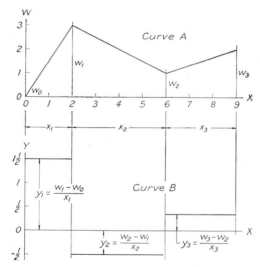

Fig. 20.1. Derived curves—slope and area relationships.

A simple example illustrating the relationship appears in Fig. 20.1, where curve B has been derived from curve A. Curve A is made up of three straight-line segments each having constant slope throughout its interval. The left-hand segment has for the value of its slope $(w_1 - w_0)/x_1$, which is numerically equivalent to ordinate y_1 of the corresponding portion of the derived curve B. Since the slope of this segment of curve A is constant and positive throughout the interval, the corresponding ordinates of curve B are constant and positive; consequently, this portion of curve B is a horizontal straight line drawn above the X axis.

The value of the constant slope for the middle segment of curve A is $(w_2 - w_1)/x_2$, which equals y_2, the ordinate for the corresponding portion of the derived curve B. The value of y_2 is negative, a fact indicated by the negative slope of this segment of curve A. As a result, the middle portion of curve B is drawn below the X axis.

The right-hand segment of curve A has the slope $(w_3 - w_2)/x_3$, which equals y_3, the ordinate for the corresponding portion of curve B. The value of y_3 is positive but is less than y_1, since the slope of this portion of curve A is less than the slope of the left-hand segment.

20.4. Area Relationship. The area under a curve may be defined as the area bounded by the curve, the X axis and any two ordinates. Areas above the X axis are considered positive; areas below the X axis are considered negative.

As has been stated, the right-hand segment of curve A (Fig. 20.1) has for its slope $(w_3 - w_2)/x_3$, which is numerically equal to y_3, the ordinate of the corresponding portion of curve B. Since

$$\frac{w_3 - w_2}{x_3} = y_3$$

then
$$w_3 - w_2 = x_3 y_3$$

where it is evident that $x_3 y_3$ is the area under curve B for this interval and that $w_3 - w_2$ is the *difference in magnitude* of the ordinates of curve A for the corresponding segment. Thus, the area relationship, which is complementary to the slope relationship, may be stated: *The net area between any two ordinates of a curve equals the difference in magnitude of the corresponding ordinates of the next higher curve.*

20.5. The Relationships and Continuous Curves. The area and slope relationships as developed in Secs. 20.3 and 20.4 for curves composed of broken straight-line segments can be shown to hold true for continuous curves by assuming a series of ordinates infinitely close to provide an infinite number of very small intervals. Curve A of Fig. 20.2, for example, is thereby approximated by a series of minute chords which approach the curve, while the adjacent derived curve B is approximated by minute straight-line segments each parallel with the X axis and approaching that curve. Consequently, the area and slope relationships which apply for each minute interval can be argued to apply in sum total to any number of adjacent minute intervals and, hence, to any continuous curve.

20.6. Observations—Slope Relationship. Figure 20.2 shows adjacent derived curves A and B. According to the slope relationship, the ordinate of any point in curve B is equal to the slope of curve A at the corresponding point. Observe that the slope of curve A is positive and is decreasing in magnitude from point d to point e and, correspondingly, the ordinates of curve B also are positive and decreasing in magnitude between the corresponding points d' and e'. The slope of curve A from e to g is negative, with the greatest negative slope at point f. The corresponding ordinates

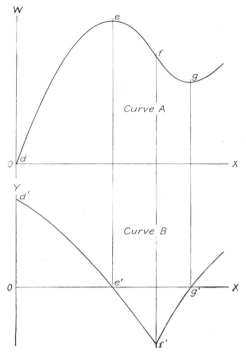

FIG. 20.2. Slope relationship.

of curve B are negative (below the X axis), and the greatest negative ordinate is at f'. Zero slope occurs at points e and g (maximum and minimum conditions for w) in curve A, and curve B crosses the X axis at the corresponding points, since these ordinates have zero values.

20.7. Observations—Area Relationship. Figure 20.3 shows the same curves as Fig. 20.2 but for the purpose of discussing area relationship. According to this relationship, an area under curve B between any two ordinates equals the difference in magnitude between the corresponding ordinates of curve A. For example, the area under B between ordinates y_1 and y_2 equals the difference between ordinates w_2 and w_1 of curve A. The area under curve B between ordinates y_3 and y_4 is negative, since it lies below the X axis, and equals the difference between the corresponding ordinates w_4 and w_3 of curve A. This difference, of course, is negative and indicated by the negative slope of A here. The total area under curve B between ordinates y_0 and y_5 is composed of positive and negative areas. The *net* total area is equal to the difference between ordinates w_5 and w_0 of curve A.

It should be emphasized that the area relationship equates an area under a curve to the *difference* between the corresponding ordinates of the next higher curve. An area under a curve does not denote the total magnitude of the ordinates of the higher curve.

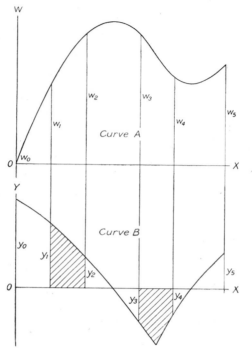

FIG. 20.3. Area relationship.

20.8. The Fundamental Problems. In a world of functionally related physical quantities constantly subject to change, it is often necessary to determine the rates of change of one variable quantity with respect to a specified change in a related variable quantity or to find a total change in one variable corresponding to a specified change in a related variable. Thus, the fundamental problems are determining rates of change and total changes.

Formal calculus has corresponding fundamental branches, the differential and the integral calculus. The two branches are, in effect, the inverse of each other. Differential calculus is primarily concerned with determining rates of change for related variable quantities through a limiting process, while integral calculus is a summation process whose primary concern is determining total change. Rates of change are found in formal calculus through an algebraic technique applied to the algebraic equation relating the variables.

In graphic calculus the equation relating the variables is replaced by its graph. Rate may then be determined through the slope relationship, and change through the area relationship of derived curves. Thus the slope and the area relationships are, respectively, the graphic counterparts of the differential and integral calculus in their more fundamental aspects.

A graph depicting related variable quantities as drawn in graphic calculus has the changing values of the independent variable represented as the abscissas and the corresponding changing values of the function or dependent variable as the ordinates.

20.9. Rate.   Rate is a ratio and may be defined as the amount of change in the dependent variable corresponding to a unit change in the independent variable.   This ratio, or rate of change, is depicted by the slope of the curve representing the variables.   For example, the slope at point P in curve A (Fig. 20.4) is the ratio $\Delta w/\Delta x$ which expresses the rate for this particular instant.   A curve with slope constantly changing, such as A, denotes rates of change that are likewise constantly changing.   Like the dependent variable, these slopes or rates are also a function of the independent variable x.   The ordinates of the next lower curve B represent this slope or rate function; hence, curve B is a rate diagram depicting the rate at which the dependent variable of curve A is changing at any instant.

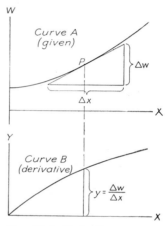

Fig. 20.4. Derivative curve, a rate diagram.

The next lower curve derived from a given curve is known as the first *derivative* curve of the given curve. The process may be continued by drawing successively lower curves as needed.   The next lower curve (not shown) derived from B (Fig. 20.4) would represent the first derivative, hence the rates of change, of B.   It would also represent the second derivative of curve A.

As rate diagrams, derivative curves are also useful in determining maximum or minimum values for a variable.   It was pointed out in connection with Fig. 20.2 that such values are indicated by zero slope in the graph of the function.   The graph of the first derivative will have zero ordinates, hence will cross the X axis at the corresponding points.

Each ordinate of a first derivative curve is the quotient of two quantities depicted by the given curve.   As a result, it can be shown by formal calculus that each successively lower curve in a bank of derived curves is one degree lower in its equation than the adjacent curve above.

20.10. Change.   The next higher curve derived from a lower curve is called the *integral* of the lower.   An integral curve is useful in determining a total change occurring in the quantities represented by the adjacent lower curve.   The ideas presented in Sec. 20.9 explaining the rate relationship between a given curve and its derivative curve, in effect, work in reverse to explain the significance attached to a given curve and its integral curve.

An area under a curve denotes the total change during the interval for the quantities represented by the graph. Thus, in Fig. 20.5, the shaded area under curve B represents the product of the mean ordinate y_m for the interval and the length Δx of the interval. Many examples could be cited. For instance, if the ordinates represent force and the abscissas distance, the shaded area would represent the work performed by the varying force of the interval as a product of the distance $(fd = W)$.

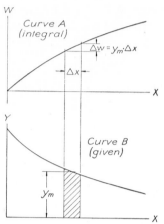

This area is depicted by the integral curve through the change Δw in its ordinates for the corresponding interval. Thus the difference between ordinates for the interval in the integral curve represents the work performed during the interval. The idea, of course, is expressed by the area relationship of derived curves.

FIG. 20.5. Integral curve, a change diagram.

A different connotation may be given the above example wherein the product of the varying force and the distance yields moment $(fd = M)$. Hence, the integral curve becomes a moment diagram instead of a work diagram.

If the area under curve B of Fig. 20.5 is assumed to be divided into a series of adjacent narrow strips such as the one shaded, it will be seen that the higher or integral curve represents a continuing summation of these areas. Thus any ordinate of the integral curve A denotes the value of the area under the lower curve B between the origin and the corresponding ordinate.

It can be shown by formal calculus that an integral curve is one degree higher in its equation than the adjacent lower curve as a result of the ordinates of the integral curve being the product of two quantities represented by the lower curve.

20.11. Example—Rate and Change Applications. Figure 20.6 contains three related curves each concerned in the motion of a body. Any one of the curves could have been given, and the others derived from it. Curves A, B, and C represent, respectively, the distance traveled, the velocity, and the acceleration of the body, all with respect to time.

Beginning the discussion with curve B, note that the slope (v/t) which happens to be constant expresses the rate of change of velocity with respect to time. The value (2 fpsps) of this rate may be obtained by inspection in this instance. Since the ordinates of curve C equal the slopes of the corresponding points in curve B, curve C represents the rate of change of velocity with respect to time. By definition this rate is acceleration $(a = v/t)$; hence, curve C represents the acceleration of the body. Similarly, rate of change in distance with respect to time, which is velocity $(v = s/t)$, is denoted by the slope of curve A; hence, curve B represents the velocity of the body. Instantaneous values of this rate may be read from B.

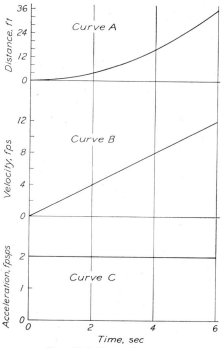

FIG. 20.6. Derived curves.

From the area-relationship viewpoint, the difference between any two ordinates of curve B equals the area under curve C for the corresponding interval. If the interval were that between $t = 0$ and $t = 4$, the difference in velocity read from curve B is seen to be 8 fps; the corresponding area under curve C is 2 fpsps $\times$ 4 sec = 8 fps, also. The student might check curve A as the integral for curve B in a similar manner.

The equations of the curves of Fig. 20.6 can be obtained with the assistance of the diagram. By observation, the equation of curve C is $a = 2$. The area under curve C between the origin and any ordinate is $2t$. According to the area relationship, this area must be equal to the corresponding ordinate of curve B, since the ordinate at the origin of curve B is zero. Therefore, the equation of curve B is $v = 2t$. By similar reasoning, the area under curve B from the origin to any ordinate will be equal to the corresponding ordinate of curve A. The area under curve B is equal to $\frac{1}{2}vt$, and since $v = 2t$, the area is equal to t^2. Hence, the equation of curve A is $s = t^2$.

20.12. Example—Composite Curves. The preceding example might be considered elementary because two of the curves are straight lines and the third parabolic. Many practical problems encountered in designing are of this nature, however. Frequently, the curves are composite, i.e., consist of several connected groups as shown by the three intervals of Fig. 20.7. When the given curves are straight lines and parabolas as in this figure, the derived curves may be obtained by simple computations using the area and slope relationships.

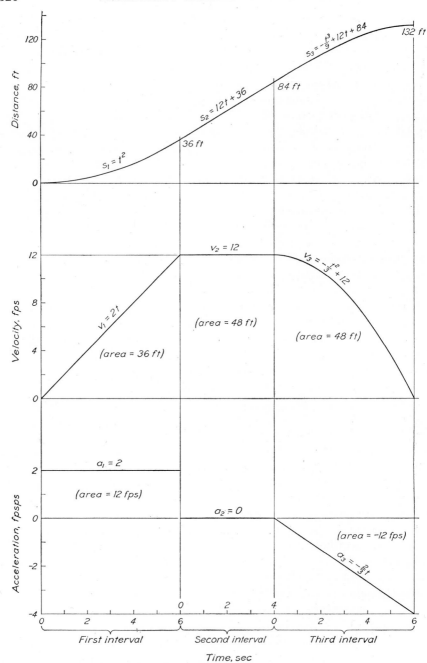

Fig. 20.7. Composite derived curves.

Figure 20.7 is a design study of the motion of a machine element. Given data stipulate that the body is to start from rest and reach maximum velocity in 6 sec with constant acceleration of 2 fps. The velocity is then to remain constant for 4 sec. Finally, the body is to be brought to rest in 6 sec with a uniform rate of deceleration.

Observe that the curves of the first interval are identical with the curves discussed in Sec. 20.11 and hence have the same equations. The constant acceleration is represented by the horizontal line with equation $a_1 = 2$. The area under this line (12 fps) equals the maximum ordinate of the velocity curve, since the initial ordinate of the latter is zero. The velocity curve is a straight line because the acceleration is constant; its equation is $v_1 = 2t$. The area under the velocity curve (36 ft) equals the maximum ordinate of the distance curve, since the initial ordinate of the distance curve is zero. The equation of the distance curve is $s_1 = t^2$.

In the second interval the constant velocity (12 fps) determined by the final velocity of the first interval is represented by the horizontal line having equation $v_2 = 12$. The acceleration is represented by the horizontal line of equation $a_2 = 0$. The initial ordinate of the distance curve is equal to the final distance (36 ft) of the first interval. Hence the final ordinate of the distance curve for this interval is equal to the initial value plus the corresponding area (48 ft) under the velocity curve, or 84 ft. This segment of the distance curve is a straight line, since the velocity is constant; the equation is $s_2 = 12t + 36$.

The body is to be brought to rest again at the end of the final interval; hence, the change in velocity must match in magnitude that acquired during the first interval. Therefore, since the rate of deceleration is constant, the deceleration is represented by a straight line having negative slope and with the area under the curve equal to the change (12 fps) required in the velocity. The equation of the line is $a_3 = -\frac{2}{3}t$.

The velocity curve in the final interval is a parabola with equation $v_3 = -(t^2/3) + 12$. The area under this parabola is $\frac{2}{3} \times 6 \times 12 = 48$ ft, which equals the difference between the initial (84 ft) and final ordinates of the distance curve for the interval. Hence, the final distance curve ordinate is 132 ft. The equation of the distance curve is $s_3 = -(t^3/9) + 12t + 84$.

The equations given for the curves may be obtained through the area relationship as explained in Sec. 20.11. An easier method will be learned in the study of formal calculus.

20.13. Methods of Graphic Differentiation and Integration. In contrast to the preceding example solved through algebraic application of the slope and area relationships, the majority of problems handled with graphic calculus have functions whose curves are irregular. Sometimes the curves are so irregular as to be characterized by the term *saw-toothed* and usually result from empirical data. The equation may or may not be determinable.

In either event, if the curve can be drawn, a solution may be had via graphics.

Although some variation is usually preferred, derived curves may be obtained through direct application of the two relationships of derived curves. Thus, a derivative curve is had by plotting slopes of the given curve as ordinates of the lower curve. And similarly, areas under a given curve may be plotted as successive differences to establish ordinates of the integral curve. Such methods require measuring slopes and areas of curves.

Slopes may be determined through drawing straight lines tangent to the curve at the required points. The trigonometric tangents of the angles made by the lines and the X axis, expressed in terms of the scale units, represent the slopes. In general, methods based on tangent lines are not desirable because tangents established by eye are usually inaccurate. It may be better to draw the tangent first and then mark its point of contact. Assistance may be had by using a transparent ruler marked along the edge with three dots equispaced at about $\frac{1}{16}$ in. By locating the outer dots on the curve, the line drawn along the ruler can be made close to the true tangent. The middle dot will help locate the point of contact.

Possibly a more reliable method is to establish lines normal to the curve at various points. This may be accomplished with a fair degree of accuracy by using a mirror. The mirror is placed on edge across the curve and rotated until the curve and its image in the mirror form a smooth, continuous curve. The normal is drawn along the back (where the image is formed) of the mirror if a glass mirror is used. The slope of the curve is the negative reciprocal of the slope of the normal. If preferred, the tangent may be established perpendicular to the face of the mirror and touching the curve.

Areas may be found by counting small squares and parts or by using a planimeter. Several well-known formulas, Simpson's rule, Durant's rule, and the trapezoidal rule, may be used to find more or less close approximations of the area of an irregular figure. These rules, however, give only the total area and not the shape of the integral curve.

A system widely used for finding an area under a curve involves dividing the area into a series of narrow vertical strips (not necessarily the same in width) and finding the average height of each. The sum of the products of the average height by the width of each strip yields the total area.

The average height or mean ordinate for a strip may be determined by drawing a horizontal line across the curve for the extent of the strip (see Fig. 20.8). The line is positioned so the crosshatched "triangular" areas as shown in the figure are equal. This may be accomplished with considerable accuracy by using a transparent straightedge and if the ordinates bounding the strips are wisely chosen so the curve is fairly regular in its curvature over the interval.

20.14. Graphic Integration and Differentiation through the Area Relationship. The area relationship of derived curves applied in conjunction with the narrow strips and mean ordinates described above provides the most generally practical avenue for obtaining derived curves through graphics. Several approaches are available. Each permits drawing either an integral or a derivative curve simply by reversing procedure.

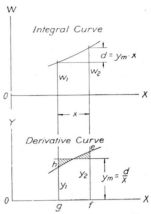

Figure 20.8 shows a narrow strip, with width x, two adjacent derived curves. A horizontal mean line of ordinate y_m has been drawn across the lower curve for the extent of the strip and positioned so the crosshatched triangular areas are equal. The actual area $efgh$ under the curve for the interval is equivalent to the product $y_m x$. Since this area according to the area relationship is equal to the difference d between ordinates w_1 and w_2 of the upper curve,

Fig. 20.8. Mean ordinate line for narrow strip.

$$d = y_m x \qquad (1)$$

or

$$y_m = \frac{d}{x} \qquad (2)$$

By establishing a series of narrow strips in connection with a given curve, Eq. (1) can be used to locate points in the integral curve and Eq. (2) can be used to establish mean ordinates for, hence permit drawing, the derivative curve.

In applying Eq. (1) to obtain an integral curve, the mean ordinate for each strip of the given curve is drawn as shown with the lower curve of Fig. 20.9. The area of each rectangle so formed is available as the product of the mean ordinate and the strip width. Since the value of the individual rectangular areas is numerically equal to the difference between ordinates for the corresponding interval of the integral curve, the integral curve can be plotted in a "step-by-step" manner as a summation of successive areas under the given curve.

The procedure is reversed in applying Eq. (2) to obtain a derivative curve. Narrow strips are established (see upper curve Fig. 20.9). The difference between ordinates bounding a strip divided by the width of the strip is numerically equal to the mean ordinate for the corresponding strip of the derivative curve. After locating the mean ordinate for each strip of the derivative curve, the curve itself is drawn in a manner so that the two small triangular areas (in each strip) between the mean ordinate line and the curve are as nearly equal as possible, yet maintaining the curve as smooth as practical.

Applying Eq. (1) or (2) as described involves, respectively, multiplication or division by the strip width. These operations may be handled several ways. A *semigraphic* method is to read the x and the y_m or d (as the case might be) values from the scales of the given graph and perform the multiplications or divisions arithmetically. The results are then plotted to obtain the required derived curve. The method is discussed in Sec. 20.15.

Speedier and, in general, preferred techniques are available for performing the multiplications or divisions and the plotting. With one, the *distance-transfer* method, special working conditions are employed that permit transfer of distances from the given curve to establish the required derived curve. For practicality, the method requires strips of equal width, which may be undesirable at times. A description of the procedure occurs in Sec. 20.17.

The *similar-triangle* method explained in Sec. 20.18 is a completely graphic technique for applying Eqs. (1) and (2) and is probably the most generally practical course open for use.

20.15. Derived Curves—Semigraphic Method. The following examples illustrate the procedure of finding integral and derivative curves by the semigraphic method.

EXAMPLE—DRAWING AN INTEGRAL CURVE. Given the lower curve B (Fig. 20.9), obtain the integral curve A. Appropriate narrow strips are established for the given curve B and extended into the space to be occupied by the integral curve. The ordinate scale for the latter is established. Mean ordinate lines are drawn for each strip of the lower curve, and their values read from the ordinate scale of the lower curve. Applying Eq. (1), $d = y_m x$, we have for the

1st strip:	$d = 10 \times 1.5 = 15$
2d strip:	$d = 7\frac{1}{3} \times 1.5 = 11$
3d strip:	$d = 3.5 \times 1 = 3.5$
4th strip:	$d = 1 \times 0.5 = 0.5$
5th strip:	$d = -1 \times 0.5 = -0.5$
6th strip:	$d = -4.5 \times 1 = -4.5$

The ordinate of the integral curve for $x = 0$ is known to be zero from the conditions of the problem. Therefore, the ordinate for the integral curve at $x = 1.5$ is $0 + 15 = 15$. Similarly, the ordinate at $x = 3$ is $15 + 11 = 26$, and at $x = 4$ is $26 + 3.5 = 29.5$, etc. After obtaining the ordinates for all points concerned, the points are plotted and the integral curve drawn through them.

EXAMPLE—DRAWING A DERIVATIVE CURVE. Given the upper curve A (Fig. 20.9), obtain the derivative curve B. Appropriate narrow strips are established for the given curve A and extended into the space to be occupied by the derivative curve. The ordinate scale for the latter is established. Applying Eq. (2), $y_m = d/x$ gives for the

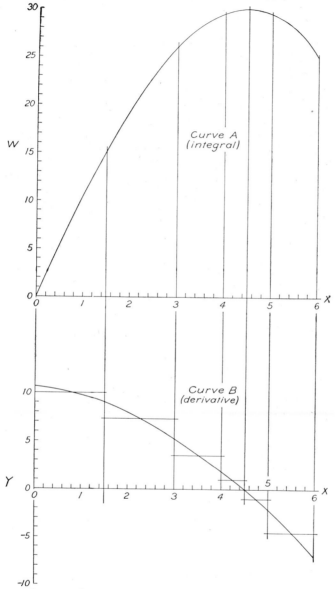

FIG. 20.9. Drawing derived curves, semigraphic method.

1st strip: $y_m = \dfrac{15 - 0}{1.5} = 10$

2d strip: $y_m = \dfrac{26 - 15}{1.5} = 7\dfrac{1}{3}$

3d strip: $y_m = \dfrac{29.5 - 26}{1} = 3.5$

4th strip: $y_m = \dfrac{30 - 29.5}{0.5} = 1$

5th strip: $y_m = \dfrac{29.5 - 30}{0.5} = -1$

6th strip: $y_m = \dfrac{25 - 29.5}{1} = -4.5$

The above-calculated values are plotted against the ordinate scale for the derivative curve, and the respective mean ordinate lines for each strip drawn. The derivative curve is then drawn as described in Sec. 20.14, being guided by the mean ordinate lines.

20.16. Ordinate Scale Ratios. The preceding example (Fig. 20.9) employs equal ordinate scales for both curves. Ordinarily, following this practice will result in either an undesirably high integral curve or an undesirably flat (hugging the X axis) derivative curve. This occurs for an integral curve because the ordinates of an integral curve represent the running sum of the area under the lower curve; hence, an integral curve tends to build in height. Conversely, the ordinates of a derivative curve result from differences between ordinates of the upper curve. Therefore a derivative curve tends to have considerably less height than the upper curve.

As a result, the ordinate scales for two adjacent curves are usually made different, with that for the lower curve the larger. It is commonly some even-value multiple such as three, four, or five times larger than the scale of the upper curve. Figure 20.10 shows derived curves having a scale ratio of 1:6. Had the ordinate scales been the same, the integral curve would extend to six times its present height.

20.17. Derived Curves—Distance-transfer Method. This method of obtaining an integral or a derivative curve applies Eq. (1) or (2) through a technique whereby distances are transferred from the given curve with draftsman's dividers to establish the required derived curve. The transfer of distances is made possible through employing special working conditions that determine a fixed "distance-transfer ratio" relating the curves. The special conditions concern the ratio between the ordinate scales of the curves and the width of the narrow strips, which are made equal so the distance-transfer ratio will be a constant value. The scale ratio and strip width are selected so that when used in connection with Eq. (1) or (2), they will yield a practical or readily useable value for the transfer ratio. The following examples illustrate.

EXAMPLE—DRAWING AN INTEGRAL CURVE. Given the lower curve of Fig. 20.10, obtain the integral curve which is to have initial ordinate $w_0 = 45$. Strips of two units width are decided upon, and the vertical lines drawn. Mean ordinate lines for the strips of the lower curve are established. The approximate range of the ordinate scale for the integral curve is needed.

Since the maximum difference between ordinates of the integral curve is equal to the area under the lower curve, this area is estimated roughly as 180 square units. Hence, the integral curve will require an ordinate scale ranging from 0 to approximately 180 plus $45(w_0)$, or 0 to 225.

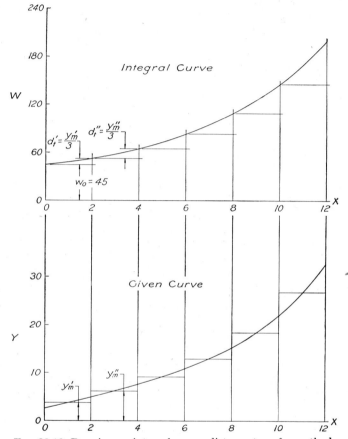

FIG. 20.10. Drawing an integral curve, distance-transfer method.

Assuming that the height of the integral curve is to be about the same as the given curve, the approximate height of the former (180) is divided by the approximate height of the latter (30) yielding 6:1 as the ordinate scale ratio. Thus the W scale will represent 60 units in the same distance that represents 10 units in the Y scale. The value 6 will be suitable as the scale multiple, since it, when divided into the strip width (2 units), results in a practical value for the transfer ratio now explained.

To transfer distances d_t from the given curve to establish the integral curve, Eq. (1), $d = y_m x$, may be written

$$d_t = \frac{y_m x}{\text{scale multiple}} \tag{3}$$

With the example at hand where all strips have width $x = 2$ and the scale multiple is 6, we have

$$d_t = \frac{y_m \times 2}{6} = \frac{y_m}{3}$$

Hence, the transfer ratio here is $\frac{1}{3}$.

To establish points in the integral curve, the initial ordinate is first plotted as $w_0 = 45$ as stipulated. Next, *one-third* the height of the mean ordinate for the first strip of the lower curve is obtained by "trial-and-error" division with the dividers. In the integral curve, this distance is added to the height of ordinate w_0 to determine the height of the ordinate bounding the right-hand side of the first strip. The remaining points in the integral curve are plotted in a similar manner as successive differences taken as one-third the height of the mean ordinate of the corresponding strip of the lower curve.

EXAMPLE—DRAWING A DERIVATIVE CURVE. Given the upper curve (Fig. 20.11), obtain the derivative curve. Narrow strips of unit width are used. In arriving at the ordinate scale for the derivative curve, it is noted that maximum slope for the given curve occurs in the first (unit width) strip. This slope is approximately $(40 - 10)/1 = 30$; hence, the mean ordinate for the first strip (the maximum such ordinate for any of the unit strips) of the lower curve will be approximately 30. Since the ordinate for this curve at $x = 0$ will be greater than 30, say 35 or 40, the value $2:1$ is selected for the ordinate scale ratio. The scale multiple is thus 2.

To transfer distances from the given curve to determine mean ordinates y_{m_t} for the derivative curve, Eq. (2), $y_m = d/x$, may be written

$$y_{m_t} = \frac{d \times \text{scale multiple}}{x} \tag{4}$$

Since, in this example, the scale multiple is 2 and the strip width is unity, the relation becomes

$$y_{m_t} = \frac{d \times 2}{1}$$

Thus the transfer ratio is 2.

In determining the derivative curve, the difference between ordinates bounding a strip of the given curve is transferred with the dividers and laid off *twice*, i.e., doubled, to locate the mean ordinate for the corresponding strip of the lower curve. The curve is then drawn as previously described, being guided by the mean ordinates.

In Fig. 20.11 it was desirable to provide an additional mean ordinate for the first one-half unit strip. Since the strip width is no longer unity, the relationship applying is had by substituting in Eq. (4).

$$y_{m_t} = \frac{d \times 2}{\frac{1}{2}} = d \times 4$$

The transfer ratio for strips of one-half unit width therefore is 4 with this example.

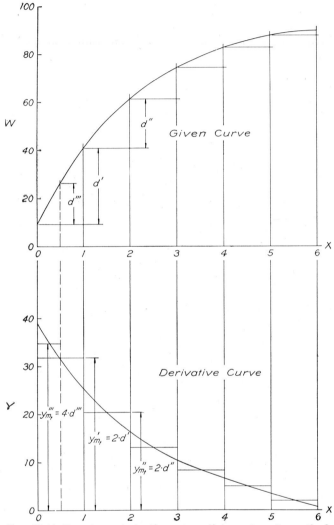

FIG. 20.11. Drawing a derivative curve, distance-transfer method.

20.18. Derived Curves—Similar-triangle Method. As has been stated, this method of obtaining an integral or a derivative curve is completely graphic and, in general, is probably the most practical course open for use. Its basis is the area relationship of derived curves. The narrow strips employed need not be of equal width. A derived curve obtained by this method is commonly, although not necessarily, superimposed upon the given curve (Fig. 20.12). Both curves ordinarily utilize the same abscissa scale. The ordinate scales, however, are usually different, **as** shown in the figure.

EXAMPLE—DRAWING AN INTEGRAL CURVE. In Fig. 20.12, consider curve B the given curve. Obtain the integral curve A. Narrow strips of appropriate widths are established, and the mean ordinates for the given curve for each strip drawn. The height of each mean ordinate is then projected to the Y axis locating points a, b, c, d, and e.

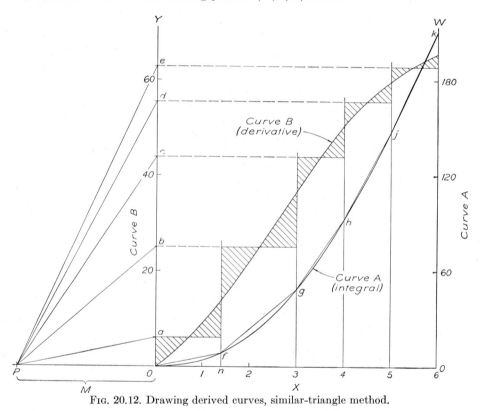

FIG. 20.12. Drawing derived curves, similar-triangle method.

A point P on the X axis and to the left of the Y axis is selected to serve as the pole. Distance M between the pole and the Y axis determines the value of the multiple relating the two ordinate scales and will be explained later. Lines, or rays, are drawn connecting the pole with points a, b, c, d, and e. To locate points in the integral curve, first a line is drawn from the initial ordinate for the integral curve (zero in this example) parallel to ray Pa and for the extent of the first strip. This line locates point f. From point f, a line is then drawn parallel to ray Pb for the extent of the second strip and locates point g. Similarly, line gh is drawn parallel to ray Pc, hj parallel to Pd, and jk parallel to Pe. The integral curve is had by drawing a smooth curve through points O, f, g, h, j, k.

The ratio between the ordinate scales of Fig. 20.12 was made 1:3 by making the pole distance M equal to 3 units on the X scale. This may be explained in connection with similar triangles Ofn and PaO for which

$$\frac{fn}{On} = \frac{aO}{PO}$$

or $$fn \times PO = aO \times On$$

Since PO is the pole distance and $aO \times On$ is the area under curve B for the interval,

$$fn \times \text{pole distance} = \text{area under curve } B$$

Thus the value of fn (read from the Y scale) multiplied by the pole distance, 3, equals the area indicated. To read ordinates of the integral curve (for example, fn) directly, the W scale was made to read three times the Y scale. The above description also explains the application of the area relationship.

An ordinate scale ratio of $1:3$ is used in this example so that both curves will have about the same height. This ratio, which determines the pole distance, is obtained by estimating the area under curve B and dividing by the maximum ordinate of that curve (a more detailed explanation is given in connection with the distance-transfer method, Sec. 20.17).

EXAMPLE—DRAWING A DERIVATIVE CURVE. Consider curve A of Fig. 20.12 as given. Obtain the derivative curve B. Appropriate narrow strips are established determining points O, f, g, h, j, and k. The ordinate scale ratio is decided upon, thus determining pole distance M and pole P as previously explained.

Rays parallel with chords Of, fg, gh, hj, and jk are drawn from pole P to intersect the Y axis and locate points a, b, c, d, and e. These points are then projected horizontally to establish the mean ordinates for the respective intervals of the derivative curve. For example, point b, determined by the ray drawn parallel with chord fg, locates the mean ordinate for the interval of fg. The derivative curve is drawn, being guided by the mean ordinate lines as previously explained.

The pole point and rays used with the similar-triangle method are often drawn within the confines of the graph proper in order to conserve space.

20.19. Constant of Integration. It has been emphasized that the area relationship equates an area under a curve to the *difference* between the corresponding ordinates of the next higher curve. The process of graphic integration thus yields the *shape* only of the integral curve and not its position with respect to the X axis. To position the curve thus, the value of one ordinate must be known from the conditions of the problem or must be assumed. Similarly with formal calculus, a value called the constant of integration obtained from known conditions of the problem is added to the equation for the integral curve to provide for initial conditions, thus positioning the curve with respect to the X axis.

Observe in Fig. 20.10 that the initial ordinate w_0 of the integral curve was given as 45 and fixes the vertical position of the curve. The initial ordinate may be zero on occasion as in Fig. 20.9.

PROBLEMS

Most of the following problems may be conveniently solved on 8½- by 11-in. plain rectangular coordinate paper of 10 or 20 lines to the inch. Solutions are to be complete with scale calibrations and captions, including units, and a title. With the problems of Groups II or III, a smooth or "fair" curve should be drawn after plotting the data.

Group I.   Composite Curves

In the following problems, construct the distance-time, velocity-time, and acceleration-time curves for the motion, and write the equations for each of the curves for each interval.

20.1. A cam follower is displaced 1.25 in. in 2.5 sec with constant positive velocity, allowed to dwell for 1 sec, then returned to the starting point in 2.5 sec with constant negative acceleration.

20.2. A cam follower is displaced 0.75 in. in 0.25 sec with constant acceleration, displaced an additional 0.75 in. in 0.25 sec with constant deceleration, then returned to the starting point in 0.5 sec, following simple harmonic motion with the varying acceleration changing from negative to positive.

20.3. A cage ascending a mine shaft 1560 ft deep first accelerates at the constant rate of 4 fpsps for 16 sec, then constantly maintains the velocity acquired until reaching the decelerating point.   The deceleration requires 13 sec, during which the velocity decreases at a uniform rate.

20.4. A gravity-type conveyor is constructed in a manner such that the objects to be moved start from rest and first travel for 8 sec at a uniformly increasing velocity and attain a velocity of 8 fps.   The objects then constantly maintain the acquired velocity for 10 sec.   Finally the objects are brought to rest at the end of the conveyor in 12 sec with the deceleration varying uniformly from 0 at the beginning to its maximum value at the end of the interval.

20.5. A sliding machine part, starting from rest, reaches a velocity of 14 fps in 7 sec with acceleration varying uniformly from its maximum value at the beginning to 0 at the end of the interval.   During the second interval the part constantly maintains the acquired velocity for 4 sec.   In the third interval the part is brought to rest in 5 sec, with the deceleration varying uniformly from 0 at the beginning to its maximum value at the end of the interval.

Group II.   Graphic Differentiation

20.6. Draw the graph of the following points and construct the derivative curve. Determine the value of x for y = maximum and for y = minimum.

x	0	1	2	3	4	5	6	7	8	9
y	6.0	4.6	3.6	2.9	2.5	2.7	3.8	5.1	5.0	4.2

20.7. The temperature D, in degrees centigrade, of a cooling body and the time T, in minutes, after the start of cooling appear in the table.

T, min	0	1	2	4	6	8	10	15	20	25	30
D, °C	100	90	81	66.5	55	46	39	28	22	18.5	17

Construct the derivative curve to determine the rate of cooling at any instant.

20.8. The following table gives the quantity of water Q, in gallons, pumped by a pumping station between 6 A.M. and various hours H of the day for a 24-hr period.

H, hr	Q, gal	H, hr	Q, gal	H, hr	Q, gal
6 A.M.	0	3 P.M.	1,500,000	11 P.M.	2,595,000
7	100,000	4	1,600,000	12	2,655,000
8	245,000	5	1,715,000	1 A.M.	2,690,000
9	410,000	6	1,885,000	2	2,710,000
10	580,000	7	2,075,000	3	2,715,000
11	775,000	8	2,255,000	4	2,730,000
12 M.	985,000	9	2,400,000	5	2,760,000
1 P.M.	1,190,000	10	2,515,000	6	2,810,000
2	1,375,000				

Construct the derivative curve to determine the rate of pumping at any instant.

20.9. A cam operating a follower utilizes a sine curve (simple harmonic motion), with θ ranging from 0 to 360°, for its displacement-time diagram. The range of θ corresponds with one complete rotation of the cam which occurs in 1 min. The maximum follower displacement is 5 in. Draw the displacement-time curve and construct derivative curves to determine the displacement, velocity, and acceleration of the follower at any instant.

20.10. The following table gives the distance S, in feet from the starting point, reached by a certain aircraft during take-off, at the end of various time intervals T in seconds.

T, sec	0	1	2	3	4	5	6	7	8	9	10
S, ft	0	4	14	39	78	132	202	284	374	472	577

Construct derivative curves to determine the velocity and acceleration at any instant.

20.11. Graphic Differentiation and Integration. An automobile accelerated under maximum power from a standstill attained the following velocities V, in feet per second, at the end of various time intervals T in seconds:

T, sec	0	2	4	6	8	10	12	14	16	18	20
V, fps	0	20.5	33.7	45.4	54.2	61.6	67.5	73.3	79.2	83.6	88.0

Construct derived curves to determine the distance and the acceleration at any instant.

Group III. Graphic Integration

20.12. The following are soundings D, in feet, for a river cross section taken at stations located S feet from one bank:

S, ft	0	20	40	60	80	100	120	138
D, ft	0	4.2	6.7	7.3	11.5	13.9	11.5	0

Construct the integral curve to determine the cross-sectional area of the stream.

20.13. The areas A, in square feet, of parallel cross sections of a road cut taken at stations located S feet from one end of the cut are as follows:

S, ft	0	20	60	100	140	180	220	260	283
A, sq ft	0	520	1950	3780	4100	2180	1390	270	0

Construct the integral curve to determine the volume of the cut between any two stations.

20.14. A contour map of the region for a proposed lake yielded the areas A, in square feet, of horizontal cross sections of the lake at various elevations E, in feet, measured from the lowest point in the lake as follows:

E, ft	0	2	5	10	15	20	25
A, sq ft	0	2830	6200	11,500	15,300	19,500	22,000

Construct the integral curve to determine the volume of the lake when filled to any elevation.

20.15. A compression test of a 7-in.-diameter by 16-in.-long concrete cylinder gave the following data, where P is total load in pounds and D is total deformation in inches.

P, lb	0	8,000	16,000	24,000	32,000	40,000	48,000	56,000	59,400
D, in.	0	0.0008	0.0018	0.0033	0.0052	0.0086	0.0147	0.0252	0.0343

Construct the integral curve to determine the work performed at any point in the test.

20.16. The table gives the total pressure P, in pounds, on an engine piston at various distances S, in inches, from the beginning of the stroke.

S, in.	0	2	4	6	8	10	12	14	16
P, lb	14,750	15,350	14,900	13,400	10,550	7150	4750	3100	2100

Construct the integral curve to determine the work done at any point in the stroke.

20.17. The table gives half ordinates O (horizontal distances, in feet, from the center-line of the shell) of a boat cross section at various heights H, in feet, above the keel.

H, ft	0	1	2	4	6	8	10	12	14	16
O, ft	4.5	11.4	14.1	17.0	18.6	19.5	20.0	20.7	21.9	24.0

Construct the integral curve to determine the area of the section.

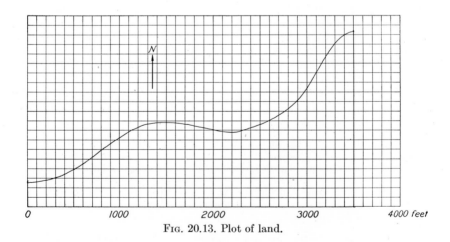

Fig. 20.13. Plot of land.

20.18. Figure 20.13 is a map of a plot of land bounded on the north by a stream. Redraw the map carefully to larger scale and (1) determine the area of the plot by constructing the integral curve; (2) divide the plot by a north-south line into two equal areas, then, similarly, into three equal areas; and (3) using north-south lines, cut off 75 acres from the west side and 100 acres from the east side of the plot. An acre equals 43,560 sq ft.

20.19. An indicator diagram for a diesel engine measures 5.5 in. in length and has the following heights, in inches, across the area at length intervals equally spaced 0.5 in. apart:

$$0,\ 1.88,\ 1.96,\ 1.08,\ 0.74,\ 0.52,\ 0.34,\ 0.26,\ 0.24,\ 0.22,\ 0.14,\ 0$$

Construct the integral curve to determine the area of the diagram, and find the indicated mean effective pressure.

$$I_{mep} = \frac{\text{area of diagram, sq in.} \times \text{pressure scale, psia per in.}}{\text{length of diagram, in.}}$$

The pressure scale is 1 in. = 200 psia.

20.20. The specific heat of mercury S, in calories per gram, at various temperatures T, in degrees centigrade, is given as follows:

T, °C	0	20	40	60	100	200	250
S, cal per g	0.03346	0.03326	0.03309	0.03295	0.0328	0.0323	0.0321

Construct the integral curve to determine the amount of heat required to raise one gram of mercury to any temperature.

20.21. The table gives information for plotting a Clark Y airfoil of any size. S is the location of the station from the leading edge in per cent of the chord length, and U and L are the ordinates from the chord line to the upper and lower surfaces, respectively, also in per cent of the chord length.

S	U	L	S	U	L
0.00	3.50	3.50	40.00	11.40	0.00
1.25	5.45	1.93	50.00	10.52	0.00
2.50	6.50	1.47	60.00	9.15	0.00
5.00	7.90	0.93	70.00	7.35	0.00
7.50	8.85	0.63	80.00	5.22	0.00
10.00	9.60	0.42	90.00	2.80	0.00
15.00	10.68	0.15	95.00	1.49	0.00
20.00	11.36	0.03	100.00	0.12	0.00
30.00	11.70	0.00	(leading edge radius = 1.50 per cent)		

Plot (to scale) an airfoil of 100-in. chord length and construct an integral curve to determine the total area.

BIBLIOGRAPHY

Davis, Dale S., "Empirical Equations and Nomography," McGraw-Hill.

Douglass, R. D., and D. P. Adams, "Elements of Nomography," McGraw-Hill.

Fairman, S., and C. S. Cutshall, "Graphic Statics," McGraw-Hill.

French, T. E., and C. J. Vierck, "A Manual of Engineering Drawing for Students and Draftsmen," McGraw-Hill.

Giesecke, F. E., A. Mitchell, and H. C. Spencer, "Technical Drawing," Macmillan.

Grant, Hiram E., "Practical Descriptive Geometry," McGraw-Hill.

Higbee, Frederic G., Sr., "Drawing Board Geometry," Wiley.

Hoelscher, R. P., J. N. Arnold, and S. H. Pierce, "Graphic Aids in Engineering Computation," McGraw-Hill.

Hood, George, "Geometry of Engineering Drawing," McGraw-Hill.

Howe, Harold Bartlett, "Descriptive Geometry," Ronald Press.

Johnson, Lee H., "Nomography and Empirical Equations," Wiley.

Levens, A. S., "Graphics in Engineering and Science," Wiley.

———, "Nomography," Wiley.

———, and H. C. T. Eggers, "Descriptive Geometry," Harper.

Lipka, Joseph, "Graphical and Mechanical Computation," Wiley.

Luzadder, W. J., "Fundamentals of Engineering Drawing," Prentice-Hall.

Mackey, Charles O., "Graphical Solutions," Wiley.

Mavis, F. T., "The Construction of Nomographic Charts," International Textbook Co.

Paré, E., R. O. Loving, and I. L. Hill, "Descriptive Geometry," Macmillan.

Rowe, C. E., and J. D. McFarland, "Engineering Descriptive Geometry," Van Nostrand.

Rule, J. T., and E. F. Watts, "Engineering Graphics," McGraw-Hill.

Schumann, Charles H., "Descriptive Geometry," Van Nostrand.

Street, William Ezra, "Technical Descriptive Geometry," Van Nostrand.

Warner, Frank M., "Applied Descriptive Geometry," McGraw-Hill.

Wellman, B. Leighton, "Technical Descriptive Geometry," McGraw-Hill.

VISUAL AIDS BIBLIOGRAPHY

The visual aids listed below and on the following pages can be used to supplement much of the material in this book. Some of them can be used in the study of more than one topic, so it is recommended that each film be reviewed, before use, in order to determine its suitability for a particular group or unit of study.

Motion pictures and filmstrips are included in the following list, the character of each being indicated by the self-explanatory abbreviations "MP" and "FS." Immediately following this identification is the name of the producer and, if different, that of the distributor also. Abbreviations are used for these names and are identified in the list of sources at the end of the bibliography. In many instances, the films can be borrowed or rented from local or state 16-mm film libraries. (A nation-wide list of these sources is given in *A Directory of 2660 16mm Film Libraries*, available for 50 cents from the Superintendent of Documents, Washington 25, D.C.) Unless otherwise indicated, the motion pictures are 16-mm sound black-and-white films, and the filmstrips are 35 mm, black-and-white, and silent. The length of motion pictures is given in minutes (min), that of filmstrips in frames (fr).

This bibliography is a selective one, and film users should examine the latest annual editions and supplements of *Educational Film Guide* and *Filmstrip Guide*, published by the H. W. Wilson Co., New York. The *Guides*, standard reference books, are available in most school, college, and public libraries.

Applied Geometry (MP, Purdue, 17 min silent). Explains construction of nine different geometric figures, from drawing a hexagon when the distance across corners is known to drawing an arc tangent to two circles.

Auxiliary Views (MP, Purdue, 18 min silent). Illustrates principles of auxiliary views and shows the construction of auxiliary views for straight- and curved-line figures.

Charts (MP, USN/UWF, 18 min). Explains the meaning, advantages, and limitations of Mercator, Gnomonic, and Lambert conformal projections.

Descriptive Geometry: Finding the Line of Intersection Between Two Solids (MP, USN/UWF, 22 min). Methods of determining intersecting lines of a cylinder and a cone by passing planes through the objects on an orthographic drawing.

Development of Surfaces (MP, Purdue, 23 min silent). Explains the construction of patterns of surfaces by means of models and drawings; describes the methods for right prism and oblique prism, right cylinder, right pyramid, right cone, and oblique cone.

Engineering Drawing (MP-FS series, McGraw). Ten motion pictures and nine follow-up filmstrips correlated with French and Vierck, *Engineering Drawing*. Titles and running times are:

1. *According to Plan* (9 min, no FS)
2. *Orthographic Projection* (18 min)
3. *Auxiliary Views: Single Auxiliaries* (23 min)
4. *Auxiliary Views: Double Auxiliaries* (13 min)
5. *Sections and Conventions* (15 min)
6. *Drawings and the Shop* (15 min)

339

7. *Selection of Dimensions* (18 min)
8. *Pictorial Sketching* (11 min)
9. *Simple Developments* (11 min)
10. *Oblique Cones and Transition Developments* (11 min)

Integral Calculus (FS series, SVE). Four filmstrips, the first three showing how the rectangular coordinate system is utilized to develop basic principles used in finding areas bounded by curved lines and volumes of solids bounded by curved surfaces, the fourth filmstrip using the polar coordinate system. Titles are:

1. *Areas by Integration* (40 fr)
2. *Double Integrals* (43 fr)
3. *Triple Integrals* (40 fr)
4. *Areas by Integration Using Polar Coordinates* (34 fr)

Intersection of Surfaces (MP, Purdue, 10 min silent). Explains by means of models and drawings the principles for finding the lines of intersection between intersecting surfaces, and discusses the problems of finding the intersection between two prisms, between two cylinders, and between cylinder and cone.

Introduction to Map Projection (MP, UWF, 18 min). Demonstrates various types of map projection and discusses the advantages and disadvantages of each projection.

Introduction to Vectors: Coplanar Concurrent Forces (MP, USOE/UWF, 22 min). Explains the meaning of scalar and vector quantities; how to add scalars and vectors; methods of vector composition and vector resolution; relationship between vector composition and vector resolution; and how vectors may be used to solve engineering problems. (Correlated filmstrip, same title, 36 fr).

Origin of Mathematics (MP, Brandon, 10 min). Background for illustrating the history of numbers, measurement, and calculation, including methods used by cave dwellers, Egyptians, Babylonians, Greeks, Romans, and Arabs.

Multi-View Drawing (MP, Purdue, 27 min silent). Demonstrates the way to represent an object by means of three orthographic views.

Periodic Functions (MP, USN/UWF, 17 min). Defines periodic functions; illustrates the graphing of sine angles; and relates sine waves to the amount of voltage produced by a generator.

Perspective Drawing (MP, Calif U, 8 min). Using a cube as a basic form, describes the one-point, two-point, and three-point perspective techniques.

Pictorial Drawing (MP, Purdue, 22 min silent). Demonstrates principles of isometric drawing by means of models and shows the construction of objects with isometric and nonisometric lines and with circles.

Practical Geometry (MP series, KB). Seventeen films, 10 to 12 min each, with the following titles:

1. *Angles*
2. *Angles and Arcs in Circles*
3. *Areas*
4. *Chords and Tangents of Circles*
5. *The Circle*
6. *Congruent Figures*
7. *Indirect Measurement*
8. *Lines and Angles*
9. *Locus*
10. *Polygons*
11. *Practical Geometry*
12. *Properties of Triangles*

13. *Pythagorean Theorem*
14. *Quadrilaterals*
15. *Ratio and Proportion*
16. *Rectilinear Coordinates*
17. *Similar Triangles*

Rectangular Coordinates (MP, USN/UWF, 13 min). Demonstrates how to use coordinates in solving problems involving time and distance and how to locate a point using two coordinates.

Sectional Views (MP, Purdue, 22 min silent). Illustrates the principles of sectioning, showing full, half, and offset sections.

Shape Description (MP, Purdue, 25 min). Demonstrates the relationship between an object itself, its pictorial representation, and its representation by three orthographic views.

Tension Testing (MP, USOE/UWF, 21 min). Demonstrates how to test the tension properties of a piece of steel—specifically, its elastic limit, yield point, and ultimate strength—and how to record and plot the data to determine the modulus of elasticity. (Correlated filmstrip, same title, 45 fr.)

Topographic Mapping by Photogrammetric Methods (MP, USGS, 95 min color). Portrays technical procedures employed by the Topographic Division of the U.S. Geological Survey in making standard topographic quadrangles, featuring the use of the multiplex method of mapping. Technical presentation for engineering students and other scientific personnel.

Vectors (MP, USN/UWF, 12 min). Explains vectors, changes in angle or magnitude, how vectors are plotted, and how the resultant is found.

Visualizing an Object (MP, USOE/UWF, 9 min). Explains how a blueprint is developed, how dimensions are shown by different views, and how special information is indicated on a blueprint. (Correlated filmstrip, same title, 39 fr.)

FILM SOURCES

Brandon—Brandon Films, Inc., 200 W. 57th St., New York 19, N.Y.

Calif U—University of California, Educational Film Sales Dept., Los Angeles 24, Calif.

KB—Knowledge Builders, Floral Park, N.Y.

McGraw—McGraw-Hill Book Co., Text-Film Dept., 330 W. 42nd St., New York 36, N.Y.

Purdue—Purdue University, Lafayette, Ind.

SVE—Society for Visual Education, Inc., 1345 W. Diversey Parkway, Chicago 14, Ill.

USGS—U.S. Geological Survey, Map Information Office, Washington 25, D.C.

USN—U.S. Department of the Navy, Washington 25, D.C. (Films distributed by United World Films, Inc.)

USOE—U.S. Office of Education, Washington 25, D.C. (Films distributed by United World Films, Inc.)

UWF—United World Films, Inc., 1445 Park Ave., New York 29, N.Y.

INDEX